Birds
Trees & Flowers

Illustrated

SPRING SCENE. *Cherry blossom and daffodils herald the spring in a Cornish orchard.*

Birds
Trees & Flowers

Illustrated

The nature lover's companion to familiar British birds, trees and flowers, fully illustrated with photographs, drawings and colour plates.

Odhams Press Limited · Long Acre · London

CONTENTS

CONTENTS

LIST OF COLOUR PLATES

GREAT TITS

CHARACTERISTICS OF BIRDS

by

BRIAN VESEY-FITZGERALD

So great are the apparent differences between birds and reptiles that it is hard to believe that the former have sprung from the latter. But it is so : birds have evolved from reptilian stock, and there is still plenty of evidence of this common ancestry visible in modern birds. Birds have feathers and reptiles have scales. A glance at the foot of a bird, from the ankle downwards, will show at once that all trace of scales has not been lost, and in some birds—like the petrels—the scales still occur on the beak. And then there are all sorts of similarities in the body structure. The skull of a bird, so very different from that of a reptile at a glance, has many points of similarity ; crocodiles and birds have the same sort of heart; the ankle-joint in birds and reptiles is made in the same way; the blood of both is very much the same. And if further proof is needed one has only to consider the egg. Birds and reptiles lay the same type of egg (the egg of a crocodile is like the egg of a goose, both externally and internally), and the unhatched bird and the unhatched reptile breathe in exactly the same way. In fact for the first few days of their lives birds and reptiles still travel the same road.

But once the road forks differences soon become pronounced. There is, for example, all the difference in the world between a three-weeks' old gosling and a three-weeks' old crocodile; and the greatest difference of all between birds and reptiles is that most birds can fly and all reptiles are flightless. There have been flying reptiles, of course (the pterodactyl was a reptile not a bird) but they have long since lost the power of flight just as some modern birds. But though there are a few flightless birds, flight is their chief characteristic.

The wing of a bird or a bat is the foreleg of the animal, in just the same way as our hands and arms are our forelegs. But in the bird and the bat the transformation has been much more drastic than has been the case in the human being, for the wing of a bird has got to fulfil very difficult and complex tasks. A glance at the wing of a dead bird will show that it is mainly made up of a whole series of parallel and tapering rods (they are *not* bones) and that these rods are fringed by many similar and much shorter rods, closely linked together to form a sort of web. These are the feathers and they are called the flight feathers or quills. The rest of the body, of course, is also provided with feathers, formed in exactly the same way, but much smaller and less sturdy. It is the quill feathers that matter so far as flight is concerned. They are arranged to overlap each other, the free edges facing the outer edge of the wing, and it is only because they are so arranged that flight is possible. On the up-stroke of the wing through the air these quills behave in much the same manner as the sails of a windmill, allowing the wind to pass through them and so lessening the pressure. On the down-stroke they behave in exactly the opposite way because the overlap comes into operation, the feathers are pressed closely together to form a fairly solid body, and so the full force of the stroke is brought into play. These quill feathers are divided into secondaries and primaries. The

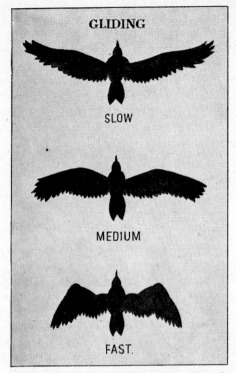

GLIDING

SLOW

MEDIUM

FAST.

Figure 1. *Wing positions are seen in fast, slow and medium gliding flight.*

sideways resembles the hull of a ship, the front end of the breastbone supports two slender rods of bone and these in turn carry the keel and the "merry-thought." That, very briefly, covers the mechanism of flight, but it must not be thought that the whole secret of flight is concentrated in the skeleton of the breastbone, the pectoral muscles and the wing. There is a great deal more in it than that—and we do not yet know all about the mechanics of flight. For example, there are large air-chambers within the body of a bird, which have something to do with flight, but precisely what is unknown. The secret of flight, which is something that cannot be explained in terms of mechanics, remains a mystery. No one, for instance, has explained how the snipe manages to fly in its twisting elusive manner.

On the other hand, we do know a great deal about many types of flight. We know how the wings work. They are not just flapped up and down, but possess a very considerable range of movement from the shoulder-joint. At some moment of flight they are thrust forwards and extended to their fullest extent; then they are driven downwards and backwards, a movement which lifts the body and forces it forwards. At the end of this sweep they are flexed (bent at the elbow and wrist joints), and at the same time they are raised and brought

secondaries are of the most importance in the stroke, for it is by them that the air is gripped. The primaries are of the most use in steering, and in some birds—like the insect-catching swifts—they have become greatly lengthened. But both feathers have this in common: the under-surface is concave. The whole under-surface of the wing is concave, though the degree varies in the different kinds of birds and in the different parts of the wing of each bird, and this arching of the wing is also of supreme importance in flight.

The most important muscles are those which provide for the power of the down-stroke. These are the pectoral muscles—the muscles of the breast—and they are so powerful that the breastbone itself would not be strong enough to support them. So there has been developed a "keel": the breastbone of a bird seen

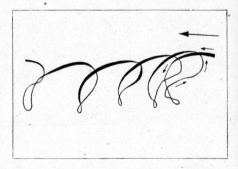

Figure 2. *A rook's flight resembles a series of figure-of-eight loops.*

BLACK-BACKED GULL. *Largest and most voracious of the gull family this bird breeds mostly on the north-west coasts of Britain. The plumage is pure white except for the dark grey mantle and black wing-tips. The flight of this bird is particularly strong.*

GOLDEN EAGLE AND GOSHAWK. *Above may be seen the golden eagle's magnificent wing-span; below, with a captured rabbit, is the goshawk, once used largely in falconry.*

YOUNG HERRING GULLS. *These young gulls keep their brown mottled feathers until four or five years old when their plumage changes to white, with a soft grey mantle.*

GANNET. *Commonly known as the solan goose the gannet, a large white sea-bird, has a wing-span of nearly six feet. It lives on fish, which it can sight from a great height, and will dive from a hundred feet in the air to ninety feet below the surface of the water in pursuit of its food. The nest is generally made of seaweed and tufts of grass or thrift, and built on a rocky ledge. Only one egg is laid, usually in early spring.*

forward above the body. The whole movement is then repeated, but it is much too quick to be followed by the eye. The whole thing is really a series of figure-of-eight loops, as is clearly shown in the accompanying diagram of the movements of the wing of a rook starting to fly, the loops getting bigger as the speed increases (Fig. 2).

It sounds simple enough; we must have seen hundreds of, say, sparrows take wing—but how? If we go out here and now and watch very carefully we still will not know. The movement is too quick. It is easier to say how birds alight. Different birds do so in different ways, of course. Ducks draw their heads backwards, tilt their bodies upwards, throw their feet forward and spread their tails, at the same time thrusting them forward so that they act as a brake. All birds use the tail as a brake in alighting.

Flight has been divided (Fig. 1) into ordinary flight, gliding flight and soaring flight. Ordinary flight is something we all know and most of us are familiar with the gliding flight of gulls. Soaring is something we are not so often privileged to see, our greatest exponent of it—the buzzard—being less common in most parts of Britain than we could wish. Gliding flight is simple in method. The bird gets up sufficient speed and having done so goes along without any movement of the wings. This sort of flight can only be conducted for a certain length of time for there is inevitably a loss of height that must be made good by strokes of the wing. Gulls, in particular, manage to get along for quite a time without wing strokes by using wind currents, but sooner or later they must return, if only momentarily, to ordinary flight. Sailing or soaring flight is the most remarkable method, for in it the bird gets along by prolonged circling without any active movement of the wings and without any appreciable loss of speed or height. The albatross,

circling round a ship, is the best known example, but vultures, buzzards, eagles and gulls (at least on cliff faces) are also experts. We do not properly understand sailing flight. We know that it is undertaken by birds with a large wing-area in proportion to their total weight; that it cannot be undertaken in a dead calm; that there are no visible wing strokes, but that there is frequent change in the tilt of the body; that in going downwind the bird loses height, in going upwind gains height; that (but this is by no means certain) the bird takes advantage of strong upward currents of air.

There is just one more point about wings that should be noted—their shape. In general the size of the wing decreases with the weight of the body to be lifted; up to a point at any rate. That sounds ridiculous at first, but a moment's reflection on the wings of a large white butterfly and the wings of a rook is

OWL IN FLIGHT. *The owl flies silently, the sound of its wings being muffled by the velvety pile which grows on the quills.*

sufficient to prove that it is true. It is a fact that birds that live in woods have short rounded wings—owls, pheasants, wrens and so on—while birds that fly only in the open have long pointed wings —gulls, swifts, swallows and so on. The reason is obvious. Short-winged birds, in general, have stouter as well as shorter quills, which is why they make more noise at the start of the flight when the wings are moved very rapidly. The loud whirr of the rising cock pheasant is familiar. But the owl, also short winged, has a very silent flight. This is caused by the fact that the quills are of very great breadth and are covered by barbules— a sort of velvet pile over them—and so the sound is muffled. Birds that fly in the open have no need of muffling, even if they are, like the owl of the woodland, birds of prey. So hawks and falcons, ducks and geese, swallows and swifts, all make a swishing sound as they fly, a sound that gives the impression of great speed.

The speed of birds is a subject for everlasting argument. Almost invariably the speed is grossly exaggerated. Without being dogmatic, it would be safe to

BLACKBIRD SUNBASKING. *The rounded wings of the blackbird and the fan-like spread of the tail are seen here. The quills of short-winged birds are generally stouter than those of birds that fly in the open, and their flight is noisier.*

RAZORBILL IN FLIGHT. *The razorbill, a common sea-bird of the North Atlantic, may be seen in spring about the cliffs where it breeds in large numbers, but returns to the open sea for the rest of the year. It ranges from America to the Mediterranean.*

say that the normal speeds of some common birds would not be greatly in excess of the following (by normal flight is meant flight unaffected by the press of danger or the assistance of a strong following wind): rook, thirty-eight miles per hour; starling, forty-three miles per hour; finch, thirty-two miles per hour; house-sparrow, twenty-five miles per hour; skylark, twenty-five miles per hour; swallow, thirty-five miles per hour; swift, seventy-five miles per hour; sparrow-hawk, twenty-five miles per hour; kestrel, forty miles per hour; goose, forty-eight miles per hour; duck, forty-five miles per hour; curlew, forty-five miles per hour; gull, thirty miles per hour; pheasant, thirty-eight miles per hour; partridge, thirty-two miles per hour. Swifts can accelerate to over one hundred miles per hour, but the two hundred miles per hour with which they are credited is very doubtful. Ducks are often credited with speeds of one hundred and fifty miles per hour, but in many years of wildfowling we have never seen a duck fly at anything approaching that speed. Roughly speaking, of two similar birds the heavier always flies the faster. Thus mallard are faster than teal, greylags than pink-feet, curlew than whimbrel.

All birds lay eggs, and in Britain these eggs are hatched by the warmth of the parent's body, either by the mother or the father, or both, sitting upon them, and incubating them. The period of incubation, of course, varies with the species and may take a month or more. Birds' eggs vary enormously in size and in colour. In general there is some relation between the size of the bird and the size of its egg. This is because a big bird needs a bit more food to start it in life than a small bird and the egg of a large bird contains more yolk than that of a small bird. But there are notable exceptions to this general rule: the cuckoo, for example, is a very much larger bird than the skylark but the eggs of the two are about the same size, while the guillemot, though about the same size as the raven, lays an egg several times larger in volume. This is because the guillemot lays only one egg in a year, and that in a place where enemies are infrequent; and here we have another general rule—that birds that lay only one egg in a year lay eggs that are comparatively very large. Again, birds that nest on the ground usually lay larger eggs than those that do not. There are exceptions to this rule also, but in the case of those birds whose chicks are born active and able to run about it is a rule without exception. The number of eggs laid has some relation to size also. The partridge may lay a dozen eggs, cover them all and hatch them all. The snipe, a smaller bird, could not possibly cover a dozen eggs and so lays only four. In shape most eggs are oval. Owls lay eggs that are very nearly round; grebes, eggs that are fat in the middle and pointed at each end; most wading birds, eggs that come to a fairly sharp point; the guillemot and the razorbill, eggs that are very much larger at one end than the other. The latter birds are related, though distantly, to the waders but the shape has become exaggerated because of the situation in which the egg is laid. A bare shelf of rock high above the sea is not a safe position and a round egg would

soon be blown off, while the sharply pointed egg merely rotates. In the case of all wading birds, the eggs are laid in the nest with the pointed ends inwards, a position which enables the sitting bird to cover them more easily.

SURFACE OF EGGS

The surface of eggs varies almost as much as the shape—kingfishers lay eggs with a beautiful gloss on their fine-grained white shells: grebes' eggs have a rough chalky surface—but even more does the colour vary. On the whole each species has a distinctive coloration—but there is at the same time enormous individual variation. Guillemots lay eggs with a simply astounding range of colour and marking variation, and so do (among others) rooks, razorbills, gulls, cuckoos and lapwings. But the guillemot's ground colour is always yellow, while the razorbill (a very closely-related bird) always lays an egg whose ground colour is green. Generally speaking, birds that lay their eggs on the ground or in nests built on the ground or in very exposed nests, lay inconspicuous eggs. About ninety British birds nest on the ground and nearly all of them lay eggs that harmonize exceedingly well with their surroundings—the lapwing, the stone curlew and the skylark are good examples. In some cases the match between eggs and surroundings is so good that one may search for a very long time for the eggs, even when one knows within a few yards where they are. The nightjar lays such eggs and so does the tern. Then again, almost all the birds that lay their eggs in holes lay white eggs. Kingfishers, owls, and puffins are good examples. It has been suggested that this is because eggs laid in holes have no need for protective coloration, but against this is the fact that the wheatear lays blue eggs in holes, while the woodpigeon and the short-eared owl lay white eggs outside holes. Though in the case

LONG-EARED OWLS AND YOUNG
Night birds of prey, found chiefly in pine woods, these owls feed on birds and mammals.

PAIR OF GREEN WOODPECKERS

*A laughing call-note and a long tongue used for catching ants are noted in this bird,
which, in many parts of Britain is known by its more familiar name of yaffle.*

CORMORANTS AT THEIR NEST

Voracious fish-eating birds which are able to swim under water, cormorants frequent inland waters, (making nests of reeds and branches) on rocky cliffs and islets.

GREAT SHEARWATER AND COMMON TERN

The shearwater (above) is an ocean-going bird; the tern (below) haunts seashores.

of most ground nesting birds the protective coloration theory holds good, it would be easy to find fault with it in many cases of birds laying in tree-nests—the hedge sparrow for example, whose lovely blue eggs can be very conspicuous, and again, the wood-pigeon—the theory that the pigmentation is of value in warding off certain rays of the sun which might be harmful to the embryo is more likely to be correct. The cuckoo alone of birds lays eggs of varying colour, but even so an expert can always tell a cuckoo's eggs. Each cuckoo lays one particular type of egg throughout her life; so consistently so, in fact, that a trained observer can recognize the egg no matter where it may be.

As a general rule among British birds, the hen does the major portion of the work of incubation. In many cases husband and wife share the work fairly evenly, and this is especially true of passerine (perching) birds. Among the ducks, geese and game birds the female does all the work, the male disclaiming all responsibility and in most cases taking no interest in his family at all. In the phalaropes, however, the position is reversed and the male does all the work once the eggs have been laid. Only in the cuckoo have both parents discarded

NIGHTJAR NESTING. *Natural camouflage makes it difficult to detect the nightjar when it settles on the ground. The bird makes no proper nest but lays its eggs on bracken or heather. Its name comes from its harsh cry.*

BLACK-HEADED GULL. *This gull is the smallest and commonest seen on British shores, and is recognizable by its deep red bill and legs. The nest is made of sticks and grass, and though the eggs vary in colour they are all blotched with dark brown markings.*

responsibility. In the majority of passerine birds monogamy is the rule and sharing of incubation occurs (by monogamy is meant monogamy for the breeding season, not for life; it is very doubtful indeed if pairing for life is at all frequent in the bird world). In the majority of ducks and gamebirds, polygamy—or perhaps promiscuity—is the rule, and the female does all the work of incubation. Geese, however, are monogamous, yet no self-respecting gander would dream of sitting on eggs, and the same is true of the partridge. The cock partridge is an excellent and devoted parent, but he does not incubate.

COLOUR AND COURTSHIP

It is commonly said that among birds it is the cock that is brightly plumaged while the hen is more soberly clad. This is true of many of our small singing birds, and also of those birds with a pronounced tendency to polygamy such as ruff, capercaillie, pheasant and blackcock. It is not true, however, of geese or partridge, nor, among passerines, is it true of the robin, the rook or the starling. Among those species in which the male is the more resplendent, he does all the courtship. He carves out for himself a territory, he sings to warn off intruders and to entice the hens, and he displays to the hen. Among those species, such as the robin, the rook, the oystercatcher, in which the sexes are alike, courtship and display seem to be mutual, either sex taking the initiative. Those are good general rules, but they do not apply to the polygamous birds such as the ruff or the blackcock, and it is doubtful whether they apply to the pheasant. In these birds the males are very much more gorgeously attired than the females—the disparity in splendour is much more pronounced than in any of the passerines—and the males do all the posturing, crowing, strutting, fighting, and so forth. They come together to do so—particularly is this so in the case of the ruffs and the black-cocks—and it is commonly said that they fight for the hens, the victors collecting the harem they require. But this is not so. They collect no harem. They do all the strutting, but it is the hens that do the choosing, and it is by no means always the most gorgeous ruff or the most belligerent blackcock that is successful with the ladies. In fact, these birds are promiscuous, not polygamous.

Display in courtship has become curiously formalized. Love flights are quite different from flights, conducted for any purpose, at any other time of the year. Fighting, too, has become formalized and is now merely a matter of display very rarely becoming serious,

though a few birds (the robin is one) will engage in combat that may become mortal. For the most part, however, fighting is largely a matter of threat. Certain postures are adopted and these are sufficient, and the victor is almost always the bird already in possession of the territory. The fighting, in fact, is done for the territory rather than for the mate. It is the ground and the food it contains that is of primary importance; the hen comes next. The colours of cocks, as well as the voice of cocks (in general it is always the cockbird that sings) are related to territory and not to the hens. They are warning colours rather than attracting colours; the songs are warning sounds before they are attracting sounds. A matter-of-fact and unromantic interpretation, but neverthe-

SHORT-EARED OWL. *Here the short-eared owl is seen alighting at its nest, a slight depression on the heathery ground. The picture gives a clear impression of the delicately striated and barred plumage of this not very common bird.*

less true. The singing blackbird is more concerned with telling his neighbours to keep out of his territory than with entertaining his mate: the red of the robin's breast is battle-dress, not wedding dress.

Just as eggs vary and colours vary, so do the nests of birds vary enormously. Some birds, such as the guillemot, the razorbill, and the nightjar, make no nest at all but simply lay their eggs on the ground: others make a scrape in the ground and lay their eggs within it as does the tern, and others put a little lining in the scrape as do some of the ducks and plovers. Some build quite elaborate nests on the ground, like the whitethroat and some of the ducks and geese, while some build domed nests on the ground like the chiff-chaff. Others dispense with building and lay their eggs in holes, like the owls, the kingfisher, the sandmartin, and the sheld-duck. Some build platforms like the wood-pigeon, some cups like the hedgesparrow, some domed nests like the magpie and the long-tailed tit. Some build huge nests like the golden eagle, and some, like the goldcrest, tiny nests. But all, even those that appear flimsy and untidy (and every wood pigeon's nest does that) are works of art, strong enough to withstand the elements, as often as not, sufficiently well concealed to avoid the eyes of enemies, warm enough to help the young to thrive. And the labour that goes into them is enormous. The long-tailed tit lines its nest with feathers—over 2,000 have been counted from one nest alone,

RAVEN FLYING. *An uncommon bird in England and Wales the raven, largest member of the crow family, frequents highland woods, mountains and rocky coasts. The nest is a collection of sticks lined with grass and wool, often found on a cliff edge.*

ANGRY STARLING. *Starlings, like sparrows, are at home in town and country. One of the commonest of British birds it is distinguished by a handsome black plumage, with a glossy purple and black sheen speckled with white during the winter months.*

and every one of those feathers had to be found and carried. The situation of a nest is usually very well chosen, too. Suitable nesting sites are not so many as one might imagine and so it is usual to find nests in much the same place each year. A blackbird that has nested in one garden for the past nine years has nested in the same bush each year, though there are plenty of other bushes that seem suitable. So, too, partridges nest in about the same place each year, as well as ducks, and tits.

NESTING SITES

Birds become adapted to their habitat, that is, the kind of ground on which they live. Guillemots will not be found inland nor wood pigeons on sand dunes. There is a reason why certain birds are to be found in certain places. And that reason, in ninety-nine cases out of a hundred, is the soil. The soil determines the life of a bird of the air just as, in the last essential, it determines all animal life.

Plants depend immediately upon the soil and the sun for nourishment, and are, in the long run, the only source of energy that keeps life going. Directly or indirectly all living creatures live upon them. Birds cannot get any nourishment from the soil itself. A few, it is true, live entirely upon vegetable matter which has come from the soil, but the majority live upon the insects or other creatures that live on the plants that live on the soil, and this is equally true of the birds of prey, though they are a stage further removed from the soil.

There are four hundred and twenty-three birds on the British list. This number, however, is most misleading,

COCK BLACKBIRD. *Known for its rich song the blackbird is common everywhere in Britain. The male bird, here seen bringing food to the nest, has jet-black feathers and a bright orange-yellow bill. The nest is made of grass, roots and mud.*

CURLEW AND EGGS. *Two features are characteristic of the curlew; its plaintive musical cry and its long curving beak. It haunts the seashore and moorlands. The brownish-green eggs are laid in a nest of grass, made amid rushes or clumps of ling.*

for a large number of them come to us irregularly and quite a lot have only been recorded on a few occasions. Actually, of the four hundred and twenty-three, only one hundred and thirty-three are resident in Britain throughout the year, while one hundred and eighty-seven have only turned up on a few occasions or only do so irregularly. The one hundred and thirty-three residents are increased every winter by twenty-six birds that come to spend the cold weather with us. These are birds that breed further north. In summer they are increased by fifty-two birds that come from further south to breed in Britain. In addition there are some twenty-three birds that pass through without stopping long every year. So in winter our bird population is made up regularly of one hundred and fifty-nine species, and in summer of one hundred and eighty-five species. But the numbers in summer are not by any means greater than those in winter, for our winter visitors come in their thousands, having no household cares. Such birds include the fieldfares which arrive in immense flocks from Northern Europe. These birds are found in the north and midlands, but severe weather will drive them south. The number of our summer visitors is limited by the number of nesting sites and the food supply available for rearing their young.

PLOVER AND CRESTED TIT. *Both the plover* (left) *and Scottish tit* (right) *show distinctive head crests and clear markings on the face and neck. In the British Isles the crested tit is found only in Scotland, where it frequents mountain pine-woods.*

FEMALE WHINCHAT. *Known as the furze-chat the whinchat (above) is recognizable by the broad white streak over its eye and its brown speckled back.*

NEWLY HATCHED STONE-CURLEWS. *Frequenting downs and wolds the stone-curlew, which is also known as the thick-knee, is a summer visitor to Britain.*

SEDGE-WARBLER FEEDS YOUNG. *Arriving in Britain in the spring the sedge-warbler makes its nest of grass, stalks and moss in a low bush or among reeds. The head is almost black in colour, the light streak over the eye being noticeable.*

COMMON BRITISH BIRDS

by

DAVID SETH-SMITH

EVERYWHERE in towns one meets the house sparrow. So common is it that we scarcely give it a second glance; yet the cock bird is quite a handsome little fellow with his black throat and whitish cheeks, contrasting with the dull brown, perky hen. Even though the house sparrow is the commonest of British town birds, it has a runner-up in the starling, especially since the latter has taken to roosting in its thousands on the buildings of some of our greatest cities. Unlike the sparrow, however, the starling is not dependent on man; village or open country suits it well, whereas the sparrow is scarce or absent at any distance from human habitation. The sparrow sleeps under the eaves of buildings and feeds on waste products and grain. For grain, in autumn it will flock to the surrounding fields; but in spring and early summer it does service in destroying hordes of insects particularly harmful to the crops.

Starlings, too, are legion, and are now common in parts of the country where some few years ago they were rare or absent. Whether their large increase is good or bad from a human viewpoint is debatable. They can cause great havoc to fruit crops, but their favourite diet consists of grubs, especially wireworms, leather-jackets and the caterpillars that prey on growing crops. When young starlings leave the nest they are brown with white throats, but at the first moult they assume the spotted dress, though without the bright iridescent blue, purple and green of the adult birds in spring.

Few town gardens or open spaces are without those champion singers, the blackbird, with jet black dress and orange bill, and the song thrush, with warm brown back and spotted breast, the former being almost always the more numerous of the two. By some, the blackbird's song is thought to be equal, if not superior, to that of the nightingale, and that of the song thrush comes a very short way behind; it has the advantage of being heard for nine months of the year, from late October until the beginning of July, the blackbird's splendid flute-like song not starting until well in February and stopping at the end of June, while the nightingale's song period is only from mid-April to the middle or end of June.

USEFUL GARDEN BIRDS

Both blackbirds and song thrushes are useful birds in gardens, the latter especially, on account of the number of insects they destroy, though, where soft fruit is grown there will be trouble unless this be protected with nets. The song thrush is a great destroyer of snails.

In their first plumage, young blackbirds resemble their blackish-brown, rather spotted, mother. At their first moult in the autumn the young cocks can be distinguished from the hens by their blacker plumage, though they do not grow entirely black until the early spring when the bill becomes orange-yellow.

Amongst the favourite visitors to or dwellers in town gardens are the tits, of which two kinds, the great tit and the blue tit, are common almost everywhere, and are to be seen searching for insects among the leaves of trees and shrubs. The great tit is easily recognized by its

HOUSE-SPARROW AND TREE-SPARROW. *Noisy and aggressive the house-sparrow (above) flourishes wherever there are buildings. Its untidy nest of straw and feathers may be seen under eaves. The tree-sparrow (below) is a country bird. Both feed on insects.*

size, glossy blue-black head with large white cheek-patches and broad black band down the middle of its yellow underparts. Considerably smaller is the blue tit—the only tit with a blue cap. Some town gardens may be favoured by visits from two other tits, the coal tit and the marsh tit, though these are more likely to be met with in country districts.

While tits feed primarily upon insects and grubs they are very fond of nuts and fat, especially during the winter months. So fond are they of nuts and fat that they will go on eating them as long as they can get them, even feeding their young on them instead of on insects, often with fatal results. The number of times the parent tits return to their young with their beaks full of small grubs and caterpillars makes

TIT FAMILY. *Tits are among the most attractive of the smaller birds. The blue tit (right), known as the tom-tit, will eat nuts or suet hung out for it. Young long-tailed tits (below) have brown and white feathers with a reddish tinge.*

SPARROWS AND CUCKOO. *Above are young house sparrows, seldom ousted by the fledgling cuckoo, but, in the picture below is the hedge sparrow, or dunnock, which is often the subject of the cuckoo's attention and seen here feeding the young impostor. The cuckoo sometimes lays as many as a dozen eggs, each in a different nest.*

WHITETHROAT AND LESSER WHITETHROAT. *Both these birds are members of the warbler family and summer visitors to Britain. The whitethroat (above) has a patch of light feathers round the throat which swells when the bird sings and which gives it its name. The lesser whitethroat (below) is smaller in size. Both haunt hedgerows and copses.*

one realize the service they render to the gardener, and helps one forget the occasional damage done to peas and pears later in the year.

Robins are to be found throughout the country and in towns with a fair proportion of open spaces. They are friendly little birds, fond of the neighbourhood of human dwellings, and with a song period covering the greater part of the year. Not that one robin will tolerate the presence of another, unless it be its mate, in its own territory. After the young are reared parents and young separate, and each bird takes up a territory of its own in which, whether male or female, it sings a song of warning to others to keep their distance. Young robins are at first spotted, but at their first moult in early autumn assume the characteristic brick-red breast which is worn by both sexes.

An unassuming little brown bird, the hedge sparrow, frequents most town gardens, hopping about beneath the shrubs and undergrowth in search of small insects and the seeds of weeds. Despite its name it is not a sparrow, possessing the narrow beak of an insect eater ; so we should do well to call it by its other name of dunnock. Its cheerful song, something like that of the wren but more musical and subdued, is heard throughout the spring and summer.

There is no hard and fast rule as to which birds are to be found in towns and which in the country, and it is quite possible to meet with many more than are mentioned in this section.

In our walks in the fields surrounded by hedges, we are sure to see birds. If there is rough grassland, or the fields are in stubble, there will be meadow pipits and during the summer months tree pipits, if there are any trees growing in the hedges. Both are rather insignificant brown birds which, in flight, show white outer feathers of the tail. The meadow pipit is with us throughout the whole year, though the birds seen in the winter are probably not those that were nesting in our district in the summer. With these, as most other birds regarded as resident species, there is considerable movement, those which nested in the north moving southward as the cold weather approaches, while those that reared their broods or were themselves reared in the south may leave us altogether in the autumn and cross to the Continent and beyond.

PIPITS AND LARKS

The tree pipit is a summer migrant, coming to us in April, and is never so numerous as the meadow pipit which it closely resembles. It is, however, easily recognized by its habit of flying upward and singing lustily as it circles round and floats down to take up a position on an upper branch of a tree. Like the meadow pipit, it nests upon the ground beneath a tuft of grass and the four or five speckled eggs vary greatly in colour.

The larks are allied to the pipits, and the skylark is common enough in most large open grasslands, where its loud, varied and continuous song, delivered as it soars to considerable heights, may be heard from early spring until July. In colour the bird is a streaky brown and on its head is a distinct crest ; it does not hop, but walks. Its long hind claws indicate a preference for the ground ; in fact, it never perches on the branches of a tree though it will sometimes do so on the top of a post, a position it may adopt while singing. It also sings occasionally while on the ground.

Skylarks feed upon insects, vegetable substances such as grain, and green leaves and shoots, including grass. In the winter, when large flocks arrive from abroad, they are sometimes rather troublesome in their attacks on young crops, though it may be doubted whether the slight pruning given by the birds does any appreciable harm to the final yield.

Fine songster as is the skylark, its

PAIR OF STOCKDOVES
Birds distinguished from the wood-pigeon by the absence of white on neck and wings.

THE HANDSOME MAGPIE

A long, glossy tail and black and white wings make the magpie a distinctive bird.

melody is eclipsed by that of its near relative, the woodlark. It can scarcely be termed common, though in certain parts of the country, especially in the south-west and south, its lovely song can generally be heard from February to June. Unlike the skylark, it perches freely and likes to sing while perched as well as during short flights. It can readily be distinguished from the skylark by its much shorter tail.

Common in hedgerows in more or less open country and, especially in winter, around farm buildings is the yellow bunting or yellow hammer. Its song—a little bit of bread and no cheese—is frequently uttered as it perches on an upper branch of a bush or tree. It has a rather longer tail than most of the finches and is easily recognized by its yellow head and underparts and chestnut upper surface which are especially bright in the spring time. The hen bird is like the cock but less bright in colour.

BUNTING FAMILY

Much larger than the yellow hammer is its relative the corn bunting, more often to be met with near the coast than inland. It is a dull-coloured bird of streaky brown plumage, something like a very large sparrow, and may be seen perched upon a post or telegraph wire or the upper branch of a bush in the hedge, its high-pitched song sounding like " the jangling of a bunch of keys."

In the south or south-west of England one may come across the cirl bunting, but it is rather locally distributed and the writer has only found it common in a few places in Devon and Cornwall. It is not unlike the yellow hammer, but the cock bird is easily distinguished by his black throat, greenish band on the chest and chestnut on the sides of the breast. The hen is very like the hen yellow hammer.

The cock bullfinch is one of our most brilliantly coloured birds, with his blue-black cap, rosy pink throat and breast and bluish-grey back. Though otherwise very like him, his mate differs in having a pinkish brown breast and browner back. One generally hears their note, a low, piping " pew-pew," and as they fly along the side of the hedgerow one notices the pure white patch above the tail. In the early spring they may visit fruit gardens and take buds and at other times the seeds of weeds and the berries of privet, rowan, and blackberry are readily taken.

Goldfinches have increased in most districts during the last few years, possibly owing to the law prohibiting their capture and sale. They are among the most attractive of all of our finches with their cheerful twittering voices, bright red faces, black caps and golden wing-bars ; and there are few prettier sights than that of a party of them feeding upon a patch of seeding thistles. One cannot mistake the bright tinkling voice of the goldfinch, whose full song has several notes much like a canary's.

The linnet, also called the brown linnet to distinguish it from the green-finch, sometimes known as the green linnet, is another very delightful bird though far less showy than the goldfinch. In its winter dress it may be described as a plain brown bird ; though in summer the cock dons a crimson crown and breast and becomes a very handsome fellow, while his mate remains dressed in sombre browns. The linnet's principal food is the seeds of various weeds and it is said to feed its young upon small caterpillars and grubs.

Two relations of the linnet are locally common in this country, the twite, of duller brown with yellow bill in the winter, sometimes called the mountain linnet and more or less confined to the north of our islands : and the lesser red-poll, commoner in the north than the south though by no means rare there. It is considerably smaller than a linnet and has a black throat and a patch of bright red on the forehead. In the spring,

TREE PIPIT AND YOUNG. *This small bird, with buff and brown plumage, builds its grassy nest on the ground, and the blotched eggs are laid in May or June. In this picture the parent bird is seen at the nest with insects to feed the young birds.*

the cock bird has pink on the chest and lower back. Its food consists of the seeds of various weeds and alder and birch.

The greenfinch is a regular hedgerow bird—if the hedge contains fairly large bushes and trees—but it also comes freely into gardens when the seeds it likes are ripening. It is recognized by its olive-green colour with patches of yellow in the wings and tail, and if seen at close range, by its stout bill. The hen is considerably duller than her mate.

One might also have included the chaffinch amongst the town birds, but it is still more in evidence in the country. Indeed it is everywhere and has claims to be considered the commonest British bird. One of our most charming birds, the chaffinch is of elegant shape and

bearing, and very pretty colouring. With its bright and cheerful song, it does more good than harm, for it is the most insectivorous of all our finches and the seeds it eats are mostly those of weeds. Its beautifully compact, ball-like nest of roots, moss and grass, is decorated or camouflaged with small pieces of lichen or bark fastened on with spiders' webs. It is tucked into the fork of a tree and is not at all easy to find, as it harmonizes wonderfully with its surroundings.

The mistle thrush may often be seen feeding, sometimes several together, out in the fields and meadows, especially in winter. It is easily distinguished from the song thrush by its larger size, greyer colour and larger and more rounded spots. Its wild song, which accounts for

GREAT TIT. *Largest of the tit family the great tit is a handsome bird of many colours with a black head and throat. Its powerful claws enable it to cling in any attitude to the bark of trees where it seeks for grubs and insects.*

its name of stormcock, is a very poor edition of the blackbird's but far louder and more disjointed, commencing with the first days of the year and generally delivered from a high leafless branch of a tree. A great consumer of berries of many kinds, even those of the mistletoe, from which its name is derived, the mistle thrush, like other thrushes, also eats quantities of insects, worms and grubs.

Rooks are the most likely of our crows to be seen, generally in flocks in the fields, and they are often accompanied by jackdaws. The jackdaw is easily known by its smaller size and the grey patch on its nape. The voices are different too, that of the rook being a distinct "caw"— though sometimes it seems to crack and become a "squark"—while the jackdaw utters a note sounding like "jack" or

"tchack." The adult rook is further recognised by its bare, greyish-white face, though young rooks have feathered faces and are not easily distinguished from carrion crows. Rooks always nest in colonies or rookeries in clumps of tall trees, generally away from actual woods; they seem to favour the vicinity of farms, villages or country houses. Whether rooks are harmful or useful to agriculture has been much debated. Actually their varied diet is roughly half animal and half vegetable matter, the former comprising earth-worms, wire-worms, grubs, and insects of all kinds found in the soil, as well as field-mice and any other small creatures they can catch, not to mention any eggs that may be discovered. There is, however, no doubt that they eat a considerable amount of

LINNETS AND YOUNG. *The linnet's song, which resembles that of the canary, may be heard on the gorsy hills it frequents. Here the male and female bird are seen with their chicks; the nest has been built in a gorse bush.*

grain when they can get it, as well as potatoes and other roots.

The jackdaw generally nests in colonies, selecting holes and crevices in which to place its nest. Sea cliffs, chalk cliffs, church towers and ruined castles are all favoured as nesting sites as well as roosting places throughout the year. Jackdaws are very numerous; their numbers seem to increase annually so that jackdaws are found taking to rabbit holes for nesting places and ousting the chough from many of its former breeding places in the south-west.

At a distance the carrion crow looks much like a rook, but a closer view shows the face to be fully feathered instead of bare as in the adult rook. Moreover, crows are generally to be seen singly or in pairs instead of in flocks, though several may roost together. The carrion crow has discovered safety in some of the London parks where it regularly breeds. Its food consists of carrion, with, in addition, young birds, eggs, all types of insects and fruit.

THE LAPWING

Also known as the peewit or green plover, the lapwing is quite common in many districts and is not only one of our most elegant birds but, perhaps, the most useful of all, for it is almost wholly a destroyer of insects and grubs. Everybody knows it by its rounded wings, its distinct black and white appearance as it flies over in large flocks, or circles, twists and tumbles in the air in the spring, uttering its delightful cry of "pee-wit" with many variations. Its head bears an elegant crest, its under parts are of purest white and its upper parts though appearing black at a distance, possess a metallic green lustre. The lapwing nests on the ground in the fields and meadows, the nest being a mere depression in the ground, lined with stalks of grass. Four eggs, shaped like a peg-top, are laid and so well camouflaged

CHAFFINCH. *Conspicuous white bars are seen on the wings of the chaffinch. The male has a pink breast; the female is duller.*

with olive-brown, spotted with black, that they are most difficult to detect.

On open fields and meadows one is likely to see the beautiful yellow wagtail any time after the end of April, for it is more of a frequenter of open and moderately dry places than are the other wagtails which like to be near water. When it first arrives the cock bird is almost as bright a yellow as a canary.

Arriving on downlands quite early in the spring, the wheatear is conspicuous as it flits from one rock or mole hill to another, showing the very distinct white of the rump and base of the tail. Sometimes it disappears into a rabbit-hole— a favourite site for its nest.

Patches of gorse may attract the whinchat which will here meet its near relative, the resident stonechat. The male stonechat is easily known by his black head and white patches on the sides of his neck, features absent from his mate. The whinchat, mostly buffish brown in colour, is recognized by its white eye-

BULLFINCH AND YOUNG. *The beautiful rose-pink breast and black head of the male bullfinch make it a striking bird. The colours of the female are duller in tone. The nest, made of twigs, roots and hair, is generally built in a low tree or bush.*

38

WREN AND NEST. *A remarkably elaborate nest is built by the wren. Domed in appearance it is made of moss, leaves, grass, wool and feathers, with an entrance hole at the side. The wren is peculiar for its silent movement among trees and bushes.*

THRUSH'S NEST. *The thrush's nest (above) is made of twigs with a smooth mud lining.*

ROOK. *The rook is the most sociable member of the crow family. The young rook below has a feathered face, but when adult this is bare.*

stripe. Both like to perch on the top sprays of small bushes, especially gorse; their food consists almost entirely of harmful insects and grubs.

We must not forget the turtle dove, the beautiful little pigeon that arrives in this country from its winter quarters in Africa at the end of April or the first days of May. It is recognized by its small size, reddish brown upper parts, and broad white band to the tail as it flies. Its food consists of the seed of many kinds of weeds; and it builds its frail nest of sticks in tall bushes and hedges that have been allowed to grow. Its purring " coo " is one of the typical sounds of early summer.

Very dense woods usually contain few birds, but those with plenty of open spaces are well favoured. Oak woods are better than those of other trees, though some birds prefer conifers. So the best kind of wood is one of mixed trees with plenty of open, grassy spaces where there are closely growing bushes.

Wood-pigeons and stockdoves are sure to be met with, though they make expeditions into the surrounding fields for their food unless acorns are plentiful in the wood. The wood-pigeon is considerably the larger of the two and may readily be told by the broad white patches on the sides of the neck—whence ringdove—and the white band across the wings, though the young birds lack the first of these. Wood-pigeons are amongst the farmer's enemies because they are most destructive to crops, feeding upon grain and green food such as clover, young cabbages and sprouting corn. In severe weather they will strip every bit of green vegetable matter visible above the snow.

The stockdove is distinguished from the wood-pigeon by the absence of white on the neck, by its smaller size and darker colour. Its note, too, is different, sounding like " hoo-up " repeated several times and frequently heard in woods containing old timber ; for this bird does

not make its nest in the open like the wood-pigeon and the turtle dove, but mostly in the hollow trunks of old trees.

The three British woodpeckers, namely, the green, the greater spotted and the lesser spotted, may all be found in any large sized wood containing old timber. They belong to a very distinct group of birds, specialized for their peculiar mode of life which is that of extracting insects from the bark of trees and boring holes in the trunks as receptacles for their nests. Thus the claws are very sharp and strong, and the toes placed two facing forwards and two backwards, as in parrots, while the legs are quite short. The tail is pointed and of very stiff feathers which form a support as the bird works on a vertical trunk. The bill is pointed and very sharp and strong, while the tongue is long and worm-like, capable of being protruded for a considerable distance to secure insects lurking beneath the bark. All feed upon insects, mostly those hiding in the bark, but the green woodpecker—also known

HAWFINCH. *Largest of the finch family this bird's powerful bill gives it the name of Grosbeak. It is not commonly seen.*

WHEATEAR. *This bird, which visits British moorlands and hillsides in summer, often makes its nest in crevices among rocks or in an old rabbit-hole. Its white rump makes it conspicuous as it flits near the ground.*

as the " yaffle " from its call—is fond of visiting ants' nests on the ground, and devouring the ants, their pupae and larvae. The greater spotted woodpecker likes nuts and has often been observed at bird tables. The woodpecker's nesting hole is a very neat piece of work. Bored horizontally into the tree-trunk for two or three inches, it then turns downwards for twelve inches or more in the case of the green woodpecker, widening out as it descends to perhaps six inches near the bottom. Somewhat smaller is the hole made by the greater spotted woodpecker, while that of the lesser spotted woodpecker is even smaller.

We can tell the greater spotted woodpecker by its smaller size and distinct black and white plumage. The male has a crimson patch on the nape which is absent on the female, but both have a crimson patch under the tail. The call is quite distinct from that of the green woodpecker, sounding like "tchick." It also drums on the tree with its bill.

On account of its small size, not much larger than a sparrow, and its liking for the upper parts of high trees, the lesser spotted woodpecker is less often seen than the others, but may often be heard, especially in the spring, uttering its call " pee-pee-pee " often many times repeated. It is not really spotted but barred with white on a black back, while, in the male, the crown is crimson.

In the spring both the greater and lesser spotted woodpeckers have the habit of drumming : a rattling sound made by an extremely rapid series of blows with the bill upon resonant boughs or other surfaces among the thick trees.

A tapping sound frequently heard in the woods may be produced by one of the woodpeckers or by the nuthatch. In many ways like a woodpecker, the nuthatch has the same type of strong, straight bill and runs up and about the tree trunks with equal facility, but does not use its tail as a support. It searches the bark for insects, but is also extremely fond of nuts, acorns and beech-mast, which it collects and pushes into holes in the bark of trees and there splits open with its strong beak. It also eats many kinds of seeds, though it feeds its young upon insects. The nuthatch is a short, stumpy little bird with a short tail and can always be recognized by its bluish-grey upper parts and buff undersurface with chestnut on the flanks and a dark stripe through the eye. It has a variety of notes, especially in the spring, but the usual one, heard throughout the year, may be described as " chuwit-chuwit " sometimes repeated many times. One always knows a nuthatch's nest in a tree-trunk hole or nesting box by the entrance being plastered round with clay, reducing it to the bare size necessary.

Another climber of tree-trunks which is common enough in woods is the tree-creeper, a very small bird of mottled brown with white underparts and a white streak over the eye, a thin, curved bill and fairly long, stiff tail used, as with the woodpeckers, as a support when climbing. Composed of small twigs, moss and roots and lined with feathers, the tree creeper's nest is generally tucked behind a piece of loose bark or other crevice.

YELLOW WAGTAIL. *Never very common the yellow wagtail is a summer visitor. It makes its nest of grass, roots and hair on the ground or in a bank. The male bird's feathers are yellow and olive-green with a blackish tail; the female is less conspicuous.*

Nearly exterminated in the severe winter of 1916-17, but now recovered as to numbers, the long-tailed tit, one of the most frail and pretty of our birds, may often be met with in family parties in the woods hunting for insects and their grubs in the leaves, twigs, cones and seed-pods of trees. The birds are whitish grey with dark markings and flushed with pink, and can always be known by their very long tails as they hang and swing aloft. Generally placed in a thorn bush or clump of brambles and sometimes in gardens, the nest is one of the most beautiful of any; an upright oval ball

WOODPECKER. *Handsomely marked with black and white, with a red patch on its nape, the greater spotted woodpecker (left) may be seen on tree trunks searching for insects and larvæ.*

WOOD-PIGEON. *Grey in colour the wood-pigeon (below) is recognizable by its large size and the white mark on its neck.*

TOWN PIGEONS. *Most of our domestic pigeons are descended from the blue rock-dove, which is common throughout Europe. They are bluish-grey in colour with a green and purple sheen on the neck. All pigeons have a power of sustained flight.*

with a small entrance hole near the top. Moss and feathers are the materials used, bound together with spiders' webs and decorated on the outside with pieces of lichen.

In the woods, too, one meets those tits that have already been mentioned as town birds and others less often seen in town, as they definitely prefer the woods. These are the marsh tit and the coal tit, neither with any bright colours such as are possessed by the great and blue tits, but mostly browns and greys. Both have black caps and white cheeks, but the coal tit has a large white patch on the nape which is absent in the marsh tit.

The coal tit has a preference for fir woods, a situation in which one is almost certain to find the smallest of our British birds, the goldcrest, a tiny, yellowish-green creature with a crest of brilliant orange-yellow, bordered with black. It is not easy to detect the presence of this bird as it hunts for minute insects among the fronds, for its thin cry of "zeec-zeec" is almost inaudible, but it is quite common and large numbers arrive every autumn from the continent. The nest is quite a work of art, built of the softest moss, felted with cobwebs and wool and lined with feathers; it is hung beneath the extremity of a branch of conifer—spruce, cypress, yew or cedar being favourites.

Another name for the goldcrest is gold-crested wren, though it is a good deal smaller than and quite different from the common wren, with its stumpy, brown-coated body and habit of cocking

JAYS WITH YOUNG. *Small birds and animals fear the jay which preys upon them. This large bird with its distinctive black and white markings on the head and wings builds an untidy nest of sticks and roots in a bush or small tree.*

its tail. The wren is to be met with in the woods as in many other places and its joyous song, so loud for so small a bird, may be heard at almost all times of the year. So long as there is cover of the right kind, such as low, thick bushes, ivy-covered slopes, overgrown banks and such like, there one will find Jenny wren, creeping about or flying low from one bit of cover to another, popping up and perching with tail erect, only as suddenly to disappear from sight.

Jays and magpies are among the most handsome of all our birds, but they can do a great deal of harm to other birds by killing them and their young and eating their eggs. These birds have greatly increased in numbers, the increase being especially noticeable in the case of the magpie, which has become excessively

numerous throughout the country. Both feed to a large extent upon insects and grubs, but in the spring birds' eggs and young birds form a large part of their food and that upon which their young are reared. In autumn, jays especially are fond of raiding gardens for vegetables and fruit. The jay is easily recognized by its pinkish body, white back and blue patch on the wing, and the magpie by its black and white plumage and long tail.

The summer migrants which appear in the woods in April and May are many and varied and at once make their presence known by their songs. The first is, as a rule, the chiff-chaff, whose song from the middle of March onwards is a repetition of its name many times over. The willow warbler follows it very closely with a cheerful melody, heard on

CHIFF-CHAFF AT NEST. *The chiff-chaff (above), which is a summer visitor to Britain, derives its name from its incessantly repeated song.*

GARDEN WARBLER. *The garden warbler (below) is of the same family as the chiff-chaff. The nest, a frail structure of dried grass, is often made among brambles.*

ROBIN. *One of the friendliest of birds the robin (above) is common everywhere in the British Isles. Its sweet song consists of many and varied notes and trills.*

NIGHTINGALE. *A shy bird with inconspicuous plumage the nightingale (below) can be easily located by its full rich song.*

every side throughout the summer. Both are small greenish birds sometimes known as leaf warblers. Another, the wood warbler, which arrives in mid-April, makes its home in beech and oak woods and has a song with two distinct phrases quite unlike that of any other bird. The first consists of a long drawn, shivering trill which may be repeated many times before the second is uttered. This is a soft " puu-puu " not generally repeated so often as the first. One may easily mistake the two phrases for the notes of two different birds. It is easy to spot this bird among the trees by the noticeable yellow streak above its eye.

We first hear the voice of the cuckoo about April 14th, whence it goes on calling until the end of June. The hen cuckoo keeps an eye on the nests, which she discovers by the movement of the birds in her particular territory. In each nest she has observed she places one egg, providing that those of the victims are at the right stage. At the same time she removes one of the eggs she finds there. As soon as it is hatched, the young cuckoo has the one object in view of turning out anything it finds in the nest, whether it be eggs or young birds. This it proceeds to do by working its body beneath the object, climbing backwards up the side of the nest and pitching it over. The young cuckoo's foster parents pay it devoted attention, not appearing to miss their own young.

Nightingales are not by any means rare, especially in the south-east of England, and their lovely song is heard from mid-April to the hatching of their young in June, when they become silent. Blackcaps and garden warblers, both delightful singers, whitethroats and lesser whitethroats all come along in April, though the spotted flycatcher, which sometimes leaves the woods and ventures into our gardens, building its nest against the wall of the house, generally waits until May before putting

SNIPE AND PARTRIDGE

Above is seen a family of common snipe at their nest; below, a pair of partridges.

A PAIR OF KINGFISHERS

There is a tropical brilliance about the dazzling blue-green upper plumage of the kingfisher. These birds nest near lakes and streams, living on insects and small fish.

A PAIR OF JAYS

The jay is a member of the crow family; it is a handsome bird with pinkish-brown plumage and black and white markings on the wings.   The head crest is speckled.

DIURNAL BIRDS OF PREY
Distinctive features of the buzzard are its broad, rounded wings and mewing cry.

in an appearance. May, too, is the month in which the nightjar arrives in Britain, but we must go into the open woodlands or the heather moors at dusk to hear its curious churring song. The nightjar flies low in the daytime and does its hunting and love-making at sunset. Its two eggs are laid on the bare ground, but are so well camouflaged as to be quite difficult to detect ; and the bird, as it squats on the ground, itself looks more like a piece of dead wood with the bark on it than anything else.

Water birds are discussed in another chapter, but we may note here a small olive-brown bird busily hunting about on the rocks for insects, and as it flies up, uttering a note sounding like " chip." Reminding us of a meadow pipit and, in fact, a very close relative of that bird, is the rock pipit. Quite common wherever there are rocks, it generally nests in holes or crevices in the cliffs and lays four or five eggs, densely speckled with grey, or grey-brown, at the end of the spring.

Parties of oyster-catchers or sea pies, curlews, dunlin and redshanks may sometimes be seen hunting for their prey in the shallows or on mud-banks, while small flocks of dainty ringed plover come swinging along the edge of the tide. Several others of the waders, which breed in the far north, visit us in some numbers during the spring and autumn migrations.

Fortunately, the kingfisher, the sole bird on our list of a really tropical brilliance, is not rare along our rivers and streams. Generally one first hears its distinctive call, " chee-chee," and sees a streak of dazzling blue disappearing along the stream. If one keeps quite still, one of these lovely birds may settle close by, on some branch or post or even on one's fishing rod, and one notices the long pointed bill and chestnut underparts. The nest is formed of fish-bones at the end of a hole in a bank.

Another fairly common bird in the neighbourhood of reed-beds is the reed

DARTFORD WARBLER. *This retiring bird (above) with its long tail is the sole member of the warbler family to reside in Britain, and is seen only in the south.*

REED BUNTING. *A broad white collar with a black head and bib make it easy to sight the cock reed bunting (below). The female has a dark brown "moustache" line.*

SNIPE. *The snipe builds a nest of grass, generally concealed in rushes on the marshes or moors. When the bird is disturbed by sportsmen it flies in an erratic zig-zag fashion until it believes it is out of danger. Its long bill is particularly useful in its search for worms, which are its chief food.*

bunting, in which the cock bird is conspicuous with his black head and throat and white collar, features lacking in the brown hen. It nests on or near the ground and feeds its young upon the seeds of marsh plants and insects. We shall not proceed far over a marsh without putting up a snipe, which starts off with many sudden twists and turns before settling on a steady course. As it flies we see its long bill and hear its cry, " scape-scape." In the spring we may hear and watch it " drumming " as it flies high, every now and then turning and diving down at a steep angle, tail spread and wings quivering to make the sound.

The pied wagtail is generally to be seen near water, but it also likes to frequent grassy meadows and the lawns of country houses where it may be watched with its tail swaying up and down, every few seconds making a rush forward to capture some small insect. Usually it builds in some hole or corner, occasionally in outbuildings or the thatch of a shed. In winter large numbers roost together in reed beds or thick bushes or trees. The very beautiful grey wagtail, with extra long tail, golden patch above and below the base of the tail and blue-grey upper parts, is not uncommon in the north and west of Britain where it frequents rocky streams. In early spring and autumn it may be seen by quite small streams and

LAPWING. *A close view of the lapwing reveals its glossy iridescent feathers and clear black and white markings. Characteristic of this bird is its long crest and heavy, rounded wings, which give it a ponderous flight. Its cry is "pee-wit".*

KINGFISHER. *This bird haunts lakes and streams that are well stocked with fish. Its feathers are brilliantly coloured; the upper parts are blue, with a greenish sheen, the under-part is chestnut. The nest is generally made in a hole on the bank of a river.*

ponds in any part of the country and even in towns.

In reed-beds, during the summer months, we expect to hear, if not to see, the sedge warbler, a small sprightly brown bird with a distinct light eye-stripe, which scolds, as one approaches its haunts, with a harsh " tuck-tuck " or a " chirr "; or sings its loud and rather grating song when disturbed, as when a pebble is tossed into the reeds. The sedge warbler arrives about the middle of April and is followed a week or so later by its relative, the reed warbler, which can be distinguished by its more musical song

and by the absence of the light eye-stripe. This bird is rarely seen north of York-shire and never in Scotland or Ireland. Haunting river reed-beds it builds itself a neat nest of dry grass, lined with wool and hair; reeds are woven into the sides of this cup-shaped structure and the nest hangs suspended. Even in stormy weather the nest is not often dislodged. The upper parts of the reed-warbler are reddish brown, the under parts being yellowish white. It is in the evening that one may most frequently hear its exuberant song, which contains a great variety of notes and is less harsh than that of the sedge warbler.

OYSTER-CATCHER AND EGGS. *Commonly called the sea-pie because of its striking black and white plumage the oyster-catcher is a good swimmer and often takes to the water for its food. The eggs, laid on the ground, are yellowish blotched with brown*

MALLARD AT REST

WATER BIRDS

by

BRIAN VESEY-FITZGERALD

IT would be possible under so general a title to include a very large proportion of the birds on the British list. For example, the dipper, the sedge-warbler, the reed-warbler and several of the wagtails could be described with every justification as water birds, since they live by streams, ponds and marshes, and indeed spend the whole of their lives in close proximity to water. On the other hand, one might exclude all those birds that are not web-footed. Let us take a middle course. Let us exclude all the passerine birds (the dipper, wagtails and so forth) because they are members of an order that is essentially terrestrial in habit and can properly be regarded as exceptions to the general rule of that order, but include the wading birds (the plovers, snipe, curlew, etc.) because they are structurally adapted for a more or less aquatic life and because nearly all of them do spend a very large part of their lives in the immediate vicinity of water, either on river-bank or sea-shore.

So this chapter will deal, so far as space allows, with the Anatidae (the swans, geese and ducks), the Ardeidae (the herons and bitterns), the Rallidae (the rails), the Phalacrocoracidae (the cormorants), the Podicipidae (the grebes), the Colymbidae (the divers), and the Scolopacidae and Charadriidae (the waders and plovers), among the land birds with aquatic habits, and with all those sea birds (the gulls, terns, auks, shearwaters and petrels) which are to be found around our coasts. The sea-birds form an easily recognizable and fairly cohesive group for they are, with very few exceptions, predominantly aquatic,

coming to land only to breed and rest. But among the others is to be found a very wide range of habit and much over-lapping so far as habitat is concerned.

Let us take the Anatidae first of all. There are on the British list three swans, twelve geese, and thirty-one ducks. Of the twelve geese only eight need concern us here for the remaining four are very rare visitors indeed, while of the thirty-one ducks, only nineteen are regular members of our fauna. The swans are the whooper swan, Bewick's swan, and the mute swan; the geese, the greylag, the bean, the pink-foot, the white-fronted, the dark-breasted brent, the light-breasted brent (these may be regarded as one species for all practical purposes), the barnacle and the Canada; the ducks, mallard, gadwall, teal, wigeon, garganey, pintail, shoveler, pochard, tufted, scaup, golden-eye, long-tailed, eider, scoter, velvet-scoter, goosander, red-breasted merganser, smew, and sheld-duck.

The geese are divided again into two groups: the grey geese (greylag, bean, pink-foot and white front), and the black geese (brent, barnacle, and Canada). The ducks are divided into three groups: the surface feeders (mallard, gadwall, teal, garganey, wigeon, pintail, shoveler), the diving ducks (pochard, tufted, scaup, golden-eye, long-tailed, eider, scoter, velvet-scoter), and the sawbills (red-breasted merganser, goosander, smew), with the sheld-duck in a little group of its own forming a sort of link between the ducks and the geese. That has made a rather formidable catalogue, but the divisions are important. We will now

review in detail some of the most interesting species.

Of the swans, the whooper breeds in northern Scotland and in winter turns up all round our coasts but never in large numbers, the mute (which is the common swan of our town parks) breeds all over the country and is now as wild a bird in many places as it is tame in others. Bewick's swan, the smallest of the three, does not breed anywhere in the British Isles and visits us only in the winter.

It is easy to tell the difference between the mute swan and either of the other two, for the mute has an orange bill with, in the male, a large black knob at the

CANADA GEESE. *Introduced into Britain as ornamental birds, these geese (left) have reverted to their wild state. They are most common in East Anglia.*

BARNACLE GEESE. *Maritime birds by nature, the barnacle geese (below) will come to land at night to feed on stubble.*

base of it, and it swims with its neck held in a graceful S-bend. Neither of the others swim with the neck curved and both have yellow bills. The whooper is much the larger of the two (as big as a mute), and the yellow occupies most of the base of the bill, while in Bewick's swan it is only a patch at the base. The whooper has got its name from the sound, *whoop-pa*, it makes on the wing, a very loud resonant trumpeting call. Bewick's swan is also vocal though in less loud tones, but the mute swan very rarely does more than hiss severely at unwelcome visitors.

There is another difference between the three. The mute is a bird of fresh water before everything else. That does not mean that it does not occur on salt water, but it will take up residence on almost any piece of fresh water, even quite small ponds in the centre of towns, and it has a fondness for rivers. Both the others, as far as Britain is concerned, are birds of the estuaries, coming to land only to feed and generally resting on the water at some little distance from the shore.

The grey geese are much more closely bound to the shore than are the black. In fact the grey geese are land birds that go to sea while the black geese are sea birds that sometimes come to land. The largest of the grey geese is the greylag, which is the ancestor of our common domestic goose. It breeds in northern Scotland but is elsewhere only a visitor in winter. None of the other grey geese breeds in the British Isles, and all of them visit us only in winter.

In the winter these grey geese spend

GREYLAG GOOSE. *Ancestor of the common domestic goose, the greylag is the only wild goose to breed in the British Isles. These winter visitors haunt the northern shores, often sleeping on the water and flying inland at dawn to feed on grass.*

GEESE IN FLIGHT. *When in flight, wild geese assume a regular V formation. Wary and suspicious birds by nature, many geese will come inland to feed on remote marshes and swamps only in the hours of daylight.*

the night on sandbanks off the shore or even sleep on the water, flighting in at dawn to feed on the stubbles or the grass of coastwise fields and flighting out again at dusk. They are astonishingly regular in their times for flighting, having due regard for the set of the tide, and are essentially day feeders.

The only exception to this rule of daylight feeding is on nights when the moon is full. They will then stay on land and feed throughout the night. They are very wary and suspicious and extremely hard to approach, but the story that a feeding flock posts sentries need not be believed. True, there is always a bird or two with head up and watchful in every feeding flock at any given moment, but this is not the result of well-laid plans on the part of the flock, merely the natural result of an extremely cautious disposition. That is, too, why the birds feed on moonlit nights. They then have sufficient light to see approaching danger, whether it be from fox or man. The black geese are entirely different in habit.

MARITIME BIRDS

Both the brent and the barnacle are maritime birds by nature, the brent exclusively so. Barnacle geese do come to land to feed, grazing on grass and very rarely visiting cultivated land (the pinkfoot has an especial fondness for cultivated land and can do a good deal of damage to crops), but they feed for the most part at night. In those districts where they are not subject to any persecution from gunners they will feed by day, which seems to indicate that their habits have been changed to meet the press of danger. Except for this night feeding tendency they are by no means so wary and suspicious as the other geese and are comparatively easy to approach.

Brent geese on the other hand hardly ever come to land, and for that matter, hardly ever fly across land. They will, in preference to crossing a very narrow peninsula, fly out to sea and round it, and so are very rarely shot by the shore gunner. Pre-eminently they are the punt-gunner's goose. They feed almost ex-

clusively on that marine weed called *Zostera marina,* coming inshore when the tide is sufficiently low to have uncovered the beds or at least made them accessible, and pulling the plants up by the roots. As a general rule brent geese are to be found where *Zostera* grows, and *Zostera* has been getting steadily less common around our shores during the last twenty years. All geese are gregarious, but none more so than the brent. A single brent is very rare indeed, and is almost certainly a wounded bird, but flocks of many hundreds are by no means uncommon off our shores during the winter months.

The last of the black geese is the Canada goose, which is the biggest of all our geese the greylag included. Canada geese have different habits from all our other geese. This is because they have been introduced and have only recently become wild birds in Britain. Like the mute swan (another bird that has only recently become truly wild, though there is no evidence that the mute swan was introduced) they are birds of fresh water rather than salt water, and prefer inland ponds and lakes to the estuaries. They feed by day and, as they are little shot at, are comparatively easy to approach; but they are beginning to acquire the wary habits of wild geese.

In recent years a tendency to flight in the manner of other geese has been noticeable and there does seem to be in winter a tendency to move to the coast. But Canada geese have not yet been seen flighting in from the sea. Grey geese are very hard to tell apart. It is easy enough to tell black from grey geese, and to tell a bernicle from a brent, for the colouring is distinctive. But the grey geese are very

confusing and when on the wing at any height it is quite impossible, even for the expert, to tell one from another. After they have been shot, adult grey geese can usually be identified without much trouble, but immature birds, even when dead, can quite easily defeat the expert.

SURFACE FEEDING DUCKS

The surface feeding ducks are relatively slenderly built birds. They obtain most of their food in shallow water, either by securing it on the surface or from the mud with a quick dabbling motion of the bill, or, if the water is too deep for that, by "up-ending" in the manner of farm-yard ducks with the head and the front part of the body submerged and the tail in the air. When "up-ended," position is

TEAL. *The smallest of the surface feeding ducks, the teal is common on lakes and pools throughout Britain, and large flocks of them may be seen at river estuaries during the winter. The drake is a handsome bird with green and chestnut head markings.*

MUTE SWAN. *A familiar sight on ponds, lakes and rivers, the mute swan is a partly domesticated bird. The nest is made of a mass of vegetation and down, and the parent birds are fierce guardians of their young. Swans feed on water-plant seeds and insects.*

maintained by paddling hard with the feet. Surface feeding ducks do rest upon the water—in particular the wigeon does so—but all of them come to land to rest, and all of them are quite at home on land, walking with ease and running quite freely if they have to do so. When resting they like to do so on one leg. Some feed on land to a certain extent—the mallard in particular—but all prefer to feed in shallow water. All swim easily and well, but the adults will only dive under exceptional circumstances, as for example when wounded, although all the young dive extremely well and often do so apparently for pleasure. All surface feeding ducks can rise from the water easily. They spring directly into the air and are very soon under way and at a

good height. All fly fairly fast and though the wing beats seem very rapid they are by no means as rapid as in other ducks. Most of them fly straight, but the teal will dodge almost as expertly as the snipe if occasion demands, and invariably at a lower altitude than the others.

No ducks—or for that matter geese or swans—glide during their ordinary flight, but when they are preparing to alight they come down in a long slanting glide. Just before they pitch the neck is craned forwards, the body dropped and the feet and tail (which is spread and acts as a brake) thrust forward so that the feet strike the water first. Whenever possible ducks take off and alight into the wind, but they seem to be able to do both with the wind behind without suffering

BITTERN AND NEST. *The bittern, once shot in large numbers, is now protected and breeds in guarded sanctuaries in Britain, where it is a winter visitor. It is a shy bird, and usually remains well hidden in the reeds of the marshes it haunts.*

THREE WELL-KNOWN WATER BIRDS. (*Right*). *Above is the moorhen, common on inland waters. It has a scarlet and yellow bill. The shoveler (centre) is a familiar bird of passage. Its spade-like bill gives it its name. The wigeon (below) is a winter visitor to Britain, but nests occasionally in Scotland.*

any noticeable inconvenience. Most of them have a conspicuously coloured patch, called the speculum, on the secondaries. This patch, which is always less brilliant in the duck than in the drake, is a very useful means of identification particularly in the ducks, who are often, and during eclipse, clad in a very similar sober garb.

All the drakes of European species assume "eclipse" plumage, closely resembling the normal plumage of birds, about mid-summer, but they do not lose the characteristic speculum. Ducks also have an eclipse plumage, assumed some weeks later than the drake, but it varies so little from the normal dress, that, as far as identification in the field is concerned, it can be ignored. During the eclipse stage the birds are to all intents and purposes flightless. During the autumn, but in one or two species a good deal later than that, the ordinary plumage is resumed.

Of the British surface feeding ducks the mallard, teal and wigeon are by far the best known since they are by far the most numerous. The mallard is the ancestor of all our coloured domestic ducks, and wild mallard drakes will sometimes take wives from the farmyard. It is a bird of catholic tastes and will frequent any water from a large reservoir or a river the size of the Thames to very small ponds or ornamental waters in town parks, and it is to be found equally at home on water high up on moorlands and flooded fields at sea-level.

In the winter very large flocks of mallard will visit the sea-shore and rest

during the day on the sea at some distance from the land. The wigeon is very much more maritime in habit, and is fond of consorting with brent geese. As a breeding bird it has increased considerably in Britain of recent years, but it is in the winter that huge numbers visit us from abroad. Though occurring far inland, it is in the main a bird of the coast and like the brent geese prefers above all things the *Zostera* beds. The teal, the smallest of our surface feeders, is less addicted than the others to the coast in winter, though sometimes large numbers, particularly in frosty weather, will gather in the estuaries. It feeds mainly at night and is very much less at ease on the land than, say, the mallard. It nests in suitable places throughout Britain. The pintail is less common but is so strikingly handsome that it cannot be mistaken when seen. The teal is generally credited with being the fastest flier of all the ducks, but this honour must go to the pintail, and in point of fact the mallard is also faster on the wing than the teal. Of the others the shoveler with its huge spatulate bill (from which it gets its name) is also unmistakable. Of recent years, it has increased as a breeding species, but is less frequently seen owing to its fondness for shallow muddy water and thick reed beds. It has a pronounced preference for fresh water and even in hard winters visits the estuaries less than any of the other surface feeders, finding adequate food among pond weeds and water insects.

The diving ducks are shorter bodied than the surface feeders. Much more stockily built and with their legs set very far back, they are quite distinct in appearance. They are not at all at home on land, walking very clumsily indeed, and they do not therefore come much to land except for breeding purposes. Generally speaking they prefer open water and do not worry about cover, and in the winter some of them are purely sea-going birds.

In contrast to the surface feeders, most of them experience considerable difficulty in rising from water, pattering along the surface for quite a distance with much heavy beating of wings before they become air-borne. When once on the wing most of them fly fast and straight with very rapid wing beats. In flight, the feet stick out beyond the tail and the broad blunt wings and short thick necks are often noticeable. In comparison with the surface feeders diving-ducks alight clumsily on the water, and not infrequently they come down with a splash out of all proportion to their size. "Up-ending" is very uncommon, all the species dive for their food. None of them feeds on land. The eclipse is less noticeable as a general rule, and there is no distinct speculum though white patches or bars on the wings are common enough.

COMMON DIVING DUCKS

Of our diving ducks the pochard, the tufted and the golden-eye are the most common. The tufted duck, in particular, has increased enormously of recent years, and like the mallard is obviously a bird very easily suited so far as accommodation goes. Some of the others, like the eider, the scoter, and the scaup are more or less plentiful in certain districts and very uncommon in others.

With the exception of the smew, the saw-bills can be recognized at once by their long slender tapering bills and generally slender build. In addition they have a mane or crest of feathers at the back of the head, and this sometimes leads to confusion with the grebes. In flight the neck is extended in a straight line with the body, giving the bird an appearance that is instantly recognizable. On land they walk as easily but not as gracefully as surface feeding ducks, though they are altogether more graceful and lively than the rather stodgy diving ducks. They, too, are divers, but they are not vegetarians, feeding for the

HERONS AND YOUNG

This water bird of marshland and lakes has a formidable bill and soft grey plumage.

TUFTED AND GOLDEN-EYE DUCKS

The tufted duck has a drooping crest, the golden-eye drake a white patch.

most part on fish. For this reason they are quite uneatable by human beings, the flesh being extraordinarily strong and rank. The smew is not a typical saw-bill, being in general appearance a diving duck, short-billed and stocky. With the exception that it likes small and shallow fresh-water pools, which are avoided by the others, it is in habits a typical saw-bill. The drakesmew, a white bird with a black patch on the side of the face, is the most handsome of all our white fowl, but it is scarce, and though it visits Britain every winter, is not very frequently seen in these islands. The duck, a much smaller bird, is grey on the back, with chestnut on the crown and neck.

The sheld-duck, a most striking black, white and chestnut bird with a bright red bill, comes midway between the ducks and the geese. It likes low lying sandy and muddy coasts about estuaries, but in the breeding season will sometimes come quite far inland. Unlike others of its family it nests in holes, and the eggs are sometimes laid quite a long way from the entrance. In flight it resembles a goose with its relatively slow wing beats which give the altogether deceptive appearance of slow flight. Though it can swim very well, and sometimes goes far out to sea, it is much less aquatic than any of the other ducks. The flesh of this bird resembles nothing so much as a box of paints.

All members of the Anatidae are able to mate only on water.

Herons, bitterns, rails, grebes and divers must be taken together. It is a very arbitrary grouping but, with the possible exception of the divers (and they are closely related to the grebes) they have habitat in common. All are primarily birds of inland waters and quiet streams. The heron, a large lavender-grey bird with a very powerful beak, is a common sight by stream and pond sides. It feeds largely on fish, but is not averse to rats, ducklings and anything

else that it can impale upon that formidable beak. It nests, for the most part, high up in tall trees, but with its long legs is obviously a wading bird intended by nature to nest on the ground. The bittern, a close relative, prefers very thick reed beds fringing meres or sluggish streams. It is an extremely secretive bird and is very rarely seen. Indeed, about 1868 it became extinct as a British breeding bird, but in 1911 bred again in Norfolk and has since done so regularly and in increasing numbers.

Of the rails only the water-rail, the moorhen and the coot interest us as water birds. All three are residents and breed regularly. The moorhen and the coot are extremely common and familiar to everyone who visits inland waters at all, and the moorhen will take up residence upon the most unsuitable stretches of water. One has even built a nest and laid eggs on a fish pond in the writer's garden, but unfortunately did not do more. The water-rail is also common, very much more so than is generally realized. But it is a bird of the thick reed beds and is of a very retiring and secretive nature, more often heard than seen.

GREBE FAMILY

Four grebes (the great crested, the Slavonian, the black-necked and the little or dabchick) are more or less common in Britain and three divers (the great northern, the black-throated and the red-throated) occur regularly though not in any great numbers. All four grebes breed in England. The great crested is fairly common and seems to be increasing, the little grebe is common and widely distributed, the other two are uncommon and only breed sporadically. Both the red- and black-throated divers breed in Scotland in limited numbers and occur also as winter visitors. The great northern diver does not breed in the British Isles and is mainly a winter visitor, but the number of birds staying

HERON. *Haunting marshes, lakes and rivers, the heron is recognizable by its dark grey wings and its powerful bill which is used to impale fish and frogs.*

through the summer appears to be increasing and it would not be surprising if they did breed in the near future.

The divers breed on inland waters, preferring the larger and deeper stretches, and outside the breeding season are mainly marine in habit staying fairly close inshore but rarely coming inland. The grebes, with the exception of the little grebe, whose tastes are quite as catholic as those of the moorhen, prefer much the same sort of breeding places though with a greater tendency to choose waters with a good cover. In winter all four resort in large numbers to the sea, living as do the divers, close to the shore, but whereas the divers are rarely to be found inland outside the breeding season, both the great crested and little grebes do not wholly desert inland waters, although in winter they show a marked preference for large waters devoid of the cover of reed-beds.

Neither grebes nor divers are really at home on land and outside the breeding season come to it as little as possible. The great crested grebe is a strong and fast flier and habitually migrates locally, flying at a considerable height. All the divers are strong fliers but are quite unable to rise quickly from the water and from small areas are unable to rise at all. As diving birds both are expert. Great crested grebes have been known to dive to the depth of twenty-one feet and habitually do so to the depth of twelve feet, while the average length of dive is twenty-six seconds with a maximum of fifty seconds. The great northern diver has been timed to stay under for more than three minutes, but forty seconds is about the average. Depths of more than thirty-three feet have been recorded for this species. The other two divers are quite as expert, the black-throated having been recorded as covering a quarter of a mile in a single dive of two minutes. Though not normally gregarious to the same extent as ducks or geese, they sometimes occur in large flocks.

As far as Britain is concerned, the two families that make up the waders contain some sixty-eight species. Of these, some are very scarce, but the majority turn up regularly every winter at any rate and sometimes in enormous numbers. Flocks

of knot, winter visitors to British shores, have been noted to aggregate five and ten thousand birds. In view of the great number of species it is evident that only a short general account can be given. Any bird lover of ordinary experience can recognize a wader at sight, even if it be a bird hitherto unknown to him. They are all birds of small to medium size—even the curlew is not really a large bird—generally with long or fairly long legs. They are birds that either run or walk, never hop. With the exception of the woodcock they are birds of open country, disdaining cover, though the snipe will sometimes join the woodcock in cover for the day. A few will breed in wooded country, however. All are more or less closely associated with water, and this is true even of the lapwing and the golden plover which may be found regularly in very dry places, because outside the breeding season these two also show a marked preference for water.

PUFFINS. *The outstanding feature of the puffin is its massive bill, which is striped with grey-blue, yellow and scarlet. These birds are found on all British coasts, but*

large numbers of them flock to the rocks of the western shores. Puffins feed on fish, for which they dive, swimming under the water with their powerful wings.

WOODCOCK. *Haunting woods and marshes, this bird (above) has a highly patterned brown plumage barred with black and chestnut. In daylight it stays under cover.*

BLACK-THROATED DIVER. *A migrant to British northern shores, the handsome black-throated diver (below) has a distinctive summer plumage of black and white.*

YOUNG DUCKS. *Most common domestic ducks (above) are descended from the mallard, a small water bird, which frequents lakes and marshes in large numbers.*

LITTLE GREBE. *A resident of inland waters, this bird (below) is known as the dabchick. Practically tail-less, it has nearly black feathers with chestnut checks.*

RINGED PLOVER. *One of the smallest of the wader family, the ringed plover haunts the sandy shores on which it seeks its food. The nest is a slight depression in a sand or pebble ridge; the eggs are speckled with brown.*

As a group, they are, indeed, birds of the narrow rim at the edge of the tide—and all can swim well when necessary. All, without exception, are masters of flight. Flight is invariably fast with rapid wing beats, and it is only the different shape of the wings that makes the lapwing, for example, appear slow.

WADER FAMILY

Waders can be divided roughly into two groups : round-headed and short-billed (the plovers), and long-headed and long-billed (curlews and sandpipers). Both types are intensely gregarious and often occur in mixed flocks of huge size. Both indulge in the most marvellously intricate communal flights, a flock of some thousands of apparently leaderless birds turning as one and moving with the precision of guardsmen. A favourite attitude with all waders is to stand on one leg, and if disturbed but not unduly pressed the birds will hop along without troubling to lower the leg. When alighting most waders hold the wings vertically above the back for a moment presenting as they do a sight of great beauty. When asleep the bill is normally tucked into the scapular feathers.

With all waders, times of feeding, with the exception of course of the breeding season and those lapwings of purely inland habit, are governed by the tides: at various times they all feed at night. At the high tide some, notably curlews, will flight inland, returning as the tide ebbs. The majority of our waders are winter visitors or passage migrants, and in general are most common in the autumn.

But some breed in Britain in considerable numbers : notably the lapwing, the golden plover, the curlew, the redshank, the woodcock, the snipe and the oyster-catcher, a large black and white bird with a ruby eye, less notably the dunlin, which is one of the commonest birds of the shore in the autumn, and the dotterel. Of them the lapwing, the curlew, the snipe and the redshank are best known for they are the most widely distributed and have also outstanding characteristics. The curlew's wild musical cry "cur-leee" is a very part of the moorlands ; the snipe's drumming is a feature of water-meadows and marshes through the spring and summer ; the redshank has well earned the nickname "warden of the marshes," for it is wary in the extreme and its shrill yelping warns all

the birds of the neighbourhood of danger ; the lapwing, one of the farmers' very best friends, is so common and its call "pee-weet," so familiar that it needs no introduction. With its rounded wings the lapwing appears clumsy in flight, but it is just as much master of aerial manœuvre as any other wader, and its acrobatics in the mating season are marvellously daring. The snipe's "drumming" is not vocal but mechanical, and is caused by the two outer feathers of the tail being held stiffly at right angles to the rest during the downward plunge so that they offer resistance to the wind. The snipe's call has none of the musical quality of the curlew's or the lapwing's, and is usually uttered only when the bird gets up from the ground when alarmed. The drumming is confined to the breeding season and is usually performed in a rough circle above the nest.

Migration is conducted for the most part at night and the birds fly over land

FULMAR PETREL. *In flight, the fulmar excels other seabirds in its ability to glide long distances without wing-beats. It builds no nest, but lays a single egg on a rocky ledge or a hollow in the turf. These birds have large breeding colonies on St. Kilda.*

HOW GULLS FLY. *The motions of the gull in flight may be followed from the top left-hand in a circular direction to the bottom left-hand. Head, tail and the wings are*

used to keep the bird evenly balanced as it alights. Like most ocean birds, gulls make use of wind currents to enable them to glide long distances without wing-beats.

frequently calling as they do so. More than once curlew have been heard passing over London, and on several occasions calls from migrating birds have been noted that have been strange to the listener. It seems to indicate that some at least must have special calls used only on migratory flights.

If that is an all too brief account of the waders the position as regards the sea birds is just as difficult. Sixty-six species figure on the British list, though some are very rare. Cormorant and shag are here included among the sea birds, because though both occur on inland water (especially the cormorant) they are essentially marine birds, earning their living in salt water but not as a rule out of sight of land. The shag is generally restricted to rocky coasts but the cormorant does not mind where it lives. They are large dark green birds of rather repellent appearance; the shag is the smaller, the male bearing a plume or tuft on the top of its head. Both shag and cormorant belong to the same family as the pelican and both are expert fishermen.

POWERFUL SEABIRDS

Seventeen gulls and three skuas are recorded as British. Certain of the gulls have only been recorded once, but these are birds of such powerful flight, used to covering enormous distances, that they may well turn up more frequently and pass unnoticed in the crowd. Some of the others are so very much alike that it is difficult to tell them apart when on the beach or in the air. Only six—the black-headed gull, the common gull, the herring-gull, the lesser black-backed and the greater black-backed, and the kitti-wake—breed in the British Isles. The common gull, by the way, is not nearly so common as the black-headed gull, which is the gull of the Thames and which is becoming more and more an inland bird, visiting towns and dustbins far from water with great regularity, and

following the plough in company with the rooks. Skuas are also gulls to all appearance, save that they are brown rather than white, but they are birds of prey, preying upon the gulls, terns and so forth of their neighbourhood. Large and powerful, they will so harry a bird that has successfully secured a fish that finally in sheer terror it will drop it, whereupon the skua swoops down and secures a free meal before it reaches the sea. Skuas will also demonstrate forcefully against a human near their nest in the breeding season, and men have been buffeted by the " bonxie," as it is also known.

In an order of its own is the gannet, a large white bird with long pointed black tipped wings, known quite commonly as the solan goose. An exclusively maritime bird, it lives by diving for fish and usually does so from a height of eighty to one hundred feet, going down like a bullet. It has been caught in a trawl ninety feet below the surface. A very powerful flier once on the wing, it will fly as much as eighty to one hundred miles from its colonies to feed.

The auks include the guillemot, razor-bill, little auk and puffin. They are all essentially maritime birds, coming only to land in the breeding season, and then being restricted to cliffs and rocky ledges. Magnificent swimmers and divers, they are also expert fliers with very rapid beats of very short wings. None makes any nest, simply laying a single egg on a rocky shelf or in a fissure, though the puffin invariably lays in a hole—generally an old rabbit burrow—on the cliff top. In winter they all go to sea and remain as a rule far from land. Exceptionally the little auk gets driven inland by very severe gales, but generally they seem able to ride out the roughest weather.

Shearwaters and petrels belong to the same order and have much in common. Twenty species have been recorded in England, most of them so rarely that they can only be regarded as accidental

LESSER BLACK-BACKED GULL. *This bird may be distinguished from the great black-backed by its yellow legs. The mottled brown plumage of the young gulls does not change to white until they are three or four years old.*

RAZORBILLS. *Razorbills are ocean birds, living on fish, for which they dive and swim under water. No nest is ever built; one buff-coloured egg is laid on a rocky ledge.*

visitors. Of the rest, the storm petrel and Leach's fork-tailed petrel breed in limited numbers and so does the Manx shearwater, while the Fulmar petrel is increasing its breeding range in a most spectacular manner. The great shearwater and the sooty shearwater visit us regularly in the autumn though never in great numbers. All these birds, like the auks, are essentially maritime, coming to land only to breed. With the exception of the Fulmar they lay their egg in a hole, generally burrowed by themselves, but the storm petrel will lay in crevices in the rocks or in holes in walls. The Fulmar lays its eggs on the bare ground or on a shelf of the rock, but occasionally in a hollow around which it will arrange stones. Like the auks, all these birds spend most of their lives out at sea, and are expert swimmers and fliers.

The terns are the swallows of the sea, swallows in shape of wings and type of flight, exquisite and dainty to view, but quarrelsome and shrewish to each other. Twelve species have been recorded in Britain, six of them very rare wanderers to our shores, five breeding regularly in restricted localities, and one, the black tern, which once bred in England, now occurring only on passage. Though by no means exclusively maritime (the common tern breeds quite frequently by inland waters) they are primarily seagoing birds, and one, the Arctic tern (which breeds in some districts of England and Wales, and plentifully in Scotland), is the greatest traveller in the world. For while some breed far north in the Arctic (Britain is about its furthest south as a breeding station) it winters on the shores of the Antarctic, a journey of some 11,000 miles made twice a year—a remarkable feat of flying.

GUILLEMOTS. *These birds remain at sea except when breeding or when a storm drives them to the shore. Their plumage is very dark brown, with white underparts, and there is white on the cheeks and throat in winter. No nest is made; a single pear-shaped egg is laid in May on the ledge of a precipitous stack or cliff.*

PTARMIGAN ON NEST. *Laying her brown-mottled yellowish eggs in a slight hollow on the heathery ground, the female ptarmigan is protected by camouflage, her speckled grey and sandy plumage merging in with the mountain landscape.*

BRITISH GAME BIRDS

by

SETON GORDON, C.B.E.

GAME birds are mainly or entirely ground-living birds of more or less chicken-like or partridge-like appearance, with short bills having an arched outline, rounded wings, and comparatively limited powers of flight, though that flight may indeed be fast. The males are often brilliantly coloured, and ornamental tail feathers, plumes, and wattles are frequently developed, though in some species both sexes are soberly coloured, browns generally predominating. There is seldom a conspicuous seasonal change of colour (the ptarmigan is an exception).

Game birds are abundant in Britain. In its true native state one species, the red grouse, is found nowhere else; and besides it we have as native game birds the ptarmigan, black grouse (commonly called blackgame), partridge and quail. On the other hand, the capercaillie, once a native, can scarcely be called so now, as the old stock died out and the species was reintroduced from abroad. Aliens now firmly established in Britain are the pheasant and the red-legged partridge.

In the true game birds are included the Phasianidae, or pheasant tribe, and the Tetraonidae, or grouse tribe. Turkeys are included in the former; also partridges and quails. The guinea-fowl belongs to this order. From the Phasianidae are derived our domestic fowls. The great family of the grouse differs from pheasant, partridge and quail, in having the nostrils entirely hidden by feathers. The legs, too, are often entirely feathered and are never armed with spurs, as in certain of the Phasianadae. A characteristic of all game birds is that they are primarily vegetarian and their young are covered with down when hatched, and are active, with open eyes, from the time they are born.

A point to be borne in mind here is that some town-bred members of the public, misled perhaps by vague reminiscences of poulterers' shops, are a little apt to confuse true game birds with others which are nothing of the kind. Woodcock, snipe, plover and other species habitually shot for food are structurally different from game birds which from early times have been protected by strict game laws.

For instance, the red grouse has been protected for many a long year by a close season extending from December 10th to the "Glorious Twelfth" of August. Partridge shooting opens on September 1st; and October 1st has long marked the opening of pheasant shooting in the British Isles.

The red grouse is generally supposed to be descended from the willow grouse, no longer found in Britain. As the glacial age receded and the lower hills of these islands were no longer snow-clad throughout the winter, the willow grouse inhabiting them found it detrimental to assume a white plumage. On a dark hillside a white-plumaged bird is an easy prey to its foes. Thus was evolved a race of willow grouse which remained dark throughout the year and in course of time lost the white wings which the willow grouse of northern lands and ptarmigan in Britain retain throughout the summer months.

In its native state the red grouse is not found south of Yorkshire and Staffordshire, but has been introduced into more southern counties such as Surrey, Devon and Somerset — on Exmoor it is now well established. Abroad it has been introduced on the continent and acclimatized in Belgium and Western Germany.

Normally the red grouse is a stay-at-home bird, but occasionally great numbers migrate from one district to another, because of bad weather or scarcity of food. On moors near the coast they have been known to be confused by a snow blizzard and fly out to sea. After a severe snowfall, accompanied by much drifting on the Langwell moors in Caithness, grouse were seen by fishing boats floating lifeless in the sea. Their haunts had apparently been rendered uninhabitable by the excessive drift and when they had taken wing the

strong wind, filled with drifting snow which prevented them from finding their bearings, had blown them away from land. That was an exceptional storm, and under ordinary conditions the red grouse has an excellent sense of direction. A grouse rarely flies more than four or five miles at a time.

During recent years the red grouse of the Outer Hebrides has been separated from its relations of the mainland as a distinct species. This bird is rather darker in plumage than the common red grouse. The Hebridean grouse is believed to have affinity with the grouse which inhabit the west of Ireland. In its behaviour the Hebridean (and Irish) red grouse does indeed in some points differ from the red grouse of the Scottish mainland. It is a much more silent bird, and when

QUAIL. *A summer visitor to Britain, the quail is a game bird frequenting fields and wastes, where it is easily able to conceal itself because of its mottled and streaked reddish-buff plumage. A grassy nest is made on the ground; the eggs which are laid in May or June are buff coloured and speckled with brown.*

GROUSE WITH YOUNG. *A resident game-bird of the British Isles, the red grouse haunts moorland country, nesting in heather. The male bird's plumage is chestnut, barred with black, with a red comb over each eye.*

disturbed does not fly so far, nor does it form into packs towards the end of the summer. But its more furtive habits may have been formed by the greater number of its enemies in the west. The egg-stealing grey or hooded crow here is common; the raven is not above taking a grouse's egg if it has the opportunity, nor is the buzzard to be trusted—in this instance it is the bird, not the egg that is the attraction. The Hebridean red grouse is certainly the later nester of the two, and eggs are rarely laid until June.

Periodically a fatal illness attacks the red grouse. It is known as grouse disease, and much time and money have been spent on its investigation. The disease has been traced to a minute thread worm, and the interesting thing is that healthy grouse are almost all infected, without harm to themselves. But when grouse become enfeebled through the overstocking of their moor or from lack of food following on a long spell of snow, the thread worms which are unable to harm a healthy bird set up acute appendicitis which is usually fatal. A late spring snowfall is probably

YOUNG PHEASANTS. *The young pheasants, when newly hatched, show distinctive plumage markings. On maturity, the feathers are chestnut, speckled with cream and black, with an iridescent sheen of green and purple.*

more injurious to red grouse than a much more prolonged snowy spell early in the winter months.

A strong, hardy bird is the male of the red grouse. We all know his defiant challenge as he rises with a whirr of wings, "Back, back, go back, back, back." In Gaelic his cry was in the olden days of clan feuds rendered as "*Cò, cò, cò, mo chlaidh, mo chlaidh*" ("Who, who, who, my sword, my sword.") The call of the hen is a subdued mewing note, and is less frequently heard.

Grouse nest in heather or, more rarely, in long hill grass. The eggs number six to eleven; they are heavily blotched with red or chocolate-brown markings. The incubation period is three weeks and the young are able to run actively the first day they are hatched. They are then very small, and a number of weeks elapse before they are full grown. In late

summer young and old often form into large flocks or "packs," and it has been recorded by careful observers that some packs consist entirely of male birds and others entirely of hens.

RED GROUSE

The red grouse is numerous on the hills of the Central Highlands up to the 2,500 feet contour line. A few nest as high as 3,000 feet, where they are in the haunts of the ptarmigan, yet the two species very rarely interbreed. Were the red grouse an offshoot of the ptarmigan, and not of the willow grouse, as has sometimes been suggested, it might be imagined that interbreeding would be frequent; were its ancestors willow grouse, this unwillingness of the two species to mix could be understood. The late Robert Hargreaves of Gaick Forest had a powerful telescope at the shooting

84

lodge for watching deer. One season he had under observation a grouse on her nest on the steep hill above the lodge, and after some days saw that several of the eggs had rolled from the nest. As he watched, the bird endeavoured to roll them uphill back to the nest, using her chin as a lever. But the task was beyond her powers, and when the observer climbed to the place he found her brooding on an empty nest and all the eggs scattered below her. The eggs were replaced, and the nest built up on the side nearest the downward slope. It was imagined that deer passing near the nest had alarmed the grouse, and that as she had flown hurriedly from the nest she had scattered the eggs. These may have been cold when they were replaced, but they hatched successfully, despite the fact that two of them had to be replaced a second time a week later, and that on this second occasion they had lain outside in the cold for certainly five hours, perhaps for many more.

The golden eagle is unpopular on a grouse moor, because its appearance sends the grouse flying wildly and at great speed out of sight. Usually an eagle takes its prey on the ground, and grouse feel safer in the air when the great bird is near. The character of the grouse's flight tells a trained observer that an eagle must be in the vicinity, for at no other times do the birds fly so high, so fast or so wildly, as though uncertain what course is to follow. An eagle at its hunting may clear a moor of its grouse in a very short time.

BIRD OF THE MOUNTAINS

The ptarmigan is a mountain dweller and is rarely seen below the 2,000 feet level. The ptarmigan is of a similar size to the red grouse from which it is distinguished above all by its white wings in summer and its pure white plumage in winter. It is an attractive bird and adds character to many a Highland hill. The scientific name of the species infers that the bird is mute—a strange misnomer, for cock ptarmigan are as vocal as cock grouse, although the cry is different. Instead of a cheery "becking," the ptarmigan's cry is a strong croak or snore; on the ground it sometimes utters a sound like the ticking of a salmon reel. Living mainly above the heather line the ptarmigan has little cover and must rely mainly on its protective plumage when its enemies appear. Sometimes it is very tame and on a hot summer day a pair of ptarmigan may refuse to take wing when disturbed, contenting themselves with running over the ground like barndoor fowls ahead of the human disturber of their peace. On cold windy days their behaviour is different; they are sometimes very wild and when they take wing fly at a great speed to beyond human sight.

PTARMIGAN'S THREE MOULTS

Most birds have two annual moults—in spring and autumn—but the ptarmigan has three. The warm brownish plumage of spring and summer is replaced in early autumn by a lichen-grey dress; in winter the plumage is snow-white, and the wings indeed remain white throughout the year.

Ptarmigan pair before the sun's heat melts the snows on the high hills, and the cock makes himself master of an area of ground which henceforward is his territory. Late snowfalls bring confusion to the ptarmigan world, for they eliminate the boundaries of the various territories. During the month of May, 1923, a month remarkable for its severity, the high corries of the Cairngorm hills in central Inverness-shire were swept by one snowstorm after another. During the last days of that May, the writer visited one of those high corries where many pairs of ptarmigan had their home. An unbroken covering of several feet of snow covered the ground. It had fallen after the male ptarmigan had chosen their territories, and the birds were now in a state of great agitation, chasing one another backwards and forwards over the snow. The opponents met sometimes on the wing, sometimes on foot and fights were frequent.

That season ptarmigan were late in nesting, and most of the birds still had eggs early in July. The ptarmigan's nest is a hollow, sometimes shallow but more rarely deeply cup-shaped. It may be lined with a few fronds of lichens or dried grass stems; sometimes the white feathers of the brooding bird form a lining, but this is perhaps accidental, as the hen ptarmigan has not always completed the moult from her winter plumage at the time the eggs are laid. The usual number

of eggs is from six to nine; they closely resemble those of the red grouse but are slightly smaller, and when the owner of the nest is seen there can be no difficulty in the identification. In their main stronghold, the Cairngorms, ptarmigan rarely nest as low as the heather line.

The ptarmigan does not begin incubation until the full clutch has been laid. Each morning, on laying her egg shortly after sunrise, she covers over her nest with grass or lichens, yet she is often careless and leaves several of the eggs exposed. The period of incubation is rather longer than that of the red grouse; the grouse incubates for three weeks and the ptarmigan for three and a half weeks. It is doubtful whether any British bird broods so closely as the ptarmigan. The

PTARMIGAN. *Game birds of the Scottish mountains, ptarmigan nest at heights up to 4,000 feet above sea-level. In winter, the plumage is white; in Spring it is barred with brown and buff; while the third change, to grey, occurs in the autumn.*

cock bird is a devoted husband and from some vantage point, say a little knoll or a boulder, mounts guard during the daylight hours. When danger is sighted he rises into the air with snorting croak, flies a little way, then alights still croaking and displaying anxiety and nervousness. It is sometimes possible to find the nest by a careful search, but care must be exercised lest the searcher should tread upon the sitting ptarmigan. When the eggs hatch a remarkable change takes place in the behaviour of the cock. He had previously been a model husband; now he leaves his mate and the chicks, joins other males in similar circumstances, and lives a communal existence at the highest levels. In the month of July these packs of male ptarmigan may be seen on the plateau of Braeriach, 4,000 feet above the sea. Male ptarmigan may occasionally remain with their mates; it seems probable, however, that this desertion of his mate by the male is only temporary, and that he rejoins her and the family before the young are fully grown or able to fly.

SNOWY NESTING SITES

Ptarmigan sometimes nest near an old snowfield, perhaps in order that the bird may cool herself during the heat of the day. The same site may be chosen year after year, although the nest is never used a second time. In an average season the ptarmigan nesting at 3,000 feet begin to lay around May 20th, but at the vertical limit of the bird's range, which rarely reaches the 4,000 feet level, the eggs are not laid until June.

The hen ptarmigan is a devoted mother. When the human wanderer has blundered upon her brood she often flutters up to his feet, trailing her white wings to attract his attention and, on the pretence of being wounded, endeavouring to decoy him from the neighbourhood of her young brood. This trick of feigning injury may not

succeed with the human being, but a fox or dog is more easily taken in and pursues the fluttering bird, who recovers the use of her wings when she has drawn the beast a safe distance from her brood. The young are able to fly at the age of ten days.

PTARMIGAN'S SOARING FLIGHT

No bird is more dependent upon the weather for the success of its nesting than the ptarmigan (it is curious that the letter P should have crept into this word, apparently from the French, for the Gaelic form is *Tarmachan*). A snowstorm may sweep their fastnesses on the Cairngorm range in any month of the summer, eggs may be buried; young may be killed. Chicks a few days old may be seen running about on a surface of new snow at the end of June. They are hardy chicks, and during these conditions are brooded closely by their mothers, but they must venture abroad from time to time to feed, if indeed all insect life is not buried out of sight in snow. Red grouse rarely soar but on occasion ptarmigan soar into a stiff breeze of wind, the wings held motionless and slightly drooping. They sometimes make long flights and appear on hills distant from their usual haunts. When the ptarmigan which live on the top of Morven in Aberdeenshire are shot too hard, instead of flying down to the lower levels of the hill they take wing in a body in the direction of Mount Keen, the nearest hill that reaches a height suitable for them and some twelve miles distant across the Dee Valley.

Ptarmigan are rarely so plentiful as to give big bags. The birds are sometimes driven. In 1886, twenty-seven brace were killed in the Forest of Gaick in the course of a single drive and in this forest sixty brace have been shot in a day. In Coire Fhearnagan, a corrie on Carn Bàn Mór in Glen Feshie Forest, in one day of the autumn of 1924, no fewer than

BLACKCOCK. *The blackcock is the male bird of the black grouse. The plumage of this game-bird is black, with white feathers on the wings and under the lyre-shaped tail. Above each eye is a bright red wattle.*

fifty-one and a half brace of ptarmigan were shot. The food of ptarmigan is varied. They eat the young shoots of ling, crowberry and bilberry, and in the autumn the fruits of Alpine plants. Insects form the chief food of the chicks. It is a grand sight to see a golden eagle pursuing a flock of ptarmigan in their snow-white winter plumage amidst the high hills. The ptarmigan scatter and fly wildly, higher and higher. The eagle sails idly around them as though enjoying the spectacle of their terror, yet rarely is seen to chase a ptarmigan in earnest for, as already mentioned, he takes his prey mainly on the ground.

The present southerly limit for ptarmigan is Ben Lomond, but in Pennant's time the species nested in the Isle of Arran. Up to recent years it nested on the slopes of Clisham, highest hill of the Outer Hebrides, but has not

been seen there for some seasons. At an earlier period it is believed to have bred on the high hills of the Lake District and Wales.

The black grouse—of which the male is termed a blackcock and the female a greyhen—is of the family Tetraonidae. A handsome bird is the blackcock, glossy black, with a lyre-shaped tail and white wing-bar. Above each eye is a bright red wattle. The female, with brownish mottled plumage, is not unlike a female red grouse, but is larger, heavier, and flies faster, though with less rapid wing beats.

In almost all parts of Britain the black grouse is decreasing. It is extinct in Wiltshire, Dorset, Hampshire, Kent, Surrey, Sussex, and Pembroke, and almost extinct in Cornwall. In South Devon it is rare, though more numerous in North Devon and in Somerset. In the English border counties it is not uncommon and on the Scottish mainland it is widely distributed. On the Inner Hebrides (the Isle of Skye and the Isle of Mull for example) it is much scarcer than it was twenty-five years ago, and has not been recorded from the Outer Hebrides or from Orkney and Shetland.

The blackcock is polygamous. Each morning at dawn the males of the species arrive at their displaying grounds. They are conservative birds, and the same knoll or heathery clearing in a pine forest may be used year after year. This display is made not only in the nesting season but even in the dead of winter.

When displaying, the blackcock droops his wings, spreads his tail and in a crouching attitude, with head close to the ground and the red wattle over the eye raised, runs excitedly backwards and forwards over the short heather, uttering an eager "bubbling" cry, quickly repeated, which has been likened to " *rōō, rōō, rōō.*" An opponent or sparring partner is soon found, and then the two face up to each other like trained boxers, advancing and withdrawing quickly. When an opening has been found in the defence, both birds suddenly spring upward into the air, striking at one another with their feet while they utter a sneezing cry of defiance, very unlike the musical bubbling pigeon-like sound used when the birds are seeking an opponent. A few greyhens may sometimes watch the display, but this goes on even when they are brooding eggs and are thus unable to take any part in the proceedings.

It is curious that the rising sun striking on the display ground should at once put a stop to the tourney. The birds then fold their outspread tails, assume a normal position and begin to feed. Peace has returned where all was activity and excitement.

BLACKCOCK DISPLAY DANCE. *When taking part in the display dance, two blackcocks face one another with spread wings, and then run to and fro in a crouching position.*

A displaying ground has the heather worn from much trampling of the birds, and feathers often lie on the ground. A fight in earnest is rare but it has been said that on occasion a bird will kill his opponent.

Greyhens nest in May. The nesting site usually chosen is below a juniper bush in the outskirts of a pine forest, or beneath the fallen branch of a tree. The eggs number from seven to ten and in shape and colour are similar to those of the capercaillie, only smaller.

Many black grouse have been shot, even in the nesting season, because of the damage they do to young plantations, for they are fond of the young shoots of larch and pine, but their chief winter food is the unopened buds of the birch. In autumn they are fond of the berries of the rowan and hawthorn, feeding also on the whortleberry and cowberry. The flight of the black grouse is easy and steady; the speed at which the birds travel is deceptive, and although they move through the air faster than the red grouse they seem to be flying more slowly. Allied forms of the species are found on the continent, from Belgium north to Norway, Sweden, Finland and north Russia, and also in the Pyrenees, Alps and Carpathians.

The capercaillie can be distinguished readily by its large size, which greatly exceeds that of the black or red grouse. A cock caper, as he shoots through or flies above the trees of a wood at the speed approaching that of an express train, is an imposing sight.

From time immemorial the capercaillie

HEN CAPERCAILLIE. *The hen capercaillie uses no nesting material, the buff-coloured eggs, mottled with brown, being laid in a slight hollow on the ground. Capercaillie feed on pineshoots, insects and berries.*

GREYHEN. *Like most game birds, the greyhen, female bird of the black grouse, makes a nest on the ground, a favourite spot being, as this picture shows, beneath the fallen branch of a tree. She lays yellowish-white eggs speckled with brown.*

PHEASANTS FEEDING

inhabited the old Caledonian Forest, but became extinct towards the end of the eighteenth century. In the year 1837 it was re-introduced into the Scottish Highlands by Lord Breadalbane, from Sweden, and the following year the Earl of Fife secured a number of these birds, perhaps from the same source, to set down in his own pine forest of Mar. The newcomers throve and multiplied, and their descendants have now spread over Scotland—north to the Dornoch Firth, west to Argyll, south to the Firth of Forth, Stirling, and even beyond it.

For the size of the bird, the song of the capercaillie is feeble. It is uttered at dawn and during the final note of ecstasy the singer is temporarily deaf and blind. In the great continental forests where this bird is stalked, these few seconds are of great value to the stalker, who rushes forward and then "freezes" before the bird is silent. After a number of well-timed rushes the hunter, if he is fortunate, reaches a point sufficiently near the bird—outlined in the tree against the sky—to shoot it. When singing, the capercaillie stands with neck held vertically, tail also vertical and fanned, and wings drooped, the body appearing to swell and the feathers of the throat to stand out.

Capercaillie nest on the ground. They prefer a forest of old native pine, and scrape their nesting hollow at the foot of a tree. The eggs are marked with red spots and blotches and number from five to nine. The hen caper sometimes

COMMON PARTRIDGE. *Game birds found in great numbers near cultivated land throughout Britain, partridges vigilantly protect their young, which are able to run actively the day after they are hatched.*

RED-LEGGED PARTRIDGE. *Introduced into Britain from France, this game bird may be distinguished from the common partridge by its bright red legs and bill.*

sits very closely, and when she leaves the eggs flutters low over the ground.

During the winter the capercaillie's food consists almost entirely of the shoots and buds of coniferous trees, but in late summer and autumn it may eat juniper berries and other fruit.

Like the black grouse the capercaillie had a wide range on the continent and is found from the forests of Russia south to the Pyrenees and the Carpathians.

The pheasant is found throughout the British Isles. It is a well-established alien of so long a standing that it is commonly believed to be a native, but this is not so. It is thought to have been introduced into England by the Romans. There is mention of it in Waltham Abbey Ordnance in the year 1059, but in Scotland it was not introduced until five hundred years later. The original British pheasant is a native of the northern slopes of the

Caucasus, but the breed is now largely composed of hybrids. The ring-necked pheasant from East China was introduced and British-reared male pheasants now usually show the white neck ring of *torquatus*, as the ring-necked pheasant is named by science. With his long tail, dark green head, red neck wattles and ear-like tufts, the cock pheasant is a handsome bird. The hen pheasant's plumage is brown and her tail is shorter than that of the cock. Flight is fast and direct, but the bird soon tires and there are instances of a pheasant alighting exhausted on the water. These birds have been known to swim when compelled to do so. In Britain the pheasant is polygamous, but is believed to be monogamous in its native habitat.

The pheasant remains shy, as well it may, for it has no cause to trust man. When disturbed it prefers to run for shelter rather than fly. Pheasants roost usually in trees but sometimes on the ground where the nest is always placed, often in the shelter of fallen branches. The eggs are olive brown in colour, unspotted; sometimes they are of a pale blue. The species is single-brooded, although eggs have been found as late as October. The food of the pheasant includes acorns and hazel nuts, beech mast and holly berries; the bird takes also insects, earthworms and slugs.

PARTRIDGES

The common partridge is found throughout Britain in suitable localities, but in some districts where it was formerly numerous it is now almost unknown. In the Isle of Skye, one of the Inner Hebrides, a good bag of partridges might have been made fifty years ago in several districts of the island, but the species has now disappeared. A reason given for this is the breaking up of the farms into crofts. The arable ground is therefore more disturbed by the human species than formerly, and the crofters' dogs range over the fields.

The partridge lives mainly in agricultural country but in the Lake District may be found up to a height of 1,500 feet above sea level. Along the northwest seaboard of Scotland it is rare.

One of the most delightful sounds of the English countryside is the calling of the partridge on a quiet, warm evening of early summer. "Kār-wit," he cries, "Kār-wit, kār-wit"; or he may rise on rapidly whirring wings and calling excitedly "krikrikri." After the young partridges are full grown they still keep with their parents; indeed, the family party remains together until the following spring when the young birds pair in their turn. Buds, flowers, and seeds are the food of the partridge. Insects, chiefly ants and their pupae, are also taken by the bird, which feeds on the grain of wheat, oats and barley.

Rather larger than the common partridge, the red-legged partridge was introduced from the continent into England in 1770. These birds were put down in Suffolk, but further importations were made and the birds liberated in many other places. In parts of England the species is now abundant, but has not as yet made itself at home in Scotland. The red-legged partridge is a more nervous bird than the common species, and its movements on the ground are quicker. The eggs are spotted with red and thus can be distinguished at a glance from the unspotted eggs of the common partridge. The red-legged partridge is a native of France, south of the Loire, and Italy; in Spain and Portugal it is replaced by allied races.

Smallest of British game birds is the quail; it resembles a minute and delicately built partridge, but the call of the male is very different—a liquid "quic, quic-ic" several times repeated. Unlike the partridge, too, it is only a summer visitor to Britain and in winter is found in tropical Africa, Arabia, and India. In Britain it is everywhere decreasing. In Ireland, it was plentiful less than a century ago, but it is now very scarce. The decrease is no doubt largely due to the great numbers of quails which have been and still are trapped in southern Europe and Africa during migration, for the quail is a dainty morsel, much appreciated by epicures.

The quail nests in fields, and the bird has been found breeding as far north as Sutherland and Caithness. The small eggs are thickly mottled with chocolate-brown. In some Highland counties it has been observed feeding on daisy and buttercup flowers. A late spring migrant, the quail arrives in Britain in May, often not until the end of that month, and leaves for its overseas flight in September. It is the only British game bird which is a migrant. When it is in this country it is rarely seen, for it is a shy bird.

CAPERCAILLIE

Game birds of Scotland, capercaillie are found chiefly in pine and spruce woods.

THE HOBBY
This diurnal bird of prey, with long pointed wings, feeds on small birds and insects.

BRITISH BIRDS OF PREY

by

F. MARTIN DUNCAN

FOR long years our most interesting resident birds of prey may literally be said to have lived dangerously, and in the face of widespread and senseless persecution the wonder is that any have managed to survive. Some, indeed, have disappeared altogether ; others no longer breed in this country and have become rare visitors, mere birds of passage, too often fated to fall victims to the sportsman's gun. Ancient superstitions on the one hand and ill-advised changes on the other have all played their part in what may eventually lead to the extermination of the few remaining species.

INTERDEPENDENCE OF NATURE

It is a regrettable position. Many of these persecuted birds are of vital importance to agriculture, and but for their presence in the countryside the successful cultivation of certain seed crops might well be seriously affected, if not rendered impossible. Many of these birds of prey, particularly the owls, form a connecting link in the complicated thread of the natural life of the countryside, and any further serious curtailment of their range and numbers will sooner or later upset the balance of nature with deplorable results to the farmer.

To demonstrate this let us take the story of one of these connecting links. A veritable jigsaw puzzle from Nature's workshop, the most important pieces fitting into it are an owl, a field-mouse, a humble-bee, a flower-head of red clover and a farmer.

On the number of owls depends the size of the population of field-mice and kindred rodents in a given district. The field-mice in turn prey upon the honey stored in the nests of the humble-bees, which alone are capable of transferring the pollen from one red clover flower to another. Therefore on the number of humble-bees visiting the red clover fields will depend the amount of fertile seed produced. The domesticated hive-bee cannot perform this important job, its tongue, or proboscis, being too short. If the farmer is a wise man and encourages or protects the owls in his neighbourhood, he will be rewarded by a higher yield of seed and fruits, for the humble-bees will be more numerous in his fields and orchards. On the other hand, should he persistently seek to destroy the owls, the yield of seed, season by season, will steadily decrease as the mice, voles and rats, no longer held in check by their natural foes, increase enormously in numbers ; the nests of the humble-bees are robbed so that their offspring die, to say nothing of the ever increasing loss and damage to the farmer's corn ricks.

CHIEF FOOD OF OWLS

The food of owls consists chiefly of field-mice, voles, and rats, also of insects more or less harmful to agriculture, and to a lesser degree small birds. The smaller prey is swallowed whole or carried in the beak, while the larger is carried securely grasped by the powerful, sharp-pointed talons, to some convenient or favourite spot where it is torn to pieces and devoured. Any small bones, pieces of fur or feathers, or beetle wing-cases and legs which may have been swallowed in the course of the meals, are later ejected as round or cylindrical pellets. Known as castings, these accumulate in considerable numbers around the favourite feeding or roosting site, or nest; and from an examination of these castings the nature of the owl's food can be accurately determined. This habit of casting up pellets containing hard, insoluble substances, is practically universal among birds of prey, whether eagle, hawk, or owl, so that the nature of their food is readily demonstrated.

CHARACTERISTICS OF BIRDS OF PREY

All birds of prey are remarkable for their strong and sharply-pointed beaks, and powerful, sharp-pointed claws. Another characteristic possessed by these birds is a waxy covering at the base of the beak, often hard, but generally fleshy in substance, and known as the cere. It is much hidden by facial bristles in the owls, but is a very noticeable feature in the hawks and eagles. There are certain external characters quite apart from the more obvious differences of shape, size and build, by which we may distinguish the hawks from the owls. Thus we have only to see the manner in which the bird is grasping the bough, or in captivity the perch, on which it is resting, to realize the family to which it belongs. If it be an owl, we shall see that it sits with its toes in pairs—two in front and two behind—for with all owls the outer toe on each foot is reversible. On the other hand, a hawk cannot do this, for all his toes are arranged like those of any other perching bird, such as a sparrow, or a blackbird; that is to say, three toes in front and one behind. The large round head and short neck, the striking development of the almost circular facial disc edged with a curious ruff of short feathers, and the great eyes, forward directed to confront the spectator, are all distinctive of the owls. Moreover, though less easily observable in the living bird, there is the distinctive difference in structure of the body plumage, for the owls have no "after-shaft" to their feathers, a structure present in most

hawks. Really a small accessory plume arising from the under-side of the main feather, this after-shaft varies considerably in size in different species of birds; it is always peculiar to the body feathers, and never found in quills or tail-feathers. In this connexion it may be interesting to note that the osprey, which no longer breeds in Britain, and is now a comparatively rare visitor, may be regarded in some respects as a connecting link between the owls and the hawk tribe. In general appearance resembling an eagle, and its prey consisting entirely of fish, the osprey is often known as the fish-hawk or fishing-eagle, but there the likeness ends for its body feathers possess no after-shaft, its outer toe is reversible, and, as in the owls, the tibia is more than double the length of the tarsus, a disproportionate difference never found in the leg bones of the hawks.

OWL FAMILY

The story of man's superstitious dread and persecution of the owl forms a curious mass of legend and folk-lore which can be traced back far in the history of the human race. No doubt this almost universal superstitious dread and awe is due to the nocturnal habits of these birds, their swift and silent flight, like ghostly phantoms, at dusk and in the moonlight; their sudden, startling, and weird cries, breaking the silence of the night, and their love of ancient ruins, church towers, and lonely places as roosting and nesting sites.

After keeping many owls as pets, and also following closely their natural life in the wild, the writer feels very strongly that their nocturnal habits are of psychological origin rather than entirely a mechanistic food reaction. Some species consistently hunt for their food during the hours of daylight, just as do hawks, and these tend to show more hawk-like characters in consequence. With their great eyes and soft plumage, these lovely

OSPREY. *A rare summer visitor to Scotland, the osprey has long, powerful wings extending beyond the tip of the tail. This bird nests on a rock or tree near the sea, using sticks, turf and seaweed, and lives solely on fish. In the photograph above, the male bird is seen returning with a fish to feed the female and young.*

birds are by nature shy and retiring creatures; they will hold their own ground and fight valiantly when cornered, but there is in their make-up none of that self-assertive aggressive swagger and dash so characteristic of the hawk family. Only when they have young in the nest do owls become really aggressive; at other times, when disturbed, they rarely stand their ground unless escape has been made impossible; but protection of offspring and self-preservation are universal instincts. Just as shy, hypersensitive folk are happiest alone or in the company of some sympathetic friend, so the owls seek security and peace through their nocturnal habits. Yet once that almost fierce reserve has been overcome—and

with quiet patience and gentle handling and speech it can be pierced—these birds of the night become devoted companions.

Of British species, the barn owl is probably the best known, being generally distributed throughout England, Wales and some parts of Scotland, chiefly in the Lowlands. It is known by various names in different parts of the country, such as screech-owl, white-owl or church owl, and unfortunately is still regarded with dislike and suspicion in many regions. Yet no bird could be better designated the farmer's friend, for it feeds chiefly on voles, field-mice and rats, capturing large numbers of these destructive creatures, particularly during the breeding season, with which to feed its young.

Usually the barn owl remains con-

SHORT-EARED OWL. *A nocturnal bird of prey, known also as the hawk-owl, this bird nests on heather or sedge, frequenting fields and moors. Here it finds the vole, which is its chief food, and which in this picture is seen being carried to the owl's brood.*

BARN OWL. *Common throughout Britain, the barn or screech owl is a bird of prey that helps rid the farmer of mice and rats. The face and underparts of the plumage are white.*

cealed during the daytime, emerging from its retreat as night draws on, seeking its prey in the dusk of late evening and through the night, and returning home towards dawn. It lives in the dark recesses of old ruins, in ancient church towers, old farm buildings, hollow trees, holes in the face of cliffs, and similar secluded situations. No nest is built, the eggs being laid on the floor of its retreat. Usually four to six in number, the eggs are pure white in colour and are laid at irregular intervals. So soon as the first one or two have been laid, the female begins to sit, and thus the young are hatched at various times. Apparently the eldest of the brood not infrequently helps with the incubation of the later eggs. Incubation may begin in March, though more usually in April or May, according to climatic conditions, and probably occupies about a month; while the fledgling period generally lasts about seven weeks.

FEEDING YOUNG OWLS

Comic-looking little creatures are the baby owls, at first clad in white down, and when hungry or disturbed, giving vent to strange sounds, difficult accurately to describe, though not altogether unlike a high pitched snoring, or the queer noises sometimes produced by the valve in a cistern. They are fed by the parent birds throughout the evening and night, an additional supply of dead mice often being placed near at hand lest the youngsters grow hungry during the day.

TAWNY OWL. *The tawny owl frequents woods, and apart from the barn owl is the commonest of British nocturnal birds of prey. The plumage is a rich brown, distinctively marked with bars and streaks of darker and lighter colours. Nesting sites vary, and a hole in a tree or a ruined building, or even the old nest of another bird may be chosen. Three or four white eggs are laid in early spring; both male and female birds share in the incubation. The tawny owl preys on rats and mice, young game and rabbits. Its cry is distinctive, being a wavering call.*

The typical barn owl stands about twelve to nearly fourteen inches in height, the female—as is usual with most birds of prey—being the larger and stronger bird. The head and upper parts are orange-buff in colour, minutely variegated with grey, brown, and white: the large facial discs are white with a brownish rim, and the plumage of the under parts pure white, the legs being covered with white hair-like feathers, and the toes armed with long needle-sharp talons.

As twilight deepens and the mice and rats come out to feed and play, the barn owls begin their nightly hunt, skimming low down along the hedge-rows, across the fields, and round the ricks and barns with noiseless flight, pouncing suddenly upon their unsuspecting prey. On still moonlight nights their weird shrieks carry far across the quiet countryside as they call to each other. In addition they have a curious whistling cry, generally more often to be heard early in the evening. Also, and particularly during the daytime if disturbed, they give vent to snoring sounds similar to those emitted by their young.

LONG-EARED OWL

The lovely long-eared owl is an equally good friend to the farmer, careful examination of large numbers of its pellets having shown that of the total food consumed, seventy-eight per cent. consisted of field-mice and voles, four per cent. shrew-mice, about ten per cent. house-sparrows and other grain feeding birds, and two per cent. injurious insects and pests.

Because it does not usually begin to hunt its prey until nightfall, the long-eared owl is more rarely observed than the barn owl, and is therefore often spoken of as a rare bird. In fact, it is more abundant than is generally imagined, its numbers during the autumn months being increased by migrants from the continent, which spend the winter with us and in spring return to their own breeding places. As a result of this annual influx, our native race is probably replenished in numbers and kept strong by the introduction of fresh blood, a certain number of the visitors mating and taking up their permanent abode in Britain. These winter visitors begin to arrive from mid-September to mid-November, and return on their homeward migration during April and May. But of migration, more will be said in a later chapter.

DAYLIGHT HABITS

Throughout the year the long-eared owl is to be found living in well-wooded country, especially in fir plantations and among groups of old Scotch pines, whose rough and tinted trunks blend with the feather pattern and colour of the bird. Daylight hours are spent by the bird perched, sound asleep, on a high branch, with its body pressed close against the trunk of the tree. If disturbed, the owl erects its ear-tufts and, contracting the feathers of its body, at the same time elongates itself so that it more than ever resembles the stump of a broken branch. This queer performance is sometimes accompanied by a repeated snapping of the beak, or a short angry cry, that sounds rather like "wack-wack, wack-wack," sharply repeated. At night the normal cry is a "whoo-hoo-hoo," repeated slowly and in varying volume of sound, but on the whole the long-eared owl is rather silent, becoming slightly more vocal during the breeding season. It is a handsome bird of rather slender build, about fourteen inches in length. The upper parts of the body are buff, mottled with brown and grey, with dark brown streaks, especially on the long, erectile ear-tufts. The facial disk is buff, with a greyish black margin and outer rim and there are dark markings round the eyes. The under parts of the

LITTLE OWL. *Once an entirely foreign bird of prey, the little owl was introduced into Britain where it is a resident. It is a fierce hunter, and in addition to preying on mice for food it will attack and kill other birds. Its small size distinguishes it from other owls; the plumage is grey-brown spotted and barred with white. This owl is fairly common; it frequents woods and chooses a hole in a tree for its nest but uses no nesting material. Its cry, a mewing sound, differs from that of other owls.*

body are warm buff and grey, with broad blackish - brown, longitudinal streaks and delicate transverse bars, while the legs are covered to the toes with fawn-coloured feathers. There is a noticeable variation of colour among different individuals, and grey as well as rufous (reddish-brown) phases of plumage exist.

The long-eared owl begins to lay early in the year, the first eggs of the season being deposited in the nest towards the end of February or early in March, the date varying with the prevailing climatic conditions. This owl usually takes possession of an old deserted nest of a crow, ringdove, magpie, or heron, or the abandoned winter drey of a squirrel, sometimes adding a little lining of small thin twigs and rabbit fur. On the Yorkshire moors and in Scotland, nests are not infrequently found among the heather. The eggs, numbering four to six, are pure white, with a smooth, rather porcelain-like surface, and the incubation period lasts about twenty-eight to thirty days. When nearly fully fledged, the young owlets often become restless and scramble in and out of the nest, using their beaks to hold on and to help in climbing back. When excited or hungry, they give vent to loud mewing cries.

SHORT-EARED OWL

The short-eared owl is essentially a bird of the open country, particularly frequenting marshlands, heather-clad moors, furzy commons, sand dunes along the coast, and, in the autumn, the stubble and turnip fields. In addition to resident birds, numbers arrive yearly from overseas at the same time that the migrating woodcocks put in an appearance, for which reason they are often called woodcock owls. These winter visitors remain until the spring, the return migration taking place from about the last week in March to early in May.

Wherever and whenever a plague of field-voles arises, short-eared owls flock to the infested region and remain there so long as food continues to be abundant. In 1890-91 there was a bad plague of voles in the south-west of Scotland, and very soon a wonderful increase in the population of short-eared owls became noticeable. Indeed, it was estimated that no fewer than four hundred pairs nested that year in the vole-infested region, and cleared it of the rodent pest.

Normally it is less generally distributed than the long-eared owl, being most frequently met with in Scotland, the moors of Northern England, and the fen country of East Anglia, becoming rarer in the south and west. Measuring about fourteen to fifteen inches in length, it is of a stouter build than the long-eared owl, and a much bolder bird. The general colouring of the plumage of the upper parts resembles that of the long-eared owl, save that the buff tint may be more pronounced and the dark pattern more blotched than streaked. The facial disk and rim are brown, while the ear-tufts are short, only becoming visible when the bird is excited and erects them. The breast and under parts are streaked longitudinally with blackish-brown, and the legs and toes feathered.

The short-eared owl breeds late in the season, the six or more creamy-white eggs being generally laid in May; in some seasons fledglings are in the nest as late as August. In the East Anglian fens the nest is a mere depression formed on top of a clump of sedges or on a mass of mown reeds, while on the northern moorlands the eggs are laid in a shallow hollow scraped in the heather. Before they are fully fledged, the little owlets become very restless and will make exploratory excursions through the heather for quite an appreciable distance, always returning to the nest for food and rest. The old birds are devoted parents and will fearlessly attack any intruder.

BUZZARD. *Haunting the wooded hills of North-West Britain, the buzzard is recognizable by its broad, blunt wings. The nest of sticks, lined with grass and leaves, is built in the top of a tree; two or three greenish-white eggs are laid.*

Wherever there are woods and cliffs suitable to its habits, the tawny owl is to be found throughout England and Wales in fair numbers, while in the Lowlands and Highlands of Scotland, it is the commonest species. Locally it is known under various names, such as brown owl, wood owl, and hooter owl. The well-known hooting note which gave rise to the last name is most frequently to be heard during the autumn and winter months; the bird's call when hunting for prey on the wing being a high-pitched rather shrill double note difficult to transcribe phonetically.

The accusation that the tawny owl habitually destroys young game birds becomes obviously absurd in the light of the truth concerning its food and habits; for young pheasant and partridge chicks are all comfortably nestled away under the mother's wings long before this owl considers conditions suitable to start abroad in search of food. Unless driven from its retreat, it never ventures

forth in broad daylight. Nevertheless, it is one of the most familiar British owls.

The breeding season starts early in the year, in mild seasons by the end of February, not infrequently by the middle of March in central and southern England, but later in the north of Scotland. Four to six smooth white eggs are laid, a hollow in the trunk of an old ivy-covered tree being a very favourite nesting site; but again, church towers, ruined buildings, old barns and out-houses, deserted nests of crows and magpies, and sheltered rock ledges on the face of steep cliffs are also utilized.

About fifteen inches is an adult bird's average length. The upper parts of the body are of varying shades of ashy-grey, mottled with brown, with large white spots on the outer webs of the wing coverts; the under parts are buffish-white mottled and streaked with brown, the tail barred with brown and tipped with white, the legs feathered to the claws; and the facial discs greyish with a dark brown border. As often occurs among birds of prey, the female is the larger of the two and she is often clad in a warmer tinted plumage.

Although now placed on the British list of resident birds, the little owl should be regarded, strictly speaking, as a very occasional and accidental visitor, as prior to its successful establishment in England in 1888 by the late Lord Lilford, the records of its appearance in this country are relatively scanty and open to doubt.

Having few natural enemies and being a good breeder, a relatively high proportion of young birds being successfully reared annually, the little owl has increased rapidly in numbers. That it does, on occasion, locally take toll of a few pheasant chicks is beyond doubt.

LITTLE OWL

As its popular name suggests, the little owl is a small bird, averaging about nine inches in height. The upper plumage is brown with triangular stripes on the head, white spots on the nape of the neck and wings, and four dull bands on the tail. The facial disk is greyish-white and not so well defined as in most owls, while the under parts of the body are dull white, streaked with brown, and the toes covered with hairy bristles. It is often very active during the daytime, particularly if many insects are about, and in the late summer captures and devours large numbers of daddy-longlegs flies. Because of its diurnal habits it attracts a good deal of attention and is often mobbed by small birds, who recognize it as one of their natural foes. In the spring the male becomes very vocal, and again to a lesser degree in the autumn. The call is monotonous, rather high pitched, and at times not unlike the yapping of an over-fed lap-dog. When angered there is a good deal of hissing and beak snapping. It is an active, comic little bird, with a grotesque

habit of alternately ducking down and drawing itself up to full height, like a feathered jack-in-the-box. It soon becomes tame in captivity, and displays little shyness or reserve in the presence of strangers, thus markedly differing from owls of strictly nocturnal habits.

FALCON FAMILY

The origin of the ancient art of falconry, or the flying of trained hawks in pursuit of game, lies buried in a distant past. Of our British hawks used in falconry, the peregrine still holds pride of place, followed by the hobby, the merlin, the kestrel, the sparrow hawk, and the goshawk, the latter now no longer resident and only a very rare and accidental visitor. A handsome bird, it was once used in falconry largely for hunting ground game.

Unfortunately, the members of the family Falconidae, which includes the hawks, buzzards, kites, and eagles, are for the most part regarded with suspicion and dislike by both farmers and gamekeepers, as preying upon poultry and game-birds, although such depredations are by no means a universal habit, but only carried out by certain species.

Once a common resident, the marsh harrier now can only be regarded as one of the rarest of our native hawks. The principal cause for its decrease is not so much due to indiscriminate slaughter as to the draining of the fen-lands in the eastern districts and the reclamation of the ancient marshes in the west country, regions which once formed the natural home of this handsome bird. Thanks, however, to strict local preservation, it is still to be seen in East Anglia, where it is often called the moor buzzard. It is a tall slender bird, with curved sharp-pointed beak and powerful claws. The adult is about twenty-one inches in length, and has a creamy-white head streaked with umber, and a brown mantle. The wing primaries are blackish,

YOUNG SPARROW-HAWKS. *Common in many woodland districts in Britain, the sparrow-hawk is a relentless enemy of other birds, which form its chief food.*

the rest of the wings and the tail being silvery-grey. The under parts are buff, striped with brown on the breast, and with chestnut on the belly and thighs; the long, slender legs and feet are bare and yellow. The female is slightly larger, and has a brown tail and under parts. Composed of reeds and dry grass the nest is built among the reed-beds, or among the dense vegetation of a marsh. Occasionally the lower branches of a tree growing on the edge or in the midst of a marsh will be utilized. From three to

six eggs are laid, usually pale-bluish-white in colour. During the breeding season the marsh harrier takes heavy toll of the eggs and young of water fowl, and also preys upon frogs, small mammals and small birds frequenting the neighbourhood.

Owing to land reclamation and modern intensive methods of farming, plus relentless slaughter, the hen harrier has been pretty nearly exterminated. It feeds on small birds, their eggs and young, field-mice and voles, reptiles and

MARSH HARRIER AND YOUNG. *Harriers are scarce in Britain, but a few visit the country every year for breeding purposes. Haunting marsh and moorlands, they make their nests on the ground. They are diurnal birds of prey, feeding on the eggs and young of water-fowl, frogs and small birds.*

MONTAGU'S HARRIER IN FLIGHT

amphibia; and though undoubtedly somewhat destructive of young game-birds at times, there is no reliable evidence that it has ever been the particular plague of the poultry-yard, as its popular name might lead one to suppose. It frequents higher and drier land than the marsh harrier, selecting such nesting sites as lonely furzy heaths and hillsides, heather-clad moorland, or a dried up marsh, where a large nest composed of roots and plant stems is built to contain the four to six bluish-white eggs, which occasionally bear yellowish-brown or rusty-red markings. It is a handsome bird, the male averaging nineteen inches in length. In the male, the plumage of the upper parts is a lovely pale slatey-grey, with the throat and breast bluish-grey, and the rest of the under parts white. So different in colour is the female that at one time this sex was regarded as a distinct species, known as the ring-tailed harrier. She is brown above, streaked with white at the nape; the under parts buffish-brown with darker bars, and the tail brown, marked with five dark bars.

MONTAGU'S HARRIER

Montagu's harrier very closely re-sembles the hen harrier in appearance, but is slightly smaller and more slender in shape, with the wings longer in proportion, giving it a greater buoyancy in flight. It is a migratory bird, coming every year to the eastern counties and breeding regularly in the fens of East Anglia, and not infrequently in other parts of the country if left undisturbed. In the fenlands the nest is made of sedges, while in furzy and heather-clad country it consists of rushes and dried grass. Four or five eggs, very pale bluish-green, occasionally marked with rusty spots, are laid towards the end of May. The male bird has the upper parts of its plumage slatey-grey with a black bar across the secondaries, the throat and breast ashy-grey, the rest of the under parts white streaked with rufous, and tail-feathers greyish with five dark bars, except on the middle pair. The female is usually brown on the upper surface, buffish-white streaked with rufous-brown below. Although like other harriers this bird hunts small birds and mammals, its food consists chiefly of grass snakes, adders, lizards, frogs and toads, insects, in-cluding large numbers of chafers and grasshoppers, and during the breeding season, the eggs and young of ground-nesting birds.

BUZZARD'S GRACEFUL FLIGHT

To our great grandfathers, the common buzzard must have been a very familiar bird of the countryside, and even in certain localities to our grandparents. Now the old epithet "common" sounds singularly out of place for a bird solely to be found in the remote and least frequented moorlands and hills of Devon, Cornwall, Wales and the Lake District, and parts of Scotland. The days when it was common in our woodlands have gone for ever and how much longer its remaining breeding haunts may be pre-served from urbanization and spoliation it is difficult to say. Yet this handsome brown bird with its plaintive cry and slow, graceful, almost eagle-like sweeping flight, does very little harm to game, and is really a good friend to the farmer, its prey consisting chiefly of field-mice and voles, rats, moles, frogs and snakes, various insects, and occasionally a young rabbit and some small birds. The male is about twenty-one inches in length. Usually it is brown on the upper surface with a few ruddy marks, with light and dark patterned markings on the breast, white patches under the wings, and twelve dark tinted bars on the brown tail; while the legs are bare of feathers and yellow in colour. There is a good deal of individual variation of colour in both sexes, old birds tending to become

GOLDEN EAGLE. *Largest of the European birds of prey in the British Isles, the golden eagle is seen only in the remote Scottish highlands. Feathered down to its feet, the golden eagle's plumage is blackish-brown, the head and back of the neck being the golden colour that gives the bird its name. The tail is grey, barred with a dark brown, but in an immature bird, such as that seen here, the tail has a broad band of white. Eagles prey on hares and rabbits, young deer and game birds.*

darker, others dark brown with a plum-coloured gloss, and in some cases with creamy white spots on the breast.

On the cliffs and crags the common buzzard's nest is built of sticks and heather lined with grass; if built in wooded country, in the fork of a tall tree, the nest may be bulky and include green leaves which are renewed from time to time. The three or four eggs are laid towards the middle of April, and are greyish-white, blotched and streaked with pale lilac and ruddy brown.

GOLDEN EAGLE

The present breeding places of our only resident eagle, the magnificent golden eagle, are confined to the Highlands and a few of the islands off the West Coast of Scotland, but there was a time, not so very distant, when it bred in parts of Derbyshire and Wales, the Cheviots, and the Lake District. Only when seen in his mountain home can one realize the lightness and buoyancy of the golden eagle's flight, and there are few more inspiring sights than to watch him on a bright sunny day soaring in wide circles, as he ascends to a great height above the lonely glen, his broad, almost motionless wings outstretched to their fullest extent. Then one can see the curious notched pinion feathers of his wings curving slightly upwards, and separated almost like the fingers of a hand. The general colour is a dark brown, tawny on the nape, the wings tawny and grey, the tail mottled with dark grey, and the legs darkly feathered to the powerful claws, which are yellow. The male's average length is thirty-three inches, the female being a larger and more powerful bird.

A favourite nesting site is a ledge on the rocky face of a precipitous cliff or crag in some wild and lonely corrie among the mountains, the projecting rocks in the vicinity of the selected ledge giving some shelter to the eggs and young from the cold winds and snow squalls which sweep down between the hills in early spring. The nest is relatively large and constructed of sticks forming a rough platform on which are placed pieces of heather and other material, while the relatively small cup-shaped depression in the centre is lined with the flattened stems of the wood-rush which grows abundantly among the Scottish hills. If undisturbed the birds return again and again, year after year, to the same nesting site, making such repairs as may be necessary each spring. Two eggs are usually laid, early in April, and vary a good deal in colour and markings. At first the nestlings are clothed in white down; and the parent birds watch and tend them with unceasing devotion, removing the fur or feathers from the prey, and dismembering it, before presentation to their hungry offspring. The golden eagle preys chiefly on the mountain hare, but will also carry off young lambs and red deer calves; it also preys upon grouse and ptarmigan, and is not above feasting on dead sheep and stags which have died on the hills. In Eastern Turkestan the golden eagle is trained for hawking and flown at deer, hares, wolves, and even the wild boar; and as one can imagine, the eagle's dash and courage is magnificent.

SPARROW-HAWKS

In the old days, when falconry was a popular sport, large numbers of sparrow-hawks were caught and trained for flight at partridges and smaller birds. It is the male sparrow-hawk that became known in the language of falconry as the "musket"—a term later applied to a firearm—but the female, being the larger and stronger bird, was the more popular for hawking. Both display considerable ferocity and ill-temper when first captured, and their successful training calls for unlimited care and patience. Unfortunately it is one of the hawks that

KESTREL. *Commonest of British hawks, the kestrel has outstandingly keen vision, and can sight a field-mouse from a height of fifty feet. Kestrels also eat many insects.*

will take pretty heavy toll of game and poultry chicks should the opportunity occur, particularly during the breeding season with a nest full of ravenous youngsters to feed. At other seasons of the year its food consists largely of house-sparrows, blackbirds and other small birds, insects, and a relatively small percentage of field-mice and voles. The plumage of the upper parts in the male bird is slatey-blue, mottled with white on the nape; the tail greyish-brown with three dark bars; cheeks bright rufous, under parts buff barred with ashy-brown, and with a rufous patch on the flanks. The nest composed of sticks, with a slight lining of softer twigs, is built in a tree, among the branches rather close to the trunk; and in this, four to six eggs, pale bluish-white and blotched with various shades of reddish-brown, are laid early in May.

At one time the kite was common in most of the wooded districts of England and Scotland, but to-day the last survivors are only to be seen in Wales, where, thanks to measures taken to protect them, a few pairs still live and breed. Its disappearance is the direct consequence of the heavy toll that it exacted during the nesting season upon young chickens in the poultry yard. Normally anything in the way of food coming easily to hand was devoured, including offal of all kinds, so that the kite can be regarded as a useful scavenger, and in addition it preys upon snakes, frogs, small mammals, and birds. The kite is handsome and graceful in its flight, the plumage of the head and neck is whitish striped with black; the mantle rufous-brown, the long, forked tail rufous, and the under parts rusty red striped with dark brown on the breast. In Wales the nest is usually built among the branches of an oak growing on some retired and thinly wooded hill-side, and is often composed of a strange assortment of materials, including sticks mixed with old rags, bones, fragments of paper, as well as samples of the "lesser linen" mentioned by Shakespeare, stolen from some cottage clothes-line. Two or three eggs, dull white or a very pale blue spotted with reddish-brown, are laid during the latter part of April or early in May.

In spite of senseless persecution, the peregrine falcon still retains a fair number of its eyries along the coasts of Dorset, Devon and Cornwall, on Exmoor and Dartmoor, along the coasts and among the mountains of Wales, the Lakes and Border country, and the coasts and mountains of Scotland. Its numbers are probably kept up and new blood introduced by the young migrating peregrines, chiefly birds of the year, known to falconers as "passage" hawks, which arrive every autumn, chiefly along the north and eastern coasts, following the hosts of wild duck migrating from more northerly regions. Some of these passage hawks certainly stay for the winter, and a few may become permanent residents. The natural food of the peregrine varies according to where the bird lives, gulls, puffins, wild duck and waders being hunted along the coast, while inland on the moors and hills

PEREGRINE FALCON. *Swift in flight and fearless in attack, the peregrine falcon preys relentlessly on other birds and was formerly used in the sport of falconry.*

pigeons, crows, magpies, rooks, partridge and grouse are taken. Although when hungry and the chance presents itself, the peregrine will take partridge and grouse, it by no means follows that these birds are its favourite prey, for it should be remembered that the peregrine as a rule captures her prey in the air, always striving to get above the quarry and then by a lightning swoop from above to strike down while in full flight. Now these two game birds are terrestrial in habit, and when a falcon is in sight, rather than take wing will squat close to the ground, and do their best to remain concealed until the danger is past.

The adult peregrine has the upper parts slatey-grey with obscure darker bars, while the under parts are buffish-white to a warm rufous tint, chest uniform or streaked, and lower down, barred with a variable amount of black; crown of head, nape, and cheeks blackish; legs yellow. In the young the upper parts are brown with buff margins, and the under parts ochreous with dark brown streaks. No regular nest is built, but a hollow scratched in the soil on the surface of some cliff ledge is a favourite coastal site; occasionally the deserted nest of a raven, crow, or heron will be utilized. Two to four eggs speckled with tints of orange-brown to rich brick-red are laid during April. The same eyrie is resorted to year after year, often genera-tion after generation, if left undisturbed. The female bird, on account of her greater size and power, was called the falcon, and the smaller male the "tiercel" or tassel, by falconers, who always held these beautiful birds in great esteem on account of their superior courage and dash.

The merlin is the smallest of our indigenous falcons, and still manages to hold its own in many parts of the country, including the moorlands of Somerset and Devon, the mountains of Wales, and northward to Scotland and the Isles. In autumn and winter it descends from its nesting haunts on the moorland hills to the low ground, the coasts and marshes, where snipe, dunlin, sandpipers and other small birds afford ample supplies of food. It is a bold, handsome little hawk, the male with the crown and mantle slate-colour, nape rufous, and throat white ; while the plumage of the under parts is buff striped with dark brown and the tail bluish-grey, broadly banded with black near the end. The female is easily-distinguished as her upper parts are a dark liver-brown, her brown tail crossed with five narrow bands of paler hue, while the cheeks, nape, and under parts are dull white streaked with brown. The moorland nesting site is usually a slight hollow scratched in the ground among the heather, a few twigs of heath forming a rough border; or, alternatively, an eyrie may be selected on some earth-covered ledge on a sea-cliff. Four to six deep reddish-brown or purplish-red eggs are laid, usually during May.

KESTREL AND HOBBY

The kestrel is still probably the most abundant of our native hawks, and un-doubtedly would be far more numerous, greatly to the benefit of agriculture throughout the country, were it not for its senseless persecution by ignorant and prejudiced people. In the country it is familiarly known as the windhover, from its habit of apparently hanging motionless in the air, hovering head to wind, supported by the rapid vibration of its wings, for a time, and then quickly gliding away to some other point; re-peating the operation again and again, until it finds some unsuspecting field-mouse, on which it swoops with light-ning rapidity. The male is a handsome bird with bluish-black head, neck, lower back and tail, the latter broadly banded with black and tipped with white; while the back is pale chestnut with small black spots. The under parts are buff streaked and spotted with black, and the bare legs and feet yellow. The female is slightly larger, and the plumage of her upper parts is rufous barred with black; and her tail has several narrow bands of black, with one broad one near the tip. Very varied nesting sites are used, from the deserted nest of a crow or magpie to a hollow in an old tree or ruin, or a cavity in the face of a cliff. Four to six eggs, usually brownish red in hue, are laid as early as the first week in April, if the weather be mild.

That most delightful little falcon, the hobby, arrives regularly in England every spring from about mid-April to the end of May, and breeds here, chiefly in the southern and south-eastern counties. After spending the summer months with us and rearing its young, the hobby usually departs during September and October for its winter quarters in tropical and southern Africa, and also in Asia. The sexes are alike in plumage, the female being slightly larger and less vivid in colour. The plumage of the upper parts is slatey-grey, becoming nearly black on the head; the nape slightly rufous, and the cheeks and throat white; while the under parts are buffish-white broadly striped with black. It breeds late in the season, seldom having eggs in the nest before the first or second week in June. Usually the deserted nest of a crow, magpie, or any other bird of suitable size, is utilized, and after the necessary repairs have been made, the three eggs, which vary a good deal in colour, some being yellowish-white closely speckled with rufous, or suffused with reddish-brown, are deposited. Although preying upon small birds, the hobby feeds chiefly upon insects, capturing large numbers of cockchafers and other beetles, dragon-flies, grasshoppers and other insects. The rapidity with which it pursues its prey, and the swiftness with which it turns and mounts after making a swoop at its quarry, is a marvellous sight to witness.

COMMON KITE. *The kite, known for its gliding flight with spread but motionless pinions, often preys on poultry.*

117

SWALLOW IN FLIGHT

THE
MYSTERY OF BIRD MIGRATION

by

SETON GORDON, C.B.E.

IN bird migration we see one of the strangest aspects of the feathered world. Put briefly, bird migration means the travelling, often over vast areas of land and ocean, of birds from their nesting ground to their winter quarters, and back again. It is only when we realize the almost incredible distances covered by certain of the birds, and try to trace the cause behind these seasonal flights, that we fully appreciate the fascination of a perplexing subject. Small wonder that widely differing theories have been advanced to account for the presence of birds in places where, seemingly, they have no business to be at all.

Years ago it was believed that certain birds solved their winter problem of lack of suitable food by hibernation rather than migration. For instance, in the sixteenth century, Olaus Magnus, Archbishop of Uppsala in Sweden, declared that swallows in autumn descended into the reeds, thence into the water below them, bound mouth to mouth, wing to wing, foot to foot. He said that fishermen often drew out these swallows in a lump: that if the fishermen were experienced they immediately returned the lump into the water, but if (through lack of knowledge) the birds were carried to a warm place, the lump was loosened by the heat and the swallows began to move and fly about. Yet they lived only a short time since they had been aroused prematurely from their deep winter sleep.

· The theory of hibernation has died hard and, until it became scientifically untenable, it was a satisfying belief for it accounted for the unexpected appearance of summer visitors in winter.

Since, however, the belief in bird-hibernation no longer exists, and that of bird migration reigns in its stead, we may as well ask ourselves the obvious question: why do birds migrate?

An explanation, which on the surface seems wholly satisfying, is that a sufficient food supply is at the bottom of it all. The swallow, house martin and swift, cuckoo, willow warbler and other species, could not find sufficient winter food in Britain. But this raises some interesting queries. Why should the blackbird remain in the British Isles throughout the year, while its first cousin, the mountain blackbird or ring ousel, migrates to Africa? Why do British-reared curlews migrate in autumn to Ireland, France, Spain and Portugal, while the curlews of Scandinavia take their places and winter with us? Why should the herring gull remain, a firm resident, in Britain throughout the year but the lesser black-backed gull, a gull of similar size and feeding habits, fly south to the coasts of Spain and Africa at the approach of winter? Why should the skylarks of the Hebrides migrate before stormy Atlantic weather sets in, but skylarks from Scandinavia, and even from Siberia, take their places as winter visitors and apparently find the food supply adequate? Why, again, should the sanderling—an attractive wader nesting far within the Arctic Circle—remain on our shores only for a few weeks, on passage, before continuing its flight toward the south, but its relative, the dunlin, a bird of similar size and feeding

ARCTIC TERNS. *Summer visitors to Britain, Arctic terns have breeding colonies on the rocky islets of the Orkneys and Hebrides.*

habits, remain on these same shores throughout the winter?

No: the food problem has much to do with bird migration but cannot entirely account for it. If food were the only issue, presumably all birds of the same species in any given locality would migrate in autumn toward the south, there to find warmer weather and more abundant food. But extensive marking of woodcock on the Alnwick estates in Northumberland has shown that some of the young birds ringed have indeed flown south, whereas others have remained throughout the winter on the ground where they were marked.

Northward migration in spring can be more easily understood than the southern drift in autumn. Like its human friends a bird has a deep love of home. Its desire is to return to the land where it was brought up, the land which saw its courtship and mating: the land where it reared its brood. That northern land may be cooler by far and more tempestuous than its winter quarters, but this is no deterrent to the wanderer eager to return. The knot, which winters in a temperate climate that rarely sees snow, migrates in summer to Grant Land, most northerly land of the North Polar Basin. Were it to reach that land in spring it would die of starvation, for the ground is frost- and snow-bound until late June. The knot must lay its eggs and rear its young during the brief Polar summer and migrate south with its young before the onset of the autumn blizzards.

On their way to summer quarters many species of birds travel in pairs, for they have mated or found their mates of the previous year before leaving their winter quarters. After the nesting season

is over, some birds migrate south in family parties. A pair of whooper swans, for example, may often be seen on some Highland tarn in October, surrounded by their cygnets: they have made the passage from Iceland in a family group.

Birds which are gregarious at their winter quarters travel usually in flocks. The formation of wild geese as they

speed across the sky attracts much
attention. The birds fly often in V-shaped
formation, but sometimes in a long line
which undulates slightly and gives the
illusion of a pennant idly waving on the
breeze. The leading member of the
flight, or "gaggle," of geese is usually
an old gander, but the leader is changed
from time to time, although it is probable

that the responsible bird is always in a
position where he can be speedily called
upon in an emergency. In migrating
birds, however, a distinct flight formation is the exception rather than the rule,
and many fly "bunched," or in straggling
flocks.

How high do migrating birds fly?
R.A.F. pilots have reported golden

plover at 6,000 feet, lapwings at 6,500 feet, and rooks as high as 11,000 feet. During the war of 1914-1918, aviators over the battle front in France saw geese flying at 9,000 feet. The Mount Everest Expedition of 1921 observed godwit and curlew, evidently on migration, at 20,000 feet, but even that great height is easily beaten by the geese observed and photographed by a scientist in India. The observer was photographing the sun, and on developing the negative saw on it a flight of geese which he found, by exact calculation, knowing the power of his telescope, to have been at an altitude of 29,000 feet above the sea.

Obviously the question arises, does travelling at this great height affect a bird's heart and breathing? No human aviator could fly at 29,000 feet without oxygen, and yet it may be inferred from this record that birds can do this without inconvenience.

Weather conditions greatly influence a migrating bird as regards the height at which it may fly. Favourable winds at the start of the flight may be succeeded by adverse air currents which can force a bird down almost to sea level. Rain may have a similar effect. The great Scottish naturalist, Eagle Clark, watched, from the Kentish Knock Lightship, chaffinches, skylarks and starlings in a heavy beam wind and drenching rain, hugging the very surface of the waves, and was amazed that they should have escaped being water-logged in that wind-driven deluge.

GOLDEN PLOVER. *In summer, this bird's plumage is speckled gold and black; cheeks, chin and underparts are also black. Haunting fields and mud-flats, golden plovers nest in northern districts of Britain; others arrive in large flocks from Iceland and the north at the approach of autumn.*

MANX SHEARWATER. *An ocean bird, which keeps close to the water in flight, the manx shearwater has breeding colonies off the west coast of Britain. Flying chiefly at night, this bird has a distinctive cry; plumage is black and white.*

Which is the greatest traveller among birds? The Arctic tern seems to hold the record, but not far behind it comes the greater shearwater. In the northern hemisphere, the Arctic tern nests within five hundred miles of the North Pole. The writer has watched a large colony of Arctic terns nesting on the mossy and shingly ground of Moffin Island, a low island off the north coast of Spitsbergen and six hundred nautical miles from the North Pole.

At the close of the northern summer the terns fly south until some of them at all events are found at the edge of the Antarctic ice-cap. They thus live in almost perpetual daylight, and make a round trip of 22,000 miles between their known haunts farthest north and those farthest south.

In the Royal Scottish Museum are two Arctic terns taken by the *Scotia* expedition in the Weddell Sea: and when the *Scotia* was locked in the pack-ice still farther south, Arctic terns were even then observed flying around the ship, in company with skuas and Antarctic and snowy petrels.

Two examples will show the great range of a young Arctic tern. A fledgling ringed in Labrador on 22 July, 1927, was found dead near La Rochelle, on the west coast of France, on the first of October of the same year. An even greater flight was made by a young Arctic tern ringed on 23 July, 1928, at Turnevik Bay, Labrador, and found lifeless at Port Shepstone, Natal, on 14 November. Only four months old, this bird had flown approximately 9,000 miles, a truly remarkable feat.

The greater shearwater is a bird of strong and effortless flight, and since it is equally at home on, or even beneath, the surface of the ocean, as in the air, its extensive migrations are less remarkable than the flights of the Arctic tern. The only known nesting haunts of the greater shearwater are the outlying uninhabited islands of the Tristan da Cunha group in the South Atlantic, 1,400 miles from the South African coast, and 1,700 miles from the nearest point of South America.

After the nesting season the greater shearwater travels leisurely toward the north but on reaching the tropical zone, where the warm waters and air-heat are apparently not to its liking, it greatly increases its speed until it has reached the cooler conditions of the northern hemisphere. It migrates northward up the western half of the North Atlantic, the first birds reaching Davis Strait in early June. At this season there are vast numbers of greater shearwaters fishing on the Grand Banks of Newfoundland, and later in the summer they are common also in Greenland waters. The cod fishers fishing the Newfoundland Banks formerly used this bird both as food and bait. The method of bringing the shearwaters alongside the boats was to feed first the small storm petrels. Seeing these little petrels fluttering above the water the greater shearwaters quickly arrived, scattered the smaller birds and proceeded to devour the fish's entrails on which the petrels had been feeding. They were caught on mackerel hooks, and seventy years ago it was no uncommon sight to see 300 to 500 shearwaters hanging from the rigging of a fishing boat. The American naturalist, R. C. Murphy, advances an interesting theory: that the numbers of greater shearwaters may be too large for each bird to nest each year on the limited nesting ground of the Tristan da Cunha island group, and that the annual breeding season may have

been replaced by a longer reproductive rhythm. An observer on the Tristan group watched the shearwaters flighting in at sunset from the ocean until in the twilight hundreds of thousands were wheeling overhead, their song rising in volume until it reached a musical roar, strange and fascinating with its background of thundering surf.

KITTIWAKES

Since this chapter began with a description of two great oceanic bird wanderers, it may be as well to consider other sea bird migrants before turning to the land birds. One of the most interesting migrations is that of the kittiwake, for it is east and west rather than north and south. Young kittiwakes ringed on the Farne Islands off the coast of Northumbria in summer have actually been recovered on the Newfoundland Banks the same autumn. After the nesting season, British kittiwakes migrate west until they have reached mid-Atlantic; at the same time, Newfoundland-nesting kittiwakes have migrated eastward from the coast of Newfoundland, and the two races share the same vast feeding grounds more than a thousand miles from land. Indeed, it has been proved by ringing that a British kittiwake may on occasion mate with a Newfoundland kittiwake and return not to Britain but Newfoundland.

When enemy submarine activity was at its greatest in mid-Atlantic, there is little doubt that the floating oil from "killed" U-boats or sinking tankers must have brought destruction to many kittiwakes. Sea birds mistake crude oil floating on the water for the oily scum which tells them that a shoal of fish—and therefore food in plenty—is near the surface; they alight upon or dive into the oil and their plumage is immediately fouled. Since the insulating layer between the sea water and the bird's skin is lost, the victim suffers from cold and, chilled and poisoned, slowly succumbs. A

POWERFUL WINGS OF BLACK TERN. *Although a small bird, the wings of the black tern are powerful enough to allow it to fly considerable distances. It is not a resident of Britain, but during spring and summer it may be seen on passage in the south-east, where it frequents inland waters. The plumage shades from light to dark grey, with blue-black head, neck and breast, and black bill and legs.*

lightly oiled bird may recover, but a heavily oiled victim is doomed.

The gannet, largest of British sea-birds and in flight the most kingly, is another extensive traveller, undertaking great ocean flights from its nesting stack to distant fishing grounds for food for its young. The date of the gannet's autumn migration is most regular. Thus in the waters which impinge upon the Isle of Skye, the season for the gannet's departure is around 10 October. The weather at the time may be fine, calm and summer-like, or wild and stormy, but the gannet's clock tells him it is time to be off and for the next six months the waters of the Minch are lonely without his long and narrow wings, snow-white beneath the summer sun and black-tipped.

It is remarkable that the young gannet should be a greater migrant than its parents. The young gannet is deserted by its parents some ten days before it makes its first flight, and thus must rely on its own intelligence during its migration.

migrate so far south. The adult solan rarely migrates south of western European waters: occasionally the normal south migration gives place to a curious northward drift, and in winter British birds have on occasion been recovered from the vicinity of the Faeroes. Gannets mistrust land and in order to avoid flying over it, make considerable detours. They never set foot on any land except their own nesting rock.

The British Isles are the main haunt of the gannet. There are no colonies in England, although a few birds have nested in recent years on the Yorkshire sea cliffs. In Wales the only colony is on Grassholm, where 6,000 pairs nest. Scotland and the Isles have eight stations, the largest colony being on St. Kilda. Eire has two colonies, both on the southwest coast.

GUILLEMOTS AND GULLS

The guillemot's migrations are not fully known, but any day in October a continuous stream of these fast-flying birds may be seen passing south-west in little parties low above the Minch at a distance of four miles and more offshore. They are all of them speeding to their winter quarters, where in winter the species occur south to the coasts of Morocco and the Canary Islands. Tens, even hundreds of thousands of these powerful-winged, ocean-going birds must pass through the Minch each autumn: the return migration in spring is not so clearly seen and the birds may follow a different route.

So firm a resident in the British Isles is the herring gull that it is noteworthy that its relative the lesser black-back should be only seen as a summer visitor. The lesser black-back is a medium-sized gull, with slatey-black back and wings:

The young solan (to give it the name by which it is almost always known in Scotland), in its black juvenile plumage with small white spots thickly sprinkled over the feathers, moves south along the Atlantic seaboard of Europe, reaching the Bay of Biscay before the end of September: it arrives above tropical waters during November, travelling along the coastal waters of West Africa as far as Senegal. Birds in their second year (the gannet is not mature until four or even five years old) do not usually it must not be confused with the greater black-back, a larger and fiercer bird, which inhabits the coasts of Britain throughout the winter. In autumn the lesser black-back migrates south, reaches the west coast of Africa by December, and is not seen in Britain again until March of the following year.

A few words may here be said of the black-headed gull, because it is the bird which gives character throughout the winter and early spring months to the ornamental waters of the London area. The Londoner rarely sees the dark chocolate hood which gives the gull its name, for this is assumed with the nesting plumage, usually after it has migrated from the London area, but the gull can be identified by its small size and narrow, pointed wings, as by its harsh scream. Most of the London gulls are natives of the countries near the Baltic, and return thither in March or early April.

SWALLOW TRIBE

Of migrants among land birds the swallow tribe have perhaps the greatest interest for nature lovers, since they live in association with man. House martin and swallow both nest in close proximity to their human friends. As the two species are often confused, it may be of interest to note the distinguishing features of each. A swallow differs from a house martin in its uniform blue-black upper parts, elongated outer tail feathers, and chestnut-red throat and forehead. In the house martin the tail is less deeply forked than the swallow, but the main distinction is the white rump, which contrasts strongly with the blue-black back and wings. The entire under parts are pure white. Many people think that swallows build their nests beneath the eaves of houses, but the species which builds under the eaves is the house martin. The true swallow nests in out-buildings. Its nest, which resembles the beginnings of a house martin's nest, is built often on a wooden rafter where it enters the wall of the building, and may be so low that it is almost possible to see into the nest from the ground.

The swallow's nest is open at the top: the martin's nest is domed. Both are built of wet mud which becomes, when dry, almost as firm as cement.

The swallow arrives in Britain before the house martin, and leaves rather earlier, generally in September.

In the *Handbook of British Birds,* Vol. 11, is an interesting map compiled and drawn by H. N. Southern, to show the rate of northern migration of the swallow over Europe during the spring. The average date of arrival in southern England is 1 April, and not until six weeks later do the birds reach northern Scotland. Southern Scandinavia is reached about 15 May, but it is not until 1 July that swallows in any numbers arrive in the most northerly districts of Norway. Some years ago the present writer had the memorable experience of seeing a migration of swallows over the Cairngorm Hills at sunrise. The birds flew only a few feet over the rock-strewn ground, moving fast and following each undulation of the pass. The ringing experiments carried out first by H. F. Witherby, a distinguished ornithologist and for many years editor of *British Birds*—his pioneer work of bird marking has now been taken over by the British Museum—show that British swallows ringed as nestlings have been reported from the south-west of the Belgian Congo, Cape Province, Orange Free State, Transvaal, Natal, and East Griqualand. Adult British swallows have been found in Natal and the Orange Free State. No less wide a traveller is the house martin, for each autumn after its nesting is over it flies south until it reaches and crosses the equator and winters in South Africa's summer.

The third member of the swallow tribe is the sand martin. It is the smallest

PAIR OF SWALLOWS
The forked tail and swift graceful flight are characteristic of this summer visitor.

THE PARASITIC CUCKOO

*Cuckoos always lay their eggs in the nests of other birds, and the young cuckoos,
when hatched, destroy the eggs or fledgelings of the foster-parents that feed them.*

of the three and may be distinguished by the uniform brown colour of the upper parts of its plumage. It is rarely found around human dwellings and nests in sandbanks or on the sides of gravel pits. It is more frequently seen fly-catching over rivers and lakes than either the swallow or the house martin. Its winter quarters also are in Africa, south of the equator.

SPEED IN FLIGHT

The swift, that dark scimitar-winged bird which circles and wheels tirelessly above villages and towns, is of a different order to the swallows and, indeed, is more nearly akin to the humming birds. The Alpine swift has been recorded in Britain as a rare vagrant, but the only swift that need be referred to here is the British species, rejoicing in the scientific name of *apus apus apus*. Swifts can be distinguished at a glance from swallows and martins by their very long and narrow scythe-like wings and uniform sooty-brown plumage. That the wings of the swift are on occasion moved alternately and not in unison would appear to be an undoubted fact, unless it be an optical illusion. It is stated that the American chimney swift was also believed to move its wings alternately, but a cinematograph film has refuted this: yet so many observers in Britain have reported the alternate moving of the wings of our own swifts that it is difficult to discredit them all.

In flight the swift is extremely rapid. According to E. C. Stuart-Baker, who timed swifts with a stop-watch over a two mile course, a speed of two hundred miles an hour was attained. Were the observer less accurate and skilled, doubt might be cast on his record for no other known bird in horizontal flight approaches that speed. Because of the length of its wings and its short, feeble, legs the swift has great difficulty in rising from level ground, and never

.T.F.—E

alights on it of its own free will, taking food, water and nesting materials on the wing. Swifts even mate while soaring in the air. They have frequently been seen to mount higher and higher at dusk and some observers have held that, in fine summer weather, they even sleep on the wing at a great altitude above the earth.

The young of the swift grow slowly, and are six weeks in the nest. It has often been asked why the swifts should begin their southward migration flight early in August, when insect food is still abundant, while the swallow and house martin linger until late September and even October. The two latter species rear a second brood; the swift, because of the prolonged fledgling period of the young, has scarcely time to do this and thus has no ties to keep it with us after

TIRED SWIFT. *This bird is able to travel great distances and is here seen resting during a migratory flight.*

WILD SWANS IN FLIGHT

the first brood is on the wing. Yet this is only a partial explanation, for why should the swift be in such haste to be off to South Africa when insect life is plentiful in its northern home?

That sweet singer the nightingale, which in Britain is found no farther north than Yorkshire, is generally known to winter in tropical Africa, but it is not common knowledge that our native robin frequently makes the overseas flight towards the south in autumn and has been recovered in south-western France. One spring day the writer found a robin dead on the snow at the crest of the Lairig pass in Inverness-shire almost 3,000 feet above the sea. The bird had evidently been on migration and perished in the snow. Nor is it generally realized that the tiny gold-crest, smallest of British birds, migrates overseas in considerable numbers before the coming of winter. So delicate and fragile a bird is ill-fitted for that great journey and alas! many meet their fate at sea or against the glass of lighthouses.

CUCKOO'S SENSE OF DIRECTION

The southward migration of the cuckoo disproves the theory that young birds are guided on that migration by their more experienced elders, for the young cuckoos do not begin the flight to Africa until a month after the adults have left. They are dependent entirely upon their own sense of direction, yet their psychic compass points unerringly to that land far to the south where they will winter.

On the other hand, fieldfares, redwings, and thrushes migrate in flocks, and so far as is known young and old travel together. Both these species nest

GANNETS. *These powerfully-winged seabirds (right) are found chiefly in the north and west of Britain, having extensive breeding colonies on Grassholm and Bass Rock.*

in the birch forests of Scandinavia and winter in Britain and in southern Europe. Fieldfares ringed as nestlings in Finnish Lapland and Norway have been recovered in the west of England. At its winter quarters the fieldfare is a shyer bird than the redwing but the opposite is true at the northern nesting sites. The redwing can be identified by its white

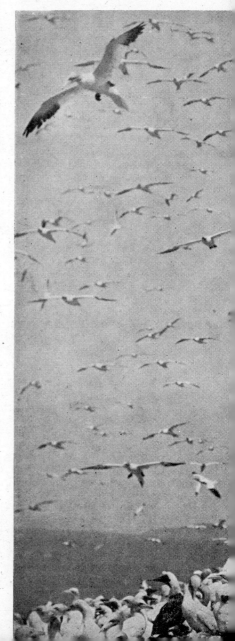

eye-stripe and chestnut-red flanks; while the fieldfare is grey, chestnut and black.

Wild geese and wild swans are strong-winged birds and migration to them must be comparatively easy. .The lordly whooper swan flies south in October from northern Norway and Iceland, to winter in Britain: the smaller Bewick's swan (named after the famous engraver and naturalist) comes to us from the Siberian tundra. One autumn day the writer saw a herd—a flock of swans is usually referred to as a "herd"—of whooper swans resting at the head of a sea loch in the Isle of Skye. The birds had evidently just arrived and were sleeping so soundly that they did not awaken as the writer passed. In the

CUCKOO. *Arriving in the British Isles early in the spring, the cuckoo quickly makes its presence known by its repetitive two-noted call. Young birds are brown but on maturity the plumage takes on a slate-grey colour, the white under-parts being barred with dark grey. In autumn, the cuckoo flies south to Africa.*

evening they were gone, and perhaps were then in the air, again speeding southward to a warmer climate.

The whooper swan and Bewick's swan can be distinguished at a glance from British semi-domesticated mute swans by the absence of the basal knob or "berry" on the bill, which is yellow; the neck, too, is less curved. Bewick's swan can be distinguished from the whooper by its smaller size and the greater area of black on the bill; while at its winter quarters it is seen more frequently on tidal waters

than the whooper. Both types are most numerous in Scotland.

Typical of the wild geese in their migrations are the brent goose and the barnacle goose. The brent is much the smallest and darkest of the geese. It comes from the far north-east, where, on the Arctic tundra and islands, it breeds in great numbers. When the writer visited Spitsbergen some years ago he found that brents were decreasing; they were much shot by Norwegians in sealing sloops, who were gathering eider eggs, for eiders and brents often nested on the same island. At some of its winter haunts in the British Isles it is present in great numbers. Two favourite winter haunts are Holy Island in Northumbria, and the Malahide estuary near Dublin, where the geese rising with thunderous clamour into the winter sky literally darken the air.

For centuries it was implicitly believed that the barnacle goose took its birth from a barnacle—hence its name. How this quaint myth arose is unknown; it was perhaps strengthened by the fact that the breeding grounds of this goose were also unknown; indeed it is only in comparatively recent years that they have been discovered in Greenland and the islands of Spitsbergen.

WILD GEESE IN LONDON

Barnacle geese winter mainly on Hebridean islets, where they crop the short green grass. They may be seen in St. James's Park, London, where they have bred at least once, and on other ornamental waters. They are handsome birds. The black, white and grey of the plumage is distinctive: the crown, neck and breast are glossy black, the face and forehead creamy white, except for a dark mark running from the bill to the eye. The rump is white; the legs are black, as is the small and delicate bill. The barnacle goose is one of the few birds that has not become used to aircraft and still panics when they appear.

The British Isles are in an unusually favoured geographical position for bird migration. They lie on the migration course of many birds which do not nest with us. We have summer migrants, winter migrants, and passage migrants. Some species can indeed be all three. The golden plover, for example, is a summer migrant to the moors, a winter migrant to the coast, and a passage migrant on its way to Iceland and Scandinavia.

B.T.F.—E*

SPOTTED FLYCATCHER. *A visitor from Africa, this bird is recognizable by its darting flight as it pursues the flies and insects on which it lives.*

THE OAK IN SUMMER

THE LIVING TREE

by

SIR WILLIAM BEACH THOMAS, K.B.E.

TREES have been called the pillars of English scenery. They are like the alphabet, which all readers must know, and their charm is acknowledged by all our world: but it was not always so. England was once almost continuous forest. Even as late as the Middle Ages it was said that a squirrel could travel ten miles in Cannock Chase and never touch the ground. There are many passages concerning the dread and terror of the aboriginal forest that covered Kent. Our civilization in early days was largely a struggle to de-forest, to make clearings for little farms and roadways. By some happy quality in the English character, terror of trees in mass gave place to love of trees in open country ; and so England to-day has fewer dense woods, but more widely dispersed individual trees than perhaps any other country. We are almost tree-worshippers, like the Druids. No compliment is dearer to us than "hearts of oak are our men", for the oak is the stoutest and most beloved of all our native trees and the most widely spread.

Though the soil and strata of Great Britain change greatly and often abruptly, particular types of trees are not for the most part confined to particular districts. Beeches like chalk and the most famous woods of beech are at High Wycombe, where they provide the raw material for the manufacture of furniture, and at Burnham: but the trees are as fine on Gloucester highlands, on Wiltshire downs and in the New Forest. Oaks are wont to flourish on heavy clay soils and the mountain ash is rightly so named. But in general a large variety of trees is to be found in all the English counties, the water-loving trees, such as sallows, willows, poplars and alders, by the rivers, dykes or marshes, and the hard woods on higher ground. The low-lying districts of both Somerset and Essex are well known for different varieties of willow, the first providing a basket-making industry, the second the material for cricket bats. Some districts have changed within memory owing to afforestation. This is true not only of the wide areas afforested—mostly with conifers—by the Forestry Commission since its formation in 1919, as on the borders of Norfolk and Suffolk, but of the New Forest, for example, where the need of ash for aeroplanes has supplanted the oak once in demand for ships. Treeless districts are rare. Single trees do not in most places—though the Isle of Wight is an exception—flourish by the sea, and where small groups of trees have survived (often of sycamore), they are wont to slope up, almost like a bank, those nearest the sea, or sometimes the west, being the lowest. Where the chalk comes very near the surface, as on parts of the Chilterns in Bedfordshire, trees are absent, though flourishing woods are near at hand; and on high, exposed places, Exmoor and Dartmoor, for example, such seedlings as those of the mountain ash, which are often numerous, seldom come to full or even half stature and there are strange patches of dwarfed oaks. A curious effect of the neglect of common land in England is that trees begin to increase over commons once kept quite treeless by grazing animals. Generally the first to establish

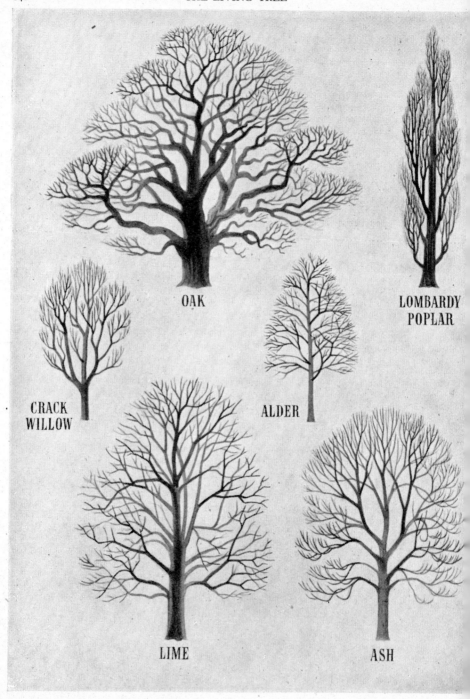

OAK

LOMBARDY
POPLAR

CRACK
WILLOW

ALDER

LIME   ASH

SHAPE OF TREES. *Stripped of summer leaves, the distinctive outline of individual*

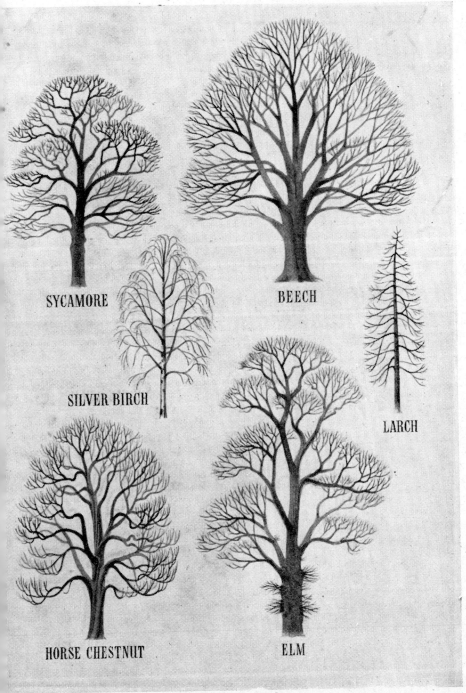

SYCAMORE

BEECH

SILVER BIRCH

LARCH

HORSE CHESTNUT

ELM

trees becomes more apparent, and the different types are easily recognizable.

TYPES OF BARK

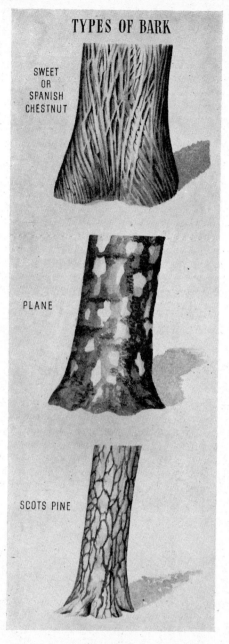

SWEET
OR
SPANISH
CHESTNUT

PLANE

SCOTS PINE

TREE BARKS. *Seen here are the twisted fissures of the bark of the sweet chestnut, the flaking, patched bark of the plane and the rough graining of the Scots pine. Plane trees are usually found in towns.*

themselves are hollies and oaks—often from acorns dropped by rooks—and elms in the neighbourhood of bordering elms.

What is a tree? The answer is not altogether simple. Some of the older botanists divided what they called erect foliage stems into four classes named, in ascending scale of size and importance, caudex, culm, stalk and trunk, but the words are not now in general use, and in any case are less important than the examples. Many of the palms (which have as a rule a long stem but no branches) are in one class, along with tree-ferns and even the dragon-tree (which lives to an immense age). The bamboos are the best example of another class. The stalk belongs to many lowly plants and to many bushes that die down after a year or two, for example, the elder. Last and greatest comes the trunk or bole, enclosed with bark proper, which is the outstanding mark of the tree as we all understand the word.

TREE TRUNKS

There are just two sorts of trunk in the general picture: trunks which rise to a good height before putting forth boughs, and trunks which are in some sort shrubby, that is, produce boughs more or less close to the ground. The tree is the crown of plant life, probably in evolution, quite certainly in human estimation. The early Scandinavians invented Yggdrasil, the Tree of Life that climbed from earth to Heaven like Jacob's ladder. Everybody admires trees and many people, including W. H. Hudson, one of our greatest writers on natural history, confessed that he was among the worshippers. There was something almost mystic in his admiration.

Exactly what sort of tree clothed England when our coal measures were laid down is in some dispute. Some think that symmetric evergreen trees more or less in the nature of araucarias or monkey puzzles, now only seen in gardens, were common, but whatever the prehistoric past, to-day an immense proportion of the trees of Great Britain are deciduous, that is lose their leaves in autumn and regain their leafage in the spring. This loss is on the whole no loss to the tree lover. Even if he has never studied trees, it is easier for a countryman to distinguish the species in winter than in summer, at any rate at a certain distance, for the prime beauty and character of a tree, as one might say of a man or a woman, is its figure, its form and shape and what is called its habit of growth. This matters most. The leaves are lovely at all periods of their constant change from early spring through summer to late autumn. Most of them persist for about eight months of the twelve, for the season is not entirely open, as sportsmen would say, till the second or third week in November. Many have more lovely flowers and catkins than is generally realized; but both flowers and leaves yield to the almost architectural grace of the form. To a considerable degree this is hidden by foliage, but it leaps to the eye as soon as the leaves fall.

At the same time the leaves, so to say, are the cause of the shape. The first thing a more or less scientific student of trees sets out to learn is the pattern of the leaves on a branch or stem. In some a pair of leaves or more come out immediately opposite one another. In others they form various sorts of spiral all up the stem. If we draw a line from one bud to the next, below or above, on the twig of an elm, lime, hazel, hornbeam, beech, chestnut or, less conspicuously, on a birch we shall pass through two buds before the spiral-circle is complete. In some species such a line will pass through three buds. In very many this spiral line passes through five buds in making the complete revolutions of the twig.

Now the buds, which will make the pattern of the branches, come up

TYPES OF BARK

OAK

BEECH

SILVER BIRCH

TREE BARKS. *The rough, furrowed bark of the oak is contrasted here with the smooth grey bark of the beech and the white papery bark of the birch, which is a hardy tree, penetrating far north.*

NEW SHOOT
SPRINGING
FROM ROOT

END OF BLACKBERRY BRANCH
SWELLING OUT TO FORM NEW SHOOT

NEW TREES WITHOUT SEEDS. *New trees and bushes are frequently reproduced without having recourse to the seed. A blackberry shoot, for example, may take root in contact with the earth, while the growth of new young plants from the roots of elms or white poplar is very common.*

in the angle or axil of the leaf, so that the position of the leaves, which is more or less constant in every species of tree, may be said to decide the future relation of the branches to one another. It would be ideally possible to foretell the shape of the tree at its summit of growth from a study of the position of the leaves on a single twig, but it generally happens that some of the buds fail to develop. The crooked pattern, for example, of many oaks is largely due to the failure of the leading bud. In a few trees, one of which is the London plane, the commonest urban tree in these days, the leaf makes a complete sheaf for the coming bud. It is worth looking at the intense fresh clean green of these buds in the smokiest town after the plane leaves fall.

Even if no bud comes out by its base the leaf leaves behind a very obvious and interesting sign of its presence. It falls not only because it has been sunburnt, battered by wind and rain and decayed

through age. It falls in some measure from its own activity. What happens in rough outline is this. As soon as the sun becomes lower and the cold increases, chlorophyll, the green fluid which is the tree's life (indeed the cause of all life, for it alone in co-operation with the sun can convert dead into living stuff)—this green flows back from the leaf into the safe harbourage of the twig; the leaves lose their greenness, often beginning from the edge and leaving a line of greenery along the centre rib. The colours of autumn appear. They are not, of course, due to the addition of new dyes, but to the loss of one sort of colouring matter. Only when it flows away are the waste colours enabled to show their various hues. On a few trees, the brown leaves hang on throughout a good part of the winter; but for the most part they fall soon after they fade. "Fall" may be thought to be the wrong word. Rather are they thrust off. Little studs of hard, barren cork are formed and help to break the cohesion between the leaf-stalk and the twig. The size and pattern of these cork studs or points vary greatly and are very conspicuous. Those on the horse chestnut have been compared with a skull but more nearly resemble an open horse-shoe with five nails, and some hold this to be the origin of the tree's unusual name.

STRUCTURE OF LEAVES

These bits of cork do more than help the ejection of the dead leaf; they heal the wound. There would be a serious wound because the leaf was not a mere decoration but a definite member of the tree. Besides the fibres which run through the leaf and hold it firm very much in the way of struts and girders in a house, there are tubes continuously connected with the stem which may be compared with the water pipes or wiring of a house. The surface covering of leaf and stalks is also continuous. When all this connection is broken, the break is sealed by the cork; and this active work is as much a part of autumn as is the more negative decay of the tissue of the leaf.

Though from a distance most trees are easiest to distinguish after the leaves have fallen, from close at hand the leaf itself is doubtless the most apparent signal of identification. The broadest difference is between the leaves that have a number of leaflets on one stem, as in the ash, the ailanthus or tree of heaven (now a common tree in towns), the so-called acacia (which thanks to William Cobbett's extravagant praise of it was multiplied all over England), or in a rather different form the horse-chestnut: and those that have single or simple leaves. But within each class the leaves are very distinct in form and character. It is possible to mistake the leaf of the hornbeam for a beech leaf or an elm leaf, but even this has an individual appearance when looked at closely. The stalk of the leaf is peculiarly individual in the poplars. Everyone

THE AGE OF A TREE. *The age of a tree may be calculated by rings on a cross-section of the bole, each one of which represents a year of growth.*

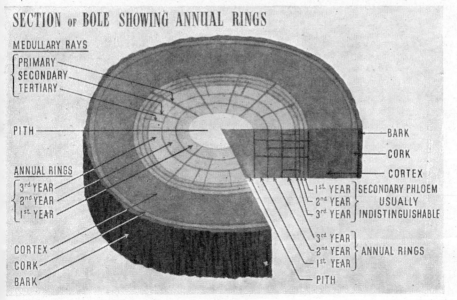

SECTION of BOLE SHOWING ANNUAL RINGS

MEDULLARY RAYS
PRIMARY
SECONDARY
TERTIARY

PITH

ANNUAL RINGS
3rd YEAR
2nd YEAR
1st YEAR

CORTEX
CORK
BARK

BARK
CORK
CORTEX
1st YEAR
2nd YEAR   SECONDARY PHLOEM
3rd YEAR   USUALLY INDISTINGUISHABLE
3rd YEAR
2nd YEAR   ANNUAL RINGS
1st YEAR
PITH

has noticed the wavering of the leaves of the aspen and many other poplars. It has indeed become a commonplace of literature. The quiver is due more to the nature of the stalk than to the shape of the leaf which suggests a spearhead. The stalk is flattened at right angles to the plane of the leaf, so that when the wind blows the leaf, taking the line of least resistance, tends to move sideways rather than up or down; curious twists and turns of motion are produced, and a singular distinctive sound is heard in the lightest breeze.

HOW TREES GROW

Magnificent though it is, the tree starts life in the same way as the smallest annual weed. The seed breaks its case. One shoot goes downward, seeming to have a natural affinity for the darkness of the earth; another shoot goes yet more directly upwards into the light. There are trees that have developed other ways of reproducing themselves. Wherever elms or white poplars grow, quantities of young trees will appear in their neighbourhood. The spreading roots, not the seeds, which are usually infertile, have grown buds and sent shoots upwards. Nevertheless, in spite of such exceptions and later developments, theoretically the origin is the seed. Though root and shoot have this strong difference of habit, the two are not in themselves opposed in nature. When a long blackberry shoot curves to the ground the buds at its tip may change to roots with astonishing rapidity and so start a new plant. Grown trees may do very much the same. When boughs sweep to the ground what would have been buds become roots and new trees are so started in life.

It is sometimes argued that trees which can multiply only in such ways, and do not set any seed, are therefore not originally native but have been introduced. Several varieties of elm, almost the commonest of English trees, are in this class, but it is hardly safe to infer that

they are therefore alien. Habits may change. It may be that a parallel exists in the habit of casting leaves before winter. This was perhaps originally induced by the severity of the frost which most broad, vulnerable sappy leaves could not endure. The organism discovered that strength was best preserved by hoarding the vital fluid and the rejection of the tender leaf during the periods of frost and complete darkness.

The buds—both leaf-buds and flower-buds—are already formed in autumn and must abide the winter. To this end they are protected both by the tightness of the folding, by the hardening of the outer fold, and often by a sort of gum or varnish particularly noticeable, for example, in the horse-chestnut and the balsam poplar. Indeed the pleasant powerful smell of this latter tree issues largely from the sticky exterior of the buds. Scientifically the covering of the bud, as indeed all parts of it, and perhaps the sepals and bracts and petals of the flower are all of the nature of leaves that have assumed different functions in the course of their evolution.

FLOWERS OF TREES

All trees, of course, are flowering trees; and the flowers, though often inconspicuous, are perhaps more characteristic of each species than any other part. A considerable majority belong to one of just two classes. They are either catkin-bearing or rosaceous—that is, in the words of the *Oxford English Dictionary*, " belonging to, characteristic of, the natural order Rosaceae, of which the rose is the type." All poplars and willows, the hazel, oak, hornbeam, alder, plane, beech, Spanish chestnut and many evergreens are alike in that they produce in spring, often before the leaves open, tassels of imperfectly developed flowers; and in all of them the flowers are of two sorts, one male, one female (staminate and pistillate). The majority carry both sorts of

SILVER BIRCH IN WINTER

LEAVES OF THE ASH TREE. *The leaves of the ash tree are among the latest to appear in the spring and they open from stout black buds. Each leaf is divided into six or seven pairs of lance-shaped tooth-edged leaflets, with a single terminal leaflet. The flowers, borne in April or May, are succeeded by the fruit, generally known as "keys," or "spinners" because of the twisted wings. These narrow, scale-like keys float to the earth when ripe and are so designed that the seed-end lands first.*

FLOWERS OF THE SYCAMORE. *The sycamore tree is not a native of Britain but was introduced from the Continent in the fifteenth century. This hardy tree grows quickly and is full grown in fifty or sixty years. The leaves are heart-shaped but cut into five lobes with jagged edges, and the flowers are greenish-yellow; these develop into winged fruits which seed freely in even poor soil.*

flowers on the same tree. A smaller number, including most willows and sallows, bear them on different trees, the male on one and the female on the other. A good example, though exceptions are found, is the holly. Only the female trees can produce the coral berries. The technical terms of botany are very numerous and chiefly used by scientific botanists; but if any be necessary for the general tree-lover it is the word *dioecious*, meaning a tree that bears both sorts of flowers, as opposed to *monoecious*, applied to trees producing only one sort of flower.

Trees that have been put in the Rose family are also numerous. They include the hawthorn, a large number of bushes or half-trees (so to call them) such as the beautiful service and beam trees; all the Prunus and Pyrus trees, such as crab apple and wild pear; and many more such as the wild cherry and mountain ash or rowan and the medlar. Outside these two classes come the lime or linden tree and the maples; the common and wych elms, which are in a class by themselves and are related to the nettles; and the ash, which is of the Olive family. It is remarkable that though they differ in family, ash and hornbeam produce a fruit known in different country places as " keys." Indeed the hornbeam and the ash are both known locally as key trees. The sycamore, which is almost unique in its success in sowing fertile seed, is a little like them. Spinning as they fall to the ground, the two flat wings that flank the seed often carry it to a considerable distance. The alien imported tree called acacia by the public but robinia by the botanists. is the only example among trees of the " butterfly " or papilionaceous family. It was introduced from the United States in the eighteenth century.

LEAF PATTERNS. *The drawing shows the position of buds on a branch.*

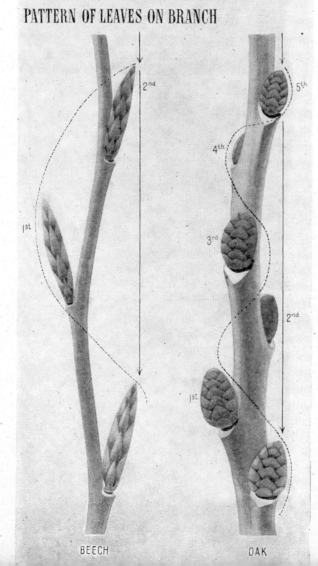

PATTERN OF LEAVES ON BRANCH

2nd

1st

5th

4th

3rd

2nd

1st

BEECH

OAK

GOAT WILLOW IN BLOOM

We cannot be said to know a tree till we can identify it by bud, leaf, flower, bark, form and trunk. In winter, even expert foresters have on occasion to verify their identification from the trunk by examination of the still tightly folded bud. Even in the winter season buds give unmistakable evidence. At some seasons the case has a curious likeness to the shard of a beetle's wing, especially when it is thrown back for the leaf or flower to emerge. Its armour is further strengthened, as we have seen, by a resinous varnish that makes it quite waterproof.

TYPES OF BUDS

When at last the envelope breaks open and falls back before being wholly rejected there may be revealed within (to take the horse chestnut as a salient example) not only the seven leaflets, but often the complete flower which looks almost as if it were wrapped up in cotton wool. Its existence at the top and centre of the shoot proclaims one reason why the shape of the boughs and twigs of the tree does not follow logically from the position of the buds; when the leading bud is a flower it does not of course grow further and the effect is the same as when a leaf bud withers or remains inactive. The flower is particularly noticeable at the end of the chestnut shoots and the dying off of the central bud in the oak. The curious crooked pattern of oak twigs is compared by Lord Avebury with the irregular indentations of the leaf: but it is due largely to the fact that some of the side buds and few of the centre buds develop.

Perhaps the best contrast with the chestnut bud, which is stout and thick, is the beech bud, which is long and pointed and has many small points of difference in structure. The ground may be littered in early spring by the rejected brown casings. It would be accurate enough to speak of the fall of leaves in spring, little though their brown shrivelled relics

seem to share with the brilliant fresh green of the leaves unfolding from what botanists have called "crumpled vernation." Though in the winter scene the buds are the first sign of identification for the expert, the trunk usually tells a true tale. Even the colours of the species have a wide range. Everyone knows the whiteness of the birch bark which can be peeled off and serve, if need be, for a writing tablet so smooth is the inner surface. The white poplar has patches and blotches of smudged grey and white. The bark of the occidental plane, so widely planted in London, drops off in considerable panels under the irregular pressure from within; and for this reason, as well as the covering of the bud by the sheath of the old leaf, the species is peculiarly well suited for growth in a dirty or sooty atmosphere. The purple smoothness of the wild cherry is quite unmistakable; and of the trunks which most saliently adorn the winter scene in England none excels the beech. The smooth, grey-green splendidly chiselled trunks suggest to some eyes a particular variety of coloured marble. It is doubtless due to the attraction of this bark that it is more often defaced by the cutting of names and initials—and has been so since Ovid described the habit—than any other tree. One of the few trees with a soft bark is an evergreen, the imported Wellingtonia or sequoia, which one can hit with one's fist and not suffer for it. Its softness is much appreciated by the little tree-creeper which makes winter snuggeries in it; but this same bird prefers to nest in a deciduous tree, that other alien the acacia, which often has a bark so deeply furrowed that a nest may be well concealed in the crevices.

The height of the trunks is not so good a pointer to the species as is generally imagined. True, many trees such as the elm and the ash tend to grow to a considerable altitude before branching, whereas the oak oftens sends forth

ELMS IN WINTER. *Common elms, which vary in their greater height and narrower girth from wych elms, are found in fields and hedges in every part of Britain. It is in winter that the full beauty of the bare frames is revealed.*

153

LARCH WOOD. *Introduced into England in the sixteenth century, larch trees were first grown as ornamental trees but were later used for their valuable timber. The straight tapering trunk sometimes approaches a height of one hundred feet.*

almost horizontal boughs of great thick-ness from the head of a short trunk; but this habit is peculiar to single, isolated oaks. In a plantation they may send up clean, tall trunks rivalling those of any other tree. It is curious that the beech, which has perhaps the most beautiful trunk, will often branch from a very short trunk even within a wood.

STRUCTURE OF TREES

The trunk's superstructure is in some measure fitted to the nature of the roots that anchor the tree. The oak's heavy boughs, thrust out at an angle that appears to be mechanically impossible, can take this shape for two reasons; the wood is of peculiarly strong, firm tissue, and the tree has tap-roots (so-called) that go very deep. It is quite difficult to dig up and transplant oak seedlings of even as little as three years' growth, so deeply has the long root penetrated; and though roots are often soft their tensile strength is enormous. Like the poplars in this regard the elm, whose boughs rise at a much sharper and safer angle than the oak's, has singularly shallow roots. Elms may be said to be erected on a stand like figures in the old Noah's arks; and in a great storm these trees may topple like ninepins. The wood, being much more brittle than oak wood and shorter in fibre than such trees as the poplar, is apt to split off without warning if for any reason the bough leans at all far outwards. No other tree has such a reputation for treachery. Countrymen have complained that it will "wait ten years to drop a limb on your head."

For the lover of the winter scene it is a happy accident that very many trunks are most highly coloured after the leaves fall. This is largely due to the reason that late autumn is the spring of the tiny mosses that flourish on the bark—especially towards the south side—of many, indeed most trees; and lichens, which are such devotees of pure air that virtually none of

them is found in London, are best seen in winter, as one might expect of a plant which is in construction a most strange combination of a moss and a seaweed.

The nature of a tree's growth may be very persuasively illustrated by old hollow trunks, such as are found, for example, on the edge of the Old Windsor Forest on the Berkshire boundary, or in Hatfield Park near the famous Queen Elizabeth oak. Though the whole of the centre of the tree is gone, leaving a comparatively thin shell, a large expanse of boughs may flourish and put forth fresh leaves and flowers for the passage of the sap is always near the surface. It is the common practice in Australia not to fell or explode trees where land is being cleared, but to "ring-bark" them. The cutting of a circular notch all round the trunk cuts off the sap and the tree dies. In the first world war thousands of trees were killed by the tethering of horses to their trunks. The animals gnawed through the bark, thus inflicting a death-blow. Truly may a tree's beauty be described as skin-deep.

BARK OF TREES

One of the features distinguishing the tree from the humbler plants, the bark itself has an interesting growth. A very few semi-trees have no bark in the full sense of the word. Two English examples are the mistletoe and the spindle in which the exterior retains a certain greenness. In other trees the shaft of the shoot is green only for a very few months. The thin skin (epidermis) allows the green life-blood to be seen. Very soon a corky substance develops below this skin, forces it off and surrounds the twig, bough or bole with a dense cover that takes on many shades of grey and brown, even of white and yellow, but never the greenness of the young twig. This cork forms at different depths in different species. It is deep, for example, in the elm and shallow in the beech. Its purpose or

effect is to protect the part of the tree that matters most (that is the *cambium* layer or lines of cells up and down which the sap flows) from wet and heat and cold. It is water-proof and a bad conductor of temperature. It has even been claimed that trees such as the alder with a certain affinity for wet places, possess a particularly strong waterproof bark. Since the trunk grows larger each year all round the circle the outer layer is subject to strain. When a trunk is cut across you can often read its exact age by counting the number of annual rings, each distinct from the other, though often the inner rings are so tightly packed together that counting may be a little difficult. Under such strain the outer bark, which often contains many dead cells of various sorts, is forced to split; and the normal, natural result is the formation of more or less upright cracks. The bark of the oak often

WOODLAND TREES. *A feature of English woodlands is the variety of trees they contain. Here, for example, may be seen the sweet or Spanish chestnut, the elm, the oak and the birch.*

quality. A good forester could at once detect the identity of any species by the pattern of the bark alone. Indeed almost any part of a tree is labelled with its name for those who have closely studied such a script; the bud, the leaf, the leaf-scar, the flower, the bark, the general form; and when the tree is felled and converted into timber, each sort of wood has quite its own pattern of grain and often an individual colour. One of the rather surprising similarities in this sphere is between the Spanish chestnut and the oak, both of them favourites with medieval architects. No pattern is more pictorial than that of the common elm, and now that methods have been discovered for preventing the wood warping, it may be expected that the use of the tree for such purposes as panelling will increase. For the elm is one of the commonest of trees; and in this its value as timber has been grossly neglected. So largely have we esteemed our trees for their beauty that we have sometimes forgotten their utility.

FORESTS, NATURAL AND MAN-MADE

It is worth noting that forests that have been planted by timber-producers differ from forests that have grown up naturally. The timber-producer's purpose is to grow trees that are alike in type and height, and his planting is done scientifically to this effect. Natural forests, in contrast, contain a variety of trees; the undergrowth of shrubs and bushes, ruthlessly destroyed by the forester, is allowed to have its own way, and though from the forester's point of view much good timber may be wasted, these natural forests form an integral part of the English landscape.

gives a singularly regular pattern of vertical crevices. But the unseen cork may form irregularly; and many are the kinds of pressure-signs that may appear. Such irregularity explains the habit of the plane in thrusting off large panels of dead bark. For no known reason, the bark of the Spanish chestnut often looks like a spiral. The thin-barked beech may stretch rather than split and no cracks become visible; the hornbeam shares this

HORSE CHESTNUT BUDS

DECIDUOUS TREES

by

SIR WILLIAM BEACH THOMAS, K.B.E.

In some countries and in the higher mountains of most countries, the evergreen is more common than the deciduous tree. It should be called rather an ever-grey than an evergreen in countries such as Australia, where the gum-tree, in its infinite variety, prevails. Of course, both classes are deciduous in the strict sense of the Latin word. The difference is that the deciduous trees lose their leaves every autumn and regain them every spring, showing bare boughs in winter, while evergreens are always green, and drop their leaves or needles much less often. Darwin thought the blackberry, which often keeps its old green leaves till the next spring, was on the way to becoming an evergreen. A few deciduous trees, especially the oak and the beech, may keep their withered leaves throughout the winter, especially if they are severely pruned or are stunted; and this is further evidence of the fact that the casting of the leaves is a vigorous active process, arrested by bad treatment or lack of vitality.

We who live in a land where deciduous trees prevail, cannot but feel that they are the more beautiful. The English scene is a continuous transformation; and though it may seem melancholy to us, the period when the leaves begin to fall is perhaps the most splendid moment of colour. Similarly, the naked boughs reveal their highest beauty of form in the winter months.

Our trees are of many species and varieties for much the same reason as our language is rich: we have absorbed many foreign examples, some of them so long ago that disputes are still heard as to whether such and such a tree is a native or not. There is even some doubt about the elm, which was a favourite in Italy at the time of the Roman invasion of Britain. The Lombardy poplar, the acacia or robinia, many poplars (including Canadian, which is more rightly named than the Italian poplar—identical with our black poplar), the Spanish and horse chestnut, the copper beech, the ailanthus or tree of Heaven, are examples of aliens that have taken a permanent place in our landscapes or boulevards. There are many others to be seen, especially in parks and gardens. One is the very beautiful tulip tree, with its strangely-shaped leaf and handsome tulip-like flower, which was introduced from North America in one species and China in another. It grows in gardens in the Home Counties into a splendid tree of eighty feet or so in height with a very ample trunk. A smaller tree, with an equally handsome flower, is to be found in most London parks and many squares and gardens, the catalpa. The colours of the flowers have been compared with those of the horse-chestnut. It was imported from the eastern United States and is now as well established in England as, say, the giant sequoia, which is usually called, in England, the Wellingtonia because it was multiplied greatly in the days of the Iron Duke.

Such trees are everywhere recognized as aliens in this country, as are, for example, the wattles which—to the dissatisfaction of Australians—were called "mimosa" when introduced in great quantity from Australia to the south of France. Such unnecessary changes of name are a

frequent cause of confusion. Examples
are numerous. The acacia, the syringa,
the juniper are all wrongly named in the
judgment of the American public and
all botanists. Other species of our most
typical native trees have been introduced.
There are, for example, thirty varieties
of the English oak in Kew Gardens,
besides a number of species imported
from different parts of the world. They
include the popular Turkey oak, which
came to us from both eastern Europe
and Asia Minor, and the pin oak (whose
leaves turn brilliant scarlet in autumn)
which came from North America. From
the English point of view they scarcely
deserve to be called oaks, for they grow
fast and their wood is not hard. We have
two English oaks, and some foresters
hold that the less common is of higher
virtue. It is always worth while taking
note of the points, so to call them, of
these most English of trees. The
commoner, sometimes called the English
oak, is to be distinguished by its rather
smaller leaves, which have next to no
stalk, while the acorns have a long stalk.
Contrariwise, the other oak, often called
the durmast oak, has no stalk to the
acorn, but a longer stalk to the leaf.
Though this oak becomes a large tree
it does not, as a rule, grow quite to the
same height as the pedunculate oak, and
is a good deal less common in the south.

ELM FAMILY

To take the elm, which perhaps comes
next to the oak in the English scene, as
many as seventeen varieties or species
are to be found. To mention the most
prominent, there is the so-called English
elm, and Dutch elm, which is a hybrid
between two other elms, one of them
the very distinctive wych elm. This is

SILVER BIRCHES. *The silver birch is common throughout the British Isles and its great virtue is that it will grow in even the poorest soil. The outer bark, which is silvery-white, is cast off in shreds; the branches are slender and drooping.*

ASH TREE ON LOCH ECK

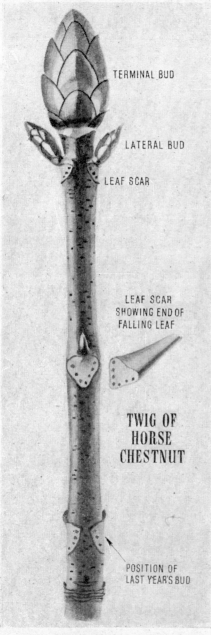

TERMINAL BUD

LATERAL BUD

LEAF SCAR

LEAF SCAR
SHOWING END OF
FALLING LEAF

TWIG OF
HORSE
CHESTNUT

POSITION OF
LAST YEAR'S BUD

HORSE CHESTNUT BUDS. *The drawing shows the position of new buds in relation to those of the previous year. The scars resemble a horse-shoe, and probably give the tree its name.*

not always recognized as an elm by the general public, as the form sometimes resembles that of an oak. The outer cases are of a light green colour, and come so early and grow so freely that in the distant view the appearance is of a tree in premature green leaf. The envelope itself, which has technical interest for botanists, allows the red seed to be seen through it; and this seed is set eccentrically some way from the centre. Unlike that of most of our species of elm, it is a fertile seed and for this, as for historical reasons, it is generally agreed to be a true native. There is some doubt about the other species, but their wide extent at least suggests that they are indigenous. They developed such astonishing success in multiplying suckers that seeds became unnecessary. The present writer has found a flourishing sucker just over seventy yards from the parent tree.

We have historical records of the appearance of some of the varieties. The wych elm is often called locally "the Huntingdonshire oak," and it is found in great quantity in that small county. What actually happened was that a hybrid of the wych elm proper was found, or produced, by a Huntingdon gardener of the name of Wood (a name still held by a local nurseryman), about the year 1775; and the variety has flourished. In general the wych elm has a strong predilection for the North of England, and is one of the few trees showing a strong local preference. When used for outdoor work the wood of the wych elm lasts rather longer than other elm wood.

It may be said that the most notorious of imported but now naturalized trees is the larch, against which the poet Wordsworth fulminated, chiefly because the very light green of the spring foliage did not seem to him to fit the scenery of the Lake Country. It is one of the very few dediduous conifers. One other, introduced about the same date, which

CHESTNUT TREE IN SPRING. *The full beauty of the horse chestnut tree is only seen when its spikes of white or rose-pink flowers are blooming, but before these arrive, the bright green leaves burst from the resin-coated buds.*

AVENUE OF LIMES. *A shapely tree, with a particularly sweet-smelling flower, the lime has always been popular for avenue planting although the period in which it is in leaf is a short one—generally from May to early autumn.*

166

has been freely planted by lakes, streams and ornamental waters, is the deciduous cypress, which has the odd habit of forming stools of wood above the roots. The great hardness of the wood of the larch has made the tree very popular with afforesters and it usually grows well. The purple flowers and the light colour of the flat, green, almost grasslike tufts of foliage are beautiful enough in most eyes. Different sorts were introduced at various dates in the eighteenth century from America, Europe and Japan. It has, perhaps, an un-English appearance, as Wordsworth said, but that a useful cross between the Japanese and European varieties made its appearance at two separate places in Scotland, interestingly demonstrates how kindly aliens take to our climate. Unlike most conifers, the larch is a hardwood tree; but there are certain dangers in the rough division of trees into hard and soft woods. Anyone who fells a sycamore and discovers that it can be split from top to bottom with a tap or two may argue the wood is soft; and its extreme whiteness (which makes it valuable for panels) suggests lack of strength. On the other hand, the craftsman who uses it for a score of purposes— the backs of hair-brushes, for example— regards it as both hard and strong, though easily worked.

SPEED OF GROWTH

In most trees the speed of growth decrees the strength of the wood. The hardest of English trees and one of the slowest in growth is the oak; one of the quickest is the soft horse-chestnut, an abrupt contrast in this respect to the true or so-called Spanish or sweet chestnut, to which it has no affinity except in name, and a rough similarity in the seedcases. But there are a few exceptions, one of them the pseudo-acacia, of which the wood is so hard that for centuries it was used as a sort of wooden rivet for ships' timbers. The

growth of the species is rapid, thanks to the great spread of roots through the rich, shallow soil. Nevertheless, "the slower the harder and the longer-lived" may be said to be the general rule.

The age of trees is in general not difficult to determine after they have fallen. When the oak beams in Westminster Hall were found to be perishing some years ago, owing to damage by the death-watch beetle, they were replaced by oak from the same Surrey forest, and it was calculated with some nicety that the substitute trees were well grown seedlings at the date when their old neighbours were felled.

LONG-LIVED TREES

Immensely old trees—such as sequoia and dragon trees and indeed olives, all very different botanically—are found in various parts of the world. The notorious dragon tree at Orotava, in the Canary Isles, was said to be 6,000 years old; but when we come to really scientific estimates, the ages of a particular oak and Spanish chestnut are put at 1,000 years; and certain cypresses, cedars and yews may have lived for three thousand years. Within Britain there is a tendency to exaggerate the ages of most big trees. It is a question whether any English deciduous tree is a thousand years old, but some few oaks may approach that limit. It was said of the oak, and the estimate only approaches the truth, that it grows for three hundred years, rests for three hundred years, and decays for another three hundred. Three hundred is a very long life for a beech and two hundred and fifty for an ash. Probably most other deciduous trees, with the exception of the Spanish chestnut, larch and perhaps the white poplar, seldom if ever live as long.

The height of trees can of course be calculated with great accuracy and here again popular beliefs are usually found to exaggerate. Some of our commoner trees

PLANE TREE. *Plane trees are not found in the wild state in any part of Britain, and they are seen chiefly in towns and cities, where they are able to stand up to smoke and fog. The dark outer bark is thrown off by the expanding light inner bark, and this process gives the trunk its mottled appearance.*

have been graded as to height in this order: larch, beech, white poplar, elm, oak, ash, hornbeam; the tallest reaching about a hundred and sixty feet, and the lowest in the list about sixty feet, but these exceed the English maxima. It is worth notice that the height bears little or no relation to the girth. Many oaks exist which have a girth of twenty-five or more feet, and sweet chestnuts hardly less, while four feet is big for a larch, and ten or twelve for an elm, though a few are bigger.

Our damp and variable climate does not tend to longevity in wood, but it is very favourable to the production of green leaf and blade, and to germination of seed. These sizes do not compare with those recorded in Australia, where a eucalyptus of about four hundred and fifty feet has been recorded, or the west coast of North America, where a coach and four has been driven through a hollow in the middle of a sequoia.

SIGNS OF DECAY

What usually brings about the fall is decay at the centre. The life of a tree lies near the circumference. Towards the centre growth and vitality cease. There is all the difference between sap and pith. Hundreds of old trees exist with a capacious hollow in the centre that may externally show little sign of age, till a gale comes and the thin outer circle, though it gave sufficient passage for the sap to feed branch and leaf, was not stout enough to withstand the mechanical pressure. An example at which thousands have wondered is of an extremely old elm in Richmond Park, which broke off long ago at some ten feet or so from the ground, but left a short and slender shell which retains life and even adds length to the one branch.

It is sometimes feared by those who delight in particular trees that the shedding of small boughs is a sign of approaching decay. Oaks, for example,

are wont to shed a certain number of branches every year; but often—indeed as a rule—this may be a sign of vitality as the active rejection of the leaf, and be brought about by very much the same agency. In other words, the tree prunes itself. Many willows indulge in what gardeners call hard pruning, and throw off yearly faggots of twigs. In all deciduous trees, except one, these rejected limbs grow lighter as they lose vitality. None becomes softer than the oak, which may decay into a material so woolly that mice make their nests in it. The larch, a tree more prolific than most of a resinous excretion, may lose boughs that actually become heavier as their vitality ebbs, so great is the amount of resin they contain.

How many sorts of English trees there are is a theme still widely discussed. The list is certainly short if by English we mean strictly native from the beginning of things. We have certainly doubled the list of our trees by our hospitality to aliens; and in a great many instances we have historical evidence of the approximate date when the naturalization of this and that species or variety was introduced. It may be said that a new interest in trees was spread abroad among all classes when John Evelyn published his *Sylva*. Trees had been imported long before that, certainly in the days of the Roman occupation, but importation accelerated after Evelyn's day and still continues.

NATIVE ENGLISH TREES

If an ordinary observer were asked to make a list of what he considered the most truly English trees, he would be inclined to include several that botanical historians class as aliens, but there would be a select class about which there can be no question. Of deciduous forest trees, excluding the bigger bushes, a full score would complete the list. One difficulty in making such a census is to decide

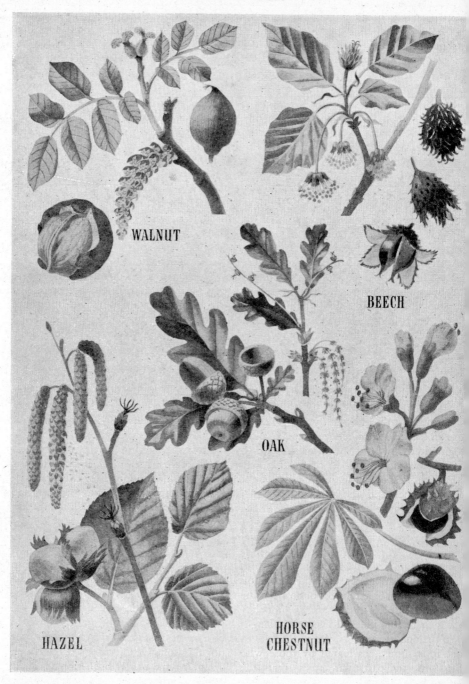

WALNUT

BEECH

OAK

HAZEL

HORSE
CHESTNUT

LEAVES, FLOWERS AND FRUIT. *These drawings show the leaves, flowers and fruit of some of the best known deciduous trees in Britain. It will be seen that the fruit of*

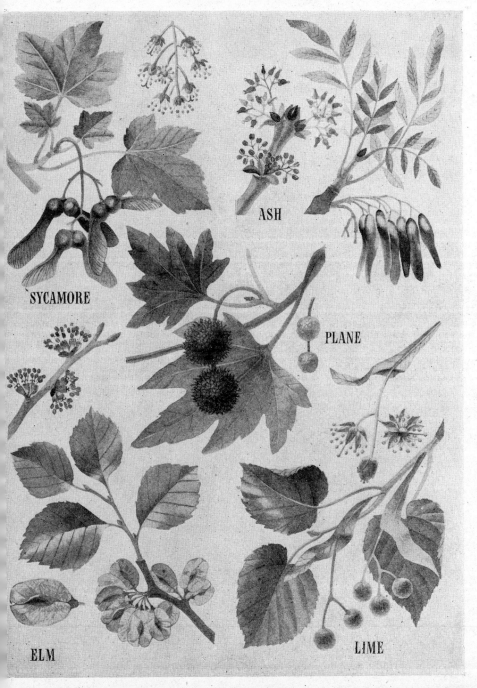

SYCAMORE

ASH

PLANE

ELM

LIME

the walnut has a double case ; a green fleshy covering which then splits to reveal the thin brown shell guarding the nut inside. Hazel nuts have a single hard covering.

OAK BRANCHES. *The oak is recognizable by its sturdy, furrowed trunk and the rounded outline of the frame.*

the difference between a tree and a shrub. Many plants regarded as hedge plants can be made into the likeness of fair-sized trees by pruning, and sometimes the pruning is done by natural causes, by situation, weather, the attacks of animals, by the close presence of other trees or bushes, by the accidental loss of side shoots. The service tree, the beam, the two wild guelders, the elder and the hazel all come into this class. Contrari-wise, of course, our gardeners make many forest trees into hedge bushes, especially the yew, the holly, the beech, and the hornbeam; and many hedges are spoiled because the nature of the tree is not realized or gardeners are in a hurry. Our ancestors would plant yews for a hedge as much as twenty feet apart; present-day gardeners will plant beeches a foot apart.

NATIVE AND FOREIGN OAKS

Popular as well as scientific opinion would put the oak at the head of a catalogue of true natives. Both the two oaks spread abroad are native; but a number of larger oaks with softer woods, notably the Turkey oak, have been imported, but are found chiefly in gardens and parks. One magnificent Turkey oak flourishes in Kew Gardens. The habit of rooks of carrying away the acorns and incontinently dropping them continually increases the spread of the oak. No other tree extends so wide a hospitality to living things, from a number of small and curious insects, whose work may be seen on the backs of fallen leaves, and in so-called oak apples. It is said to be the host of some 2,000 insects in all. Birds, squirrels, mice and rats are all fond of acorns, which may also supply a useful food for pigs and poultry.

The beech, which rejoices especially in the chalk that lies beneath a great part of southern England (on the east coast as far north as the Humber), has claim to second place in use and first in beauty. The boughs stretch out their slender tips like a hand trying to extend its reach. When the brown covering is cast off in spring, the green leaves have a silky sheen and presently uncrumple into a leaf singularly smooth and bright. The male flower catkins are attractive and the triangular beech nuts or mast are a rich

food when they emerge from their hard spring cases. No autumnal scene excels the old gold of a beech wood, and no trunk is more finely coloured or smoother. It often carries one peculiarity: little round bark-encircled knobs, of which the cause remains quite unknown. Few trees are more popular in gardens than the purple and copper beeches that derive from it.

Elms are the most numerous trees in the Midlands and the most conspicuous in the English landscape. The field elm seldom if ever sets seed, though it produces a mass of imperfect flowers before the leaf. Of recent years it has been liable to a fungus disease carried chiefly, it is thought, by the elm-bark beetle which prefers to lay its string of eggs underneath the thick bark. The queer pattern made by the grubs which tunnel their way out at right angles to the line of the eggs is familiar to most country folk. The poet Browning, thinking of

England, put first the opening of the "tiny leaf," which is rough and has some likeness to the nettle. The wood, though hard and, in dry condition, very durable, is brittle and beautiful. The contrast between the dark brown of the central wood and the white outer wood is as a rule singularly abrupt.

The birch, with its white trunk and slender, graceful twigs, a favourite with artists, also has a dwarf form. Both are British and there is a variety marked by its height and a more pendent, weeping habit. A very tall and singularly beautiful specimen with the full weeping pattern adorns a very old nursery-garden in Tunbridge Wells, but this variety is chiefly of a more northern district. Both flourish on high rocky ground and are often associated with conifers; but they have also been used for afforesting marshy ground—as in western Scotland —and they have sown themselves in scrub spinneys, in, for example, a deep marshy watershed near the Welsh border of Herefordshire.

LIMES AND POPLARS

Very popular for avenues, the lime is a singularly shapely tree and may reach a great height. The sweetly-scented flowers (much used in France as a tea) give the bee-keepers a highly treasured "honey-flow" and are remarkable for the wide bract at the base of the spray. The small round nuts contain one or two seeds. The underbark is the chief source of bast, which makes a fairly tough and weather-proof string popular with gardeners. The buds of winter and early spring are of a very salient redness, break early into leaf, and are among the very first to colour and fall.

Of the poplars, which have almost a monopoly of the landscape in parts of France, four sorts are truly native of Britain: the black poplar, the aspen, the white poplar or abele, and the grey, if this last be a true species: but so many

more have been introduced that distinctions are apt to be lost. The black or Italian poplar grows at a great rate and to a large size. One of this race, probably in Italy, "sported," that is produced a queer form known to botanists as fastigiate (i.e., narrowed or tapering). That is to say the boughs hugged the trunk in a sort of faggot. So was produced the Lombardy poplar, now spread abroad in most countries, especially the Argentine Republic. Botanically it is indistinguishable from the black poplar, and all the millions of trees of this character must have come from cuttings or suckers, owing their origin to the original "sport." The whole race of poplars, as of willows, prefers a watery site, but will grow in most soils. A curiosity is the immense proportion of infertile seed, equipped with a woolly appendage. When it falls, the ground in a great circle round the trunk may look as white as a tablecloth.

The aspen is the most shapely of the poplars and exhibits in an exaggerated form a peculiarity of the family. The spear-head leaves have long stalks flattened at right angles to the plane of the leaf, so that they bend easily from side to side but not up and down. This gives the leaves their dancing shade and quaint and distinctive shiver. Of the sorts introduced in recent years perhaps the most widely spread is the Canadian poplar, which has larger leaves than any of the British species. The balsam poplar, that emits a pleasing and powerful scent, especially from the gummy buds, has a yet larger leaf. This also is to be found in the wild as well as in parks and gardens, and itself has several varieties.

Though very common in hedgerows, the field maple is seldom seen as a tree. All the same, it is a truly British tree, whereas the sycamore, also of the same species and yet more widely distributed, is not. Both trees are wont to give beautiful examples of leaf arrangement—

BEECH WOOD. *Distinguished for the smoothness of its grey trunk, the beauty of its translucent green leaves in spring and the fiery colour these assume in autumn, the beech is also a useful tree to the forester. Its shade prevents evaporation from the soil and its fallen leaves, rich in potash, give nourishment to the earth.*

a "mosaic patterning" designed to allow each leaf its place in the sun. This demand for light in all green leaves is answered in most trees by the arrangement of the shoots, the placing of the leaves and the superior length of the lower branches, which often, as in ash and horse-chestnut, also grow more vertical towards the tips. The leaf of our maple is wont to turn yellow rather than the red which flames so conspicuously on the larger-leafed Canadian or sugar maple; but it is a beautiful addition to the autumn scene, while the sycamore leaves are drab and often marked by spots of a black fungus. Bright colour belongs only to the ruddy stalks of the leaves, a like colour of parts of the seed-case, and a bright red-orange fungus that commonly attacks the new shoots.

ALDERS AND WILLOWS

The alder is as widely distributed about Britain and Europe as any tree. It is regarded by botanists as a close cousin of the birch, but resembles it only in the structure of the flowers. In other respects the trees are poles apart; and no species is so closely confined to a waterside site. As in the hazel, the male catkins appear in autumn, but the fertile flowers not till the spring. On the other hand, the woody cases of the seeds, like little fir cones, hang conspicuously on the bare boughs throughout the winter, suggesting a certain likeness to the larch. Everything about the tree, except in early spring, is singularly dark, from the deeply-coloured, saw-edged leaves to the brown bark.

The willow includes more British species than any other tree, but many of them, such as the very common sallows and the osiers, more nearly resemble bushes than trees. There are certainly as many as fifteen species and a host of varieties; but the most beautiful, the Babylonian or weeping willow, is a new-comer from Asia, probably not introduced till the opening of the nineteenth

century. Its dispersal has been wide and rapid beyond that of any other tree except perhaps the Lombardy poplar, which is its opposite in form. Both are common in the Argentine and the weeping willow, introduced into St. Helena in Napoleon's day, supplied cuttings which now hold up the banks of Australian rivers. No genus of tree grows so readily from slips or cuttings. The white willow is indigenous, but is less famous than its close cousin, the cricket bat willow, which owes its vogue and high value to the long fibre of its timber. Two species at any rate, sometimes known as the Huntingdon and the Bedfordshire willows, will grow to a great height and at astonishing speed. No tree has been so generally pollarded. The short and often rotting trunk with a flourishing head of young branches is a commonplace of riverside scenery. These younger shoots are so bendable, again owing to the length of fibre, that they can be woven into a hurdle, or the frame of a boat, or a basket, or what you will, but more useful for the finer purposes, such as basket making, are the naturally bushy osiers, for example, in quantity along the streams and ditches of Somerset and about Essex marshes. Our country people are apt to call some of these "palms," partly because the silvery male catkins and the golden female catkins are ripe about Palm Sunday, being among the earliest flowers, partly because palms and willows are associated together in one passage in the Bible. It is a growing habit to plant little beds of willows close to English apiaries, for they give the bees an early and rich supply of pollen.

More rightly known as the rowan is the mountain ash, which has no affinity with the ash proper. It may be called a connecting link with our wild fruit trees. The individual florets are very like the flowers of the pear, and the bright coral-red berries are not unlike pear and apple

SILVER BIRCH IN SUMMER

TREES IN EPPING FOREST. *Once rich in forest-land, England possesses few larg[e]*
tracts of wooded country. Epping forest, once part of the great Essex forest [of]
Waltham, contains many ancient beeches (such as the one above) and hollies, oa[k]
and, above all, the very local hornbeam. It was once a royal hunting groun[d.]

their inner structure. No tree in the st is so intolerant of neighbours; it rows to its greatest height on exposed illsides in west Scotland and north-west ngland, and it has given its name to everal districts in Wales; but it is also idely spread and a favourite in suburban laces. Walking across the almost treeless owns of Dartmoor, one comes upon equent seedlings, and the tree has the apacity of flowering and fruiting in a ery dwarf state where weather and soil revent a fuller growth.

WILD FRUIT TREES

The wild cherry which multiplies self readily by both seed and sucker is tore generally admired than any of our owering trees, such as the beam tree and ild senna tree and crab and pear which te all near relations. The wild cherry's ery early white flowers, borne very eely, light up the spring scene in the tome Counties as in wilder districts f the north. Vigorous discussions ill proceed on its claims to be in-igenous. That cherries were intro-iced by the Romans to both Italy and ngland is beyond question; but the idence suggests that these were more early akin to the orchard cherries, hich have an edible fruit. The wild tree rows rapidly, has useful timber, and the owers and leaves add a crowning beauty the spring and autumn in many istricts.

Both of our common orchard fruits the classes of Pyrus and Prunus, have eir wild counterparts. In the Pear class, te pear, the crab-apple—of which there e several wild varieties—and the tedlar all have good claim to be umbered among our wild trees, and nong the plums are the black-thorn id bird cherry. The prevalence of the edgerow, in which all growths are able to severe pruning, has tended to :duce a good many trees to the status f bushes: the white-thorn or quick,

the black-thorn or sloe, the maple, the white beam, the service tree, the crab, and even the hornbeam and beech are so tamed, as well as the hazel, the guelders, the spindle, the privet and many more.

Imported and naturalized trees are as numerous as native trees, if we reckon by varieties, not species, and some of them are as common as the natives. The elm and sycamore have been discussed in connection with their native cousins, the wych elm and the maple. Perhaps others so suggest a native origin. Though the sycamore reaches its pitch in about sixty years and is, therefore, short-lived, it is one of the hardiest of trees, delighting in high and exposed positions. Its relation-ship with the other maples, especially the Canadian, is suggested by the sweet, sticky exudation from the leaves, which is one of many characteristic marks. It has been given several relations, which have nothing to do with it, as even the botanical names would imply. It is known as pseudo-platanus because its leaves are shaped like those of the plane, and the Greeks called it sycamore because of a certain superficial likeness to both fig (which is the meaning of the first half of the word) and mulberry (indicated in the second half).

VALUABLE CHESTNUT WOOD

Next in importance come the two so-called chestnuts. The Spanish chestnut is much the older importation and some think it may be a native. At any rate, it is now completely naturalized. The hard oak-like timber has been valued by English builders for centuries; and there are living trees that rival the larger oaks. The long catkins, which have suggested heads of barley to some observers, and the narrow leaves, strange seed-cases with their half-furry, half-thorny surface, and the desirable nuts within it give it a rare distinction.

The horse-chestnut is not, of course, among the catkin bearers. It was

BEECH ROOTS. *A feature of the beech tree is the frequent appearance of its roo* *above the soil. In this picture the roots have been exposed by the falling or cutti* *away of the land, but the growth of the tree is not affected.*

probably introduced into England, maybe from north India or Tibet, towards the end of the sixteenth century; and soon proved a favourite, especially for avenues. It is, strictly speaking, unique in several respects. The candelabra-like flower-head has no fellow. The very large buds of winter contain leaf and flower in singular, if tiny, perfection, long before the brown sticky scales are thrown off. The almost woolly leaves at first droop and then stretch out smooth leaflets, usually seven in number of a pure greenery, lil an open hand. In no other tree do suc leaflets emerge from a single point. Tl tree may grow to a great size; and fe trees grow so fast though the actu period of growth in each year is sing larly short. There is one tree in Cambridg shire that carries over thirty heav boughs covering a circle of more tha twenty yards' diameter. It is general held that the name "horse" derives fro the pattern left by the fallen leaf, but it

ot unlikely that "horse" (frequently
sed as a synonym for "coarse") was
iven it to contrast its fruit with the
veet, edible Spanish chestnut.

Many of the aliens excel in beauty of
ower; horse chestnut, acacia, tulip-tree,
atalpa, Judas tree, snowy mespilus, and
thers of yet greater rarity; but in the
ndscape none excels the native wild
nerry. The towns rather than the
ountry are the chief hosts of most of
ne more recent immigrants. The plane
the favourite of London planters and
ne variety is said to have appeared
aysteriously in London streets. There
as a scare at one time that the rough
ed cases which hang on the twigs
aroughout the winter were a cause of
aroat and nose maladies; but it was
ghtly disregarded. Of the two quite
istinct sorts of plane, the occidental
as smaller seed-heads and a smaller but
ery much more indented leaf.

Another later immigrant, chiefly urban,
rowing in favour in English towns and
arks, is the ailanthus or tree of Heaven,
ith its large ash-like (or pinnate)
aves. Though it grows as well as the
lanes in the midst of towns, it is a little
nfortunate that both have large leaves,
ery unpopular with scavengers and
rivers of horses. The litter is trouble-
ome and slippery.

THE WALNUT

While the planes are seen chiefly in
owns, the walnut was planted many
enturies ago in many a glebe and park
nd splendid examples are to be seen.
here are several varieties and, most
nfortunately for many orchards, a
reat number of small fruited, but
uicker growing varieties were widely
istributed in England; and these, if not
ithout beauty, are useless for their
uit. Walnuts, like mulberry trees, are
ot slow in growth, but often advance
owly because the young shoots are apt
o be cut by frost, even in tolerably mild

winters. The check happily does no more
than slow down the progress of growth
and add to the hardness of the wood.
Walnut trees were probably introduced
into Britain about the middle of the
fifteenth century, and because of their
valuable fruit their cultivation has always
been encouraged. In addition to the
fruit the walnut tree also yields valuable
timber, for although the grain is coarse,
at least, to some tastes, the dark-brown
colour of the mature wood is attractively
marked with streaks of lighter shades
and black, and is also capable of bearing
a high polish. Walnut is, accordingly,
a popular wood for furniture manufacture. Again, a combination of the
qualities of lightness and toughness
make it an ideal wood for the making
of stocks for rifles and shot-guns.

The age of the walnut tree may be
gauged from the state of its bark and the
colour of its wood. When young the grey-
brown bark is smooth, but deep furrows
develop with age and the tree takes on a
rugged appearance. The wood of young
trees is white but gradually deepens in
colour as the tree becomes mature.

LANDSCAPE'S CROWNING GLORY

Deciduous trees, both native and
immigrant, are the crowning glory of the
English scene and the most beautiful
expression of the progress of the seasons.
They make winter hardly less lovely than
spring. The broad domes of the elms,
and broader domes of the oaks, the
narrow poplars and slender willows, the
ash trees and horse-chestnuts with
spreading boughs that lift upwards at the
tips, the wide spread of the tapering
beeches, the even cones of the limes, the
complicated filigree of the urban planes
dotted with the round seed-cases, the
white trunk and graceful droop of the
birch—all these appeal to the eye as a
large character of a most legible script
announces the individuality, each of its
own peculiar beauty.

THE BEECH WOOD

CYPRESSES AND YEW HEDGE. *Two types of cypress have been importe into Britain; the common cypress, which came from the Mediterranean area in t fifteenth century, and Lawson's cypress, a native of North America. Both are us as ornamental trees in England. Yew is frequently used for ornamental hedge*

EVERGREEN TREES

by

RICHARD MORSE, F.L.S.

IF we had set out to study the ever-green trees of this country in the earlier days of its history, our task would have been a light one, for barely half a dozen species of such trees are real natives of Britain. As the centuries have rolled by, however, there has been a continual introduction of new species from abroad. The few, therefore, have grown to be many, and our first task to-day, in any effort to distinguish one kind from another, will be to arrange this large assemblage in some sort of reasonable order.

A very simple first step can be taken by dividing all the trees that grow in this country into two main groups, namely, (1) the broad-leaved trees, and (2) the narrow-leaved trees, or conifers. The broad-leaved trees include most of the common species of our woods and hedgerows, such as the oak, the elm and the sycamore. The narrow-leaved group, on the other hand, is made up mostly of those trees that are popularly known by such names as pines and firs.

Now the broad-leaved trees are, with few exceptions, deciduous trees. The conifers, on the other hand, are mostly evergreen, and hence stand out with conspicuous clearness in the winter landscape. It follows from this, of course, that by far the greater part of the present chapter will be devoted to the conifers, and it is to these that we must now turn our attention.

The conifers, as a class, form such an important and well-defined group that they deserve a few introductory remarks of a general character before we select certain individual species for separate study. They have a number of family characteristics that are of considerable interest to the student.

All these trees, for example, bear flowers of a very primitive nature, in which sepals and petals are entirely lacking. The flowers of a conifer, moreover, are of two different kinds, one male and the other female. The two sexes are never combined in one flower, as they so often are in our ordinary flowering plants.

Furthermore, the conifers belong to that big division of plants known as the naked-seeded plants, or gymnosperms. It is true that many of them have their seeds protected from the weather by the woody scales of the cones that they bear, but not one of them ever has its seeds enclosed in an ovary, or seed-case. The conifers, in fact, are the living representatives of a very ancient group of plants—a group that came into existence long before ovaries of any kind had been evolved.

Another interesting characteristic of these trees is their unusual habit of growth. The typical conifer has a strikingly straight trunk, from which successive tiers of branches spring out at regular intervals; and since the branches of each tier are shorter than those of the tier next below it, the tree comes to assume that well-known conical, or pyramidal, form familiar to everyone in the ideal Christmas tree. There are, of course, some exceptions to this, but the habit, nevertheless, is very characteristic of the group.

Then again, as we have already noticed, the conifers are mostly evergreen

CORSICAN PINES. *This coniferous tree is yet another importation into England, where it has been found a particularly useful and hardy tree for " fixing " sandy soils and providing shelter in bleak country. Roughly pyramidal in shape, it grows as high as one hundred feet; the dark-green leaves are pairs of spiny " needles."*

SCOTS PINE. *The free growth of a tree depends on soil, weather and general climatic conditions. The Scots pine, when grown at a great height and on stony ground, tends to become stunted in appearance, the upper branches being short and spreading, while the lower branches frequently die. In the picture above, the branches have been swept in one direction by the force of the wind.*

trees, though this must not be taken to mean that their leaves are permanent structures. The leaves of the evergreen conifers, like those of deciduous trees, are cast off at intervals, but as they are not all cast at the same time, the trees themselves are never bare. It is, in other words, the tree as a whole that is evergreen, and not the individual leaves. That is why the floor of a pine forest is soon covered with a thick carpet of fallen "needles."

These leathery, needle-like leaves must be looked upon as an adaptive character in the trees concerned. The typical conifer is a drought-plant, or xerophyte. It grows in an environment where it needs to conserve its water content; and the water-vapour that it exhales from its tough, hard foliage, is very much less than that given off by a broad-leaved tree, such as an oak or a sycamore.

It will be seen, therefore, that a pine tree and an oak prepare themselves for the winter season in two quite different ways. So far as our trees are concerned, the British winter, in spite of its heavy rainfall, is really a dry season, for the soil is mostly too cold for proper absorption to take place. The oak meets this difficulty by throwing off its broad leaves and thus checking its loss of water. The pine, on the other hand, produces leaves which are not only

SCOTCH FIRS

strong enough to withstand the winter's cold, but which lose so little water that there is no danger of its ever becoming desiccated.

Now the evergreen conifers that grow in this country to-day are of so many different kinds that it will be a very great help in our study of them if we try, as a first step, to think of them in groups. Such names as pine, fir, cedar and cypress are used very loosely in our everyday language, and we shall not get very far with our studies until we know the real significance of these names, and can use them with botanical precision.

PINE FAMILY

Let us think of the pines first. A true pine is one that belongs to the genus known as *Pinus*—a genus containing well over eighty species. Many of these species are cultivated quite commonly in this country, and every one of them is, of course, a pine of one kind or another. They have been grouped in the genus *Pinus* because they have certain characters in common; and some at least of these characters should be observed and remembered by everyone who wishes to gain a closer acquaintance with this interesting tribe of trees.

It will be noticed, for example, that the leaves of these pines do not grow singly, but in bundles. In some species there are only two leaves in each bundle; in others there are three; and in others five. These numbers, moreover, are constant for each species, and are therefore a great help to identification.

It will be noticed also that these leaf-bundles of the pines hold very tightly together. They do not fall to pieces when the foliage is cast from the pines, but remain intact. If, therefore, the living foliage of a particular tree is beyond our reach, we can discover the nature of its leaf-bundles by examining the fallen leaves on the ground below.

Most of the pine trees that are grown in this country have their leaves in bundles of two, and the commonest of them all is the Scots pine. It is also the only one that is a true native of Britain, all the other species having been introduced from abroad.

SCOTS PINE

While the Scots pine is still young, it has the typical, pyramidal form of a conifer. As it grows older, however, the lower branches die, and are often broken off by the wind. The leading shoot also frequently dies, and then the upper branches spread out broadly to form the big, flattened crown so characteristic of this tree in the later stages of its growth.

Although it is not one of our largest conifers, a well-grown specimen of the Scots pine may reach a height of a hundred feet or so, with a trunk measuring a yard or more in thickness; and such a tree, with its rich, coppery-red bark glowing in the rays of the setting sun, is an object of great beauty.

The needles of the Scots pine are usually about two or three inches in length, and are of a bluish-green colour. The flowers appear in the spring, and the cones that follow them remain upon the tree for three years. A mature tree in the late springtime, therefore, will show not only the new cones of the present year, but also the green ones of last year, the brown ones of the year before, and the old, empty ones of the year before that. The fully grown cone reaches a length of about two inches.

In speaking of the Scots pine it is important to remember that this tree is sometimes referred to as the Scotch fir— a name that, from a botanical point of view, is very misleading. As will be seen later in this chapter, the true fir differ widely from the pines, and not one of them is a native of Scotland.

The timber of the Scots pine has a yellowish colour and a resinous scent

EDAR OF LEBANON. *Generally grown for ornamental purposes on lawns and parks, this cedar has a distinctively flattened head, the main trunk being comratively short. The ever-green leaves are needle-shaped and generally last for about four years, and the fruit is a closely-scaled purple-brown cone.*

It is widely used for building and other purposes, and is often spoken of as yellow deal.

A tree that is often confused with the Scots pine is the Corsican pine. This, as its name indicates, is a native of Corsica, though it grows plentifully also in Spain, Italy and other parts of southern Europe, often forming large forests. It was introduced into Britain as long ago as 1759, and has been widely planted here as a timber tree. Its wood, however, is inferior to that of the Scots pine, and is suitable only for the rougher types of building work.

In its general appearance the Corsican pine resembles the Scots pine rather closely. It is true that both trees vary a good deal in shape, but, as a general rule, the Corsican pine retains its lower branches for a much longer period, and is therefore much more pyramidal in form. Its leaves, moreover, although sheathed in pairs, are usually much longer than those of the Scots pine, as well as much darker in colour.

The cones of the Corsican pine are fairly distinctive too. They are larger than those of the Scots pine, and often grow in pairs, each cone standing out almost horizontally from the twig. When ripe, they are of a tawny yellow colour and have a polished surface.

A variety of the Corsican pine, known as the Austrian pine, is also often cultivated in Britain. Its timber, however, is of relatively little value, though its durability makes it useful for outside work. The tree is grown chiefly for ornamental purposes in parks and large gardens, or as a shelter for more tender trees in exposed places. It is a native of Austria and neighbouring countries and was introduced into Britain in 1835.

ROOTS OF SCOTS PINE. *Although this tree prefers a deep soil it will grow successfully on shallow sandy shores. In addition to its usefulness in binding loose soil with its spreading roots, its fallen needles provide nourishment for other plants.*

RUNK OF YEW. *The peculiarly ridged appearance of the trunk of the yew is*
e to the fact that new trunks are constantly growing from the lower part of the
ain stem, with which they eventually coalesce. It is reputed to be the longest-lived
' all trees, and in the past it was valued for its durable but elastic timber.

The Austrian pine differs from the Corsican pine in having longer, stouter and stiffer needles and larger cones. The cones, moreover, have distinctly rounded bases, whereas in the cones of the Corsican pine the bases are flat.

A number of other foreign pines with their leaves in bundles of two can be found growing in many parts of Britain, the stone pine and the cluster pine being typical examples.

STONE AND CLUSTER PINES

So striking a form has the stone pine that it attracts everyone's attention. When grown in this country, it has a relatively short trunk, sending out its large branches not far above the level of the ground. These branches spread themselves out in a characteristic, umbrella-like fashion, giving the tree a strange, squat appearance that can be immediately recognized.

Though widely grown for its picturesque appearance, the stone pine is of little value as a timber tree. The date of its introduction to Britain does not appear to be known, but it has certainly been grown here for several centuries. It is a native of Mediterranean countries, and is often a striking feature in the Italian countryside.

The outstanding feature of the cluster pine, as is suggested by its popular name, is its habit of forming its cones in dense clusters, a cluster sometimes consisting of as many as seven or eight large, shining cones. Its leaves are stiff, sharply pointed, unusually long (often as much as eight inches) and of a dark green colour.

Like the stone pine, the cluster pine is a native of the Mediterranean regions, often forming large forests along the shores. In favourable circumstances it reaches a height of a hundred feet or more. It was introduced into Britain at the end of the sixteenth century.

We now come to those pines whose leaves are in bundles of three, and of these the most familiar is the Monterey pine. It is a native of California, and was introduced into Britain in 1833. It is not quite so hardy as some of the other pines, and is grown chiefly in the south-western counties of England.

A well-grown Monterey pine may reach a height of a hundred feet or more. It will be recognized not only by its dense masses of bright grass-green foliage, made up of slender needles measuring about six inches in length, but also by its large, uneven, bright brown cones, which are almost, if not quite, as long as the leaves.

A number of other pines with leaves in bundles of three are occasionally grown for ornamental or forestry purposes. One of the most striking of these is the western yellow pine, which is native of western North America. It was introduced into Britain in 1826, and has always attracted attention by reason of its extraordinarily long needles (which often reach a foot in length) and its prickly cones.

WEYMOUTH PINE

Of the pines whose needles are in bundles of five, probably the most famous is the Weymouth pine—so named after Lord Weymouth, who cultivated it on a large scale in the early part of the eighteenth century. Its real home is in eastern North America, where it is highly prized for its valuable timber, known as white pine.

The cones of the Weymouth pine are very distinctive. They are about six inches in length, slightly curved, usually slender, pendulous, and covered with loosely arranged scales. The leaves also are slender and elegant, and are of an attractive, light-green colour.

The famous blue pine of the Himalaya is another species with five-bundled leaves. It was introduced into this country in 1823, and is a gene-

R WOOD. *The silver fir is believed to have been introduced to Britain from the ntinent at the beginning of the seventeenth century. Its straight tapering trunk, hich has a greyish-brown bark, often grows to a height of one hundred and twenty et. The timber, which is inclined to be soft, is used chiefly for interior work.*

favourite in large gardens. It closely resembles the Weymouth pine in general appearance, but differs in having larger cones and longer leaves.

Turning now from the pines to the firs, let us notice that, although the members of these two groups have much in common, there are outstanding differences between them. The pines that are grown in this country, as we have already seen, bear their leaves in bundles. The true firs, on the other hand (*i.e.*, those belonging to the genus *Abies*) never have bundled leaves, but only single ones.

There are differences also in the cones. A pine cone, when at last it falls from the tree, does so bodily. Country people often gather these cones in large quantities and use them as fuel. But a fir cone extends its career in quite a different way. Retaining, with its central axis, a tight hold upon the twig, it sheds its scales piecemeal, liberating its seeds at the same time.

THE SILVER FIR

The most familiar of the true fir trees grown in this country is the beautiful silver fir. It is not a native of Britain, but of southern and central Europe, having been introduced here as far back as 1603. Nowadays, however, it is not much grown for timber, though it is still a favourite conifer for large parks and gardens.

When grown under favourable conditions, the silver fir becomes a large and handsome tree. Its leaves, apart altogether from their habit of growing singly, are very different indeed from those of the pines. They are seldom more than an inch or so in length and are of a silvery-white colour underneath—a conspicuous character from which the tree has derived its popular name.

Although a number of other true firs have been introduced into Britain from time to time, the majority of them are not widely grown, and scarcely call for

mention here. There are, however, two other conifers which, though not true firs, are commonly called by that name and which, because of their great importance as timber trees, are cultivated on a large scale in many parts of the country.

SPRUCE AND DOUGLAS FIRS

One of them, popularly known as the spruce fir, ought really to have the word fir deleted from its name, and to be referred to merely as a spruce tree. Its proper name is the common, or Norway spruce. It is not a native of Britain, but of Norway and other parts of Europe, though it has been cultivated in the former country since 1548.

In the true firs the cones are erect and, as we have just seen, the cone scales are shed separately. In the spruces, on the other hand, the cones are pendulous and fall bodily from the twigs. The common spruce affords an excellent illustration of both of these points of distinction.

While it is still young the common spruce, on account of its regular pyramidal form, is greatly favoured as a " Christmas tree." In its later years it grows to a great height, and its massive trunk, measuring a yard or more in diameter, gives us the timber known as white deal.

The other so-called fir is one of a small group of trees known as the Douglas firs, which differ from the true firs in number of ways. The cone of a Douglas fir, for example, can be recognized once by the long, three-pointed bract that project between the scales of the cone itself. This cone, moreover, is pendulous, not erect; and it falls from the tree bodily, not in pieces.

The commonest member of this group of conifers is the Oregon Douglas-fir, or "Oregon Douglas," as the forester simply calls it. This is the one that is often spoken of as *the* Douglas fir, though it were a true fir and the only

PRUCE FIRS IN WINTER. *Seen here under winter snow are young spruce firs, hose pyramidal outline is a familiar sight at Christmas time. The spruce reaches considerable height on maturity and its wood is used for resin, pitch and wood pulp.*

ne of its kind; but the Colorado Douglas- and the Japanese Douglas-fir are also ccasionally grown.

The Oregon Douglas is one of the nest of all our coniferous trees, aching, under favourable conditions, a eight of well over a hundred feet. It as introduced into Britain about 1827, d has received its name from its troducer—David Douglas, the famous otanical explorer. The timber of British-own trees, however, is not of so fine a uality as that which, under the name of)regon pine, has been largely imported om America.

Very different indeed from the pines, e firs, the spruces and the Douglas-firs e those handsome conifers known as edars, of which three quite distinct inds are commonly grown in the ritish Isles.

As a group, the cedars are easily recognizable trees, not only by their general form, but also by their leaves and their cones. The shoots produced by these trees are of two kinds, known as long shoots and short shoots. The long shoots bear their leaves singly, but the leaves of the short shoots are in dense clusters resembling small, round brushes. The only other conifers that bear their foliage in this way are the larches; but as all the larches grown in this country are deciduous trees, whereas all the cedars are evergreen, that fact alone serves to distinguish them—at any rate in winter.

And in summer, when cedars and larches are both in full foliage, the difference between their cones can be seen at a glance. Cedar cones are large, barrel-shaped structures, from three to five inches in length and from two to three inches in diameter. Larch cones,

CYPRESS. *Grown for its valuable timber abroad, in Britain the cypress is always cultivated as an ornamental tree.*

on the contrary, are mainly egg-shaped and are rarely more than an inch and half in length. Moreover, like fir cone cedar cones shed their scales while sti upon the tree, whereas the cones of th larches fall bodily.

The most familiar of our three ceda: is the famous cedar of Lebanon. It is favourite ornamental tree for large lawn where its immense branches, spreadin out in their characteristic, horizont: fashion, give it a majesty that immediate: attracts attention. It is a native of Palestine and neighbouring lands, an was introduced into Britain in th seventeenth century.

TYPES OF CEDARS

The Atlantic cedar—or Atlas cedar, a it is sometimes called—is very closel related to the cedar of Lebanon, an may be merely a geographical variety of it. Its home is in the Atlas mountair of north-west Africa, where it form immense forests containing few othe trees. It differs from the cedar of Lebanon in having usually only on main stem instead of several, and in it densely hairy twigs and smaller cones.

The third kind of cedar, known as th Indian cedar, or deodar, is a native of th Himalayan mountains, and was intro duced into Britain in 1822. It has much narrower crown than the othe two kinds, and usually forms a ta pyramid. Its leading shoot, moreover, i pendulous, and the tips of its branche droop gracefully. Its leaves, too, ar distinctive, being double the length of those of its relations, and of a delicate silvery-green colour.

The cedars, like the firs, have ha their name misapplied to a number of other trees, and care must be taken tha these so-called cedars are not confuse with the true cedars above described Thus the tree known as the white ceda is really a kind of cypress, and so als is the so-called Oregon cedar. Even th amous red cedar, whose aromatic wood is so widely used in the making of "cedar" pencils, is not a true cedar but a juniper; and the tree known as the Japanese cedar is equally false to its name.

The leaves of all the conifers thus far described in this chapter are of the long-narrow, or needle type. Not all of them, it is true, equally well deserve the name of needles, for some are distinctly flattish, but they can all be distinguished at once as belonging to more or less closely related trees. In that group of conifers known as the cypresses, however, we meet with leaves of quite another kind. They are small and scale-like, closely pressed to the stems that bear them, and they overlap one another to such an extent that the twigs themselves are hidden from view by their own foliage.

LAWSON'S CYPRESS

By far the commonest of these cypresses is the species known as Lawson's cypress, which was introduced into this country from North America in 1854. It is a tall, handsome tree, with a crown that is almost cylindrical in form; and a well-grown specimen, in a park or large garden, is sufficiently striking to attract anyone's attention. The parsley-like aroma that is given off when the leaves of this tree are bruised is an interesting aid to identification.

Lawson's cypress is the one that has been given the misleading name of Oregon cedar, referred to above. The so-called white cedar is really a much smaller cypress that comes from Florida and is sometimes grown in gardens.

Closely related to Lawson's cypress is the Italian, or Mediterranean, cypress, which is a native of south-eastern Europe and the Orient. It was introduced into Britain as long ago as the sixteenth century, but is not such a hardy tree as Lawson's cypress, and seldom thrives except in the warmer regions of the south and west. It can be distinguished at once by its very much larger cones.

Several other coniferous trees, to which the general name of arbor vitae has been given, are commonly grown in parks and gardens, and are often mistaken for cypresses, which they closely resemble. Three of the best-known species are the Chinese arbor vitae, the American arbor vitae and the giant arbor vitae. They can be distinguished from the cypresses by their cones, the scales of which overlap like tiles on a roof instead of merely touching at their edges, and lack entirely the characteristic central stalks of cypress cone-scales.

Readers who have followed the present chapter from its beginning will have noticed how deeply indebted we are to other countries for our coniferous trees. We have no native fir tree, no native Douglas-fir or spruce, no native cedar, cypress or arbor vitae, and only one native pine. The next tree on our list, therefore, will be of special interest because it is our very own. It is the common juniper—a tree as truly British as the oak itself.

THE JUNIPER

By many folk the juniper will be remembered as little more of a tree than the familiar gooseberry tree of our gardens, yet in favourable circumstances it can—and sometimes does—attain the size and form of a proper tree, twenty or thirty feet in height.

The juniper is so strikingly different from the other trees that grow in this country that it is one of the easiest of all conifers to identify. Its leaves are awl-shaped, rigid and sharply pointed, and are arranged round the stems in alternating whorls of three. Its cones, moreover, instead of developing a woody structure, become fleshy, and are more

HOLLY. *Hollies ar
found throughout th
British Isles and thoug.
they are generally counte.
as small trees they ma
grow as high as forty fee.
The bark is smooth an
pale grey, and the woo.
underneath, which is har.
and fine-grained, is fre
quently used as a substi
tute for box wood or
when dyed, for ebony. I.
the picture to the left ma
be seen the oval leather
leaves, which break ou
into sharp spines. Thes
are said to have de
veloped as a protectio
against browsing catt.
and it is often found tha.
leaves beyond the reac
of cattle have no spines
The white male and femal
flowers are borne o.
different trees; the berrie
ripen to scarlet in Sep
tember, and the small seed
cases are found inside*

like bluish-black berries than cones. They are, in fact, usually spoken of as juniper berries, and are collected in large quantities for use in the manufacture of gin.

A considerable number of foreign junipers are cultivated in this country, largest of them all being the so-called red cedar already referred to above. It provides not only the wood for "cedar" pencils, but also the well-known cedarwood oil, which is used in the making of soap and furniture polishes. Its botanical name is *Juniperus virginiana*, which commemorates the fact that it was first known in Virginia. It was introduced into Britain in the seventeenth century.

In striking contrast to the small-sized junipers is that extraordinary giant, the famous big-tree of California, some times known as the Wellingtonia. It wa introduced into this country in 1853, an is now quite extensively cultivated fo ornamental purposes. Probably few, any, of our British specimens have ye reached a height of much over a hundre feet, though in their native land they ar frequently nearly three times that size

Closely related to the Wellingtonia and even exceeding it in height (thoug not in bulk) is the equally famou redwood, which is also a native of th Pacific coast of North America. It wa introduced into Britain some seve years or so before its cousin, though it i not so widely planted nor so familiar te most people. It is one of the tallest tree in the world, and has been known te reach a height of nearly three hundre nd fifty feet in its native American soil.

An unmistakable character of these wo giants is their very thick, fibrous, lmost spongy bark. This is specially loticeable in the redwood, where it can e struck a hard blow with the closed ist without any fear of damage to the and.

The two trees, however, can quite asily be distinguished from one another. The leaves of the Wellingtonia, for xample, which are almost scale-like in haracter, are only about half an inch in ength; and by pressing themselves losely to the twigs, and overlapping at heir bases, they completely cover their own stems, as the leaves of the cypresses do. Redwood leaves, on the other hand— or at any rate the more conspicuous of them—are longer and flatter, and spread themselves outwards in two opposite ranks, thus giving the twigs a characteristic, double comb-like appearance.

It is a common belief that the conifers can always be distinguished from other trees by the woody cones that they bear, and it is true that, as a general rule, they can be so distinguished. There are, however, several exceptions to this rule, one of which has already been referred to in the case of the juniper. Another exception, even more conspicuous, can be seen

CONES OF WEYMOUTH PINE. *Introduced into Britain by Lord Weymouth, who popularized its cultivation early in the eighteenth century, this pine is a native of North-east America. The needles grow in bundles of five and are blue-green in colour while the cones (seen on the right) are long and narrow, with widely-spaced scales. Not until the cones are two years old do they bear any seeds. As timber, the Weymouth pine is particularly valued because it has no tendency to shrink when seasoned, and its pale reddish-brown colour also makes it attractive for furniture and interior work. In Britain this pine is limited as a plantation tree because it is liable to attack from insects and fungal diseases, but it is frequently chosen as an ornamental tree for parks because of its graceful proportions and dense feathery foliage.*

.T.F.—G*

PINE

CEDAR

SILVER FIR

SPRUCE

CYPRESS

LARCH

FRUITS OF CONIFERS. *In this drawing, the fruits of different conifers comm*
in Great Britain are seen. The cones of the cypress are small, and the scales, befo
ripe, are packed closely to form a more or less globular fruit. The seeds esca
when the scales separate. The larch is a deciduous conifer, losing its leaves each yea
The seeds of spruce and silver fir do not ripen until about a year after formatio

n the common yew, where the fruit akes the form of a brilliant scarlet 'berry," so soft and so succulent that it s eagerly devoured by many of our fruit-eating birds.

The yew, nevertheless, is a true conifer, and it has, like the juniper, the distinction of being a native of Britain. t is, of course, much planted in gardens and churchyards, though it is genuinely wild in many parts of the country, and in favourable circumstances can hold its own against all competitors.

The so-called berry of the yew is not, of course, a true berry. It is a soft, juicy cup with an olive-green seed in its centre—a fruit so different from most others that it is an important aid to identification. The leaves of the trees are distinctive, too. Like those of the red-wood, they spread themselves outwards in comb-like fashion along the twigs, each leaf being dark green and polished above, but pale and unpolished beneath.

An interesting variety of the common yew, known as the Irish yew, is often cultivated, especially in churchyards. Its branches, instead of spreading out broadly on all sides, stand almost erect, giving the tree a general form not unlike that of the Lombardy poplar. But apart altogether from this difference in shape, the Irish yew can be distinguished by its leaves, which, instead of growing in two distinct ranks, stand out irregularly all round the twigs.

We have now come to the end of the list of conifers chosen for inclusion in this chapter, and must turn our attention to the *broad*-leaved evergreens referred to in the opening paragraphs. They are only three in number, and are not in any way related to one another, their broad, leathery leaves, which remain green all through the winter, being the one outstanding character that unites them in the present group.

Probably the most familiar of the three is the common holly, which is a true native of Britain and can be found growing wild in most parts of the country. Its spinous leaves, highly glazed on their upper sides, and its clusters of scarlet fruits, distinguish it at once from all our other wayside trees.

CHARACTERISTICS OF HOLLY

A point of special interest about the holly is that its male flowers are usually found on one tree and its female flowers on another. A tree that bears no female flowers cannot, of course, bear fruits; hence we may often see one tree almost blazing with its masses of scarlet "berries," while another near at hand has none at all. The small white flowers are produced in great abundance, and usually open in May. Their sexual characters can easily be made out with the aid of a pocket-lens.

It should be noticed also that holly leaves vary a great deal in their spininess. Sometimes there is only one spine on a leaf and sometimes there are many, while all kinds of intermediate stages can be found, often on the same tree. Usually, however, the number of spines diminishes gradually from the lower branches to the upper ones. The lower branches, it has been said, need much protection from browsing animals, whereas the upper ones need little or none; and the tree is supposed to respond—with a glimmer of intelligence—to its needs. Unfortunately for this argument, however, there seems to be no real evidence to support it.

Several foreign hollies, and a considerable number of varieties of our own species, are grown in parks and gardens, and it is always interesting to compare them one with another. The Himalayan holly, for example, has longer leaves with shorter spines; the American holly has fruits that grow singly instead of in clusters; the so-called inkberry, as its name implies, has fruits that turn black as they ripen; while the species known as the winter-berry is not even an evergreen, but has soft leaves that fall in the autumn.

Our second broad-leaved evergreen is the box, which is also usually considered to be indigenous to Britain, though there are said to be reasons for doubting this. It does, however, grow in an apparently wild state in several parts of the country.

VALUE OF BOXWOOD

The box, like the juniper, is known to most folk merely as a shrub, yet it is just as capable as the juniper of growing into a tree twenty or thirty feet in height if circumstances favour it. It is not one of the most interesting of our trees to watch, since it changes but little from month to month, or even from year to year. Its very slow growth, however, has one great advantage. It enables the box to build an extremely hard wood, with a fine, close grain that is specially valued by the manufacturer of such things as chessmen and mathematical instruments.

Box occurs as a native tree in a few areas only in Britain; namely, those where chalk downs, on which box flourishes, predominate. The best-known of these box-growing districts is Box Hill, in Surrey, but they are also to be found in Buckingham and Gloucestershire. The box tree is found in abundance in Mediterranean areas.

The leaves of the box have the usual leathery texture associated with evergreens. They are more or less oval in shape, about one inch in length, and grow in opposite pairs along the twigs. The flowers appear in the spring, but they are small green things that are seldom noticed; and the fruits that follow them are little more conspicuous, being nothing but small, woody capsules containing a few black seeds.

Several varieties of the box are cultivated in gardens, the commonest being the dwarf kind that was once so widely used for permanent edgings There is also a golden weeping variety and one whose leaves are rather prettily bordered with white.

The last of our three broad-leaved evergreens is the evergreen oak—or holm oak, as it is frequently called. It is not a native of Britain, but of the Mediterranean region, from which it was introduced into this country in the sixteenth century.

A well-grown evergreen oak is a magnificent tree. Although growing to a height of seventy or eighty feet, it retains its lower branches for a very long time; and when these almost sweep the ground, as they often do, and are densely covered with foliage, the whole tree assumes the form of a massive and gigantic bush.

The evergreen oak is closely related to our own native oak, though it differs from it not only in its evergreen habit and its bush-like form, but in a number of other ways too. Its leaves, for example are much smaller than those of the common oak and lack altogether the familiar wavy margins. Their under sides, moreover, have a felty covering that gives them a characteristic, greyish green appearance. The bark differs in being thin, black and scaly.

The acorns borne by this tree are similar to those of the ordinary oak, but are brown in colour, longer, and more slender in form, and more deeply buried in their cups. They differ also in having a longer life, since they do not mature until the autumn of the year following their formation.

Finally, it should be remembered that although we speak of this tree as the evergreen oak, it is not by any means the only one that is evergreen. Several other evergreen oaks are occasionally cultivated in Britain, including the famous cork oak of southern Europe. The species described above, however, is the one most commonly seen.

WELLINGTONIA. *The Wellingtonia, or Big Tree, which is a native of California, was introduced into Britain in the middle of the nineteenth century, and has since been planted in many parklands as an ornamental tree. The picture above gives an idea of its sturdy trunk, which may reach a height of one hundred and twenty feet.*

WILLOW TREES

WATERSIDE TREES

by

RICHARD MORSE, F.L.S.

OUTSTANDING among British trees as real lovers of the waterside are the willows. They form so essential a part of our riverside scenery that it is difficult to think of the one without the other. Their light and graceful appearance endears them to all, and to walk beneath their cool, silvery foliage on a hot summer's day is a refreshment in itself.

Closely related to the willows, and similarly delighting in a moist soil, are the poplars. These two groups of trees—at any rate so far as British botany is concerned—constitute the family known as Salicaceae. It will therefore be helpful to us, in our study of them, if we look first at a few of the general characteristics of the family as a whole.

A good many of the willows are shrubs —in some cases quite small shrubs—and do not therefore come within the scope of this chapter, but all the poplars are trees. In spite of much variation in size, a number of family resemblances between the two groups stand out quite clearly.

First, as already mentioned, there is the love of moist places. There are, it is true, important exceptions to this, but the fact remains that willow and poplar trees, as a general rule, need a plentiful supply of water, and seldom flourish for long unless they can get it. Perhaps that is one reason why they are such quick-growing trees. Associated with this rapid growth is the softness of their timber. To the forester they are appropriately known as *softwoods*, and are in striking contrast with such familiar *hardwoods* as the oak and the beech.

The willows and poplars, moreover, are all deciduous shrubs and trees. Their buds (with rare exceptions) are arranged in spiral fashion along their twigs. Their leaves are always simple, never compound. Their flowers are in the form of catkins, the male catkins growing on one tree and the female on another. Their fruits are small capsules which, on splitting open, liberate large numbers of tiny seeds, each bearing a minute tuft of white, silky hairs.

The fact that willow and poplar trees are of two sexes must be carefully noted. It is not sufficient to be able to say that a certain tree is a particular kind of willow or poplar. We must be able to say whether it is a male or a female tree. If the tree is examined when it is in flower or fruit, the question of sex can easily be settled.

Passing now from the resemblances between the willows and the poplars, let us glance for a moment at a few of their differences, noting especially those that are likely to help identification.

If it is springtime, and the trees are in flower, it will be noticed that, whereas the catkins of the willows are more or less erect or horizontal, or at any rate stand out stiffly from the twigs, those of the poplars are long and pendulous, and may often be seen dangling in the breeze, thus reminding one of the familiar "lambs' tails" of the hazel.

The catkins of the willows, moreover, are rich in nectar, or honey, and so are much visited by the bees, which are responsible for the scattering of their pollen. Poplar catkins, on the contrary, contain no nectar at all, and rely chiefly upon the wind for carrying their pollen from tree to tree. Furthermore, while anthers of willow flowers are usually yellow, and thus give the male catkins a bright golden colour, the anthers of the poplars are conspicuously red or purple.

In summer time, when the flowers have faded and gone, it will be the differences between the leaves that attract our attention. The leaves of the willows are usually long and narrow (though there are exceptions to this), and their stalks are quite short, whereas the leaves of the poplars are always broad, and their stalks long.

And in the winter, when even the leaves themselves have all disappeared the trees can be distinguished by the buds that stud their bare twigs. Willow buds, for example, are remarkable in being encased by one single scale (made of two scales fused together), but the

ALDERS. *Although alders may reach a height of one hundred feet in rich, moist soil and a damp climate they usually grow no larger than bushes. The wood is soft but durable when under water and is often used for submerged piles.*

CRACK WILLOW. *Crack willow and white willow are the two most common of the species in Great Britain. The former (seen above) bears its name because of the ease with which its twigs are broken off when pressed against the shoots from which they grow. This tree flourishes best in a cold, wet soil.*

buds of the poplars show several scales. Owing to a gummy exudation, these scales are often quite sticky to the touch.

As far as identification is concerned, the willows of this country form a very puzzling group, though as the great majority of them are shrubs rather than trees, our task in the present chapter is considerably lightened. In point of size, the two outstanding members of the group are the white willow and the crack willow, both of which form large trees some eighty or ninety feet in height.

The most conspicuous feature of the white willow, and the one from which it has derived its popular name, is the silvery whiteness of its foliage. The undersides of its leaves are clothed with a dense covering of silky hairs, and, when the slender twigs are swaying to and fro in the breeze, they give to this willow a lightness of colour unique among British trees.

If the white willow is allowed its freedom, its branches form a tall crown, oblong rather than round—a form quite its own, and one that a practised eye can distinguish at a glance. Very often, how-

WILLOW CATKINS

ever, its freedom is interfered with, for its crown is cut bodily away at a point about eight feet above the ground. When this is done, the decapitated trunk responds by sending out great masses of slender branches, so that the natural form of the tree is completely lost. Such trees are known as pollard willows, and their multitudinous twigs—often spoken of as osiers—are used in a large number of rural industries.

CRICKET-BAT WILLOW

Of considerable commercial importance is a variety of the white willow, known as the cricket bat willow because it provides the best of all woods for the making of cricket-bats. This tree has a narrower crown than the true white willow, and the undersides of its leaves, which lose most of their hairs as the summer advances, assume that bluish-grey colour from which its botanical name is derived.

The crack willow differs from the white willow not only in the broader, rounder form of its crown, but also in its much larger leaves, which altogether lack the dense silky hairs so conspicuous in the other species. It differs, too, in the peculiar, brittle character of its twigs, which snap off with a cracking sound when pressed against the branches that bear them. It is this character that has given the tree its specific name of *fragilis*.

At first, this fragile nature of the crack willow's twigs may appear to be a disadvantage to the tree, for the ground beneath it, after a heavy gale, is often littered not only with broken-off twigs, but with quite large branches, too. The loss, however, rarely seems to be serious, and should perhaps be looked upon as a kind of natural pruning from which the tree ultimately benefits. The crown of this species, like that of the white willow, is often completely transformed by ruthless pollarding.

The white and crack willows are probably both natives of this country, but the beautiful weeping willow is an importation from China. In most of its characters it resembles our own crack willow, but is distinguished at once by those long, pendulous twigs that have made the tree a universal favourite for planting beside ornamental waters.

No other British willows can compare in stature with the two species already described, though there are several species which frequently depart from their shrubby habits and become small trees, attaining, perhaps, a height of twenty feet or more.

One of these is the beautiful bay-leaved willow, which is found chiefly in northern England and southern Scotland. Its popular name is a useful reminder that its foliage resembles that of the common bay tree of our gardens, the leaves being not only broad, dark green and glossy, but fragrant, too. Owing to its small size, this willow is of little value as a timber tree, though it is often cultivated for its beauty and its sweet scent.

Another distinguishing feature of the bay-leaved willow is referred to in its specific name of *pentandra*, which denotes that each little flower in its male catkins contains five stamens. True, this number is not always strictly adhered to, for there are sometimes as many as ten, but as most of our other willows have only two stamens in each flower, this large number is a reliable aid to identification. The individual flowers, however, are small in size, and a pocket lens will be needed for careful counting.

The almond-leaved willow is another species that is often no more than a shrub, but that may, in favourable circumstances, become a small tree; and here again both the popular and the botanical names afford useful help in identification. The leaves, for example, are not only similar in appearance to

ALDER AND SILVER BIRCHES

those of the almond tree, but even smell and taste faintly of almonds. They are about three or four inches in length, dark green above but paler beneath, and tend to be rather narrower than those of the bay-leaved willow. Its specific name, *triandra*, refers to the three stamens to be found in each male flower of this species—a character at once distinguishing it not merely from the bay-leaved willow, but from all its commoner relations too.

Yet another difference between these two interesting willows can be observed in the dates of their flowering. The almond-leaved species flowers in April, covering itself with a wonderful array of yellow blossom. The bay-leaved kind, on the other hand, is seldom at its best until May or even June. In fact, it is usually regarded as the latest of all our willows to come into flower.

Far more widely spread than either of the two species just described are two other small willows popularly known as sallows. They are most familiar, perhaps, as hedgerow shrubs, for although both of them flourish by the waterside, they are not bound to it, and may often be found in woods and meadows far removed from any pond or stream. It is chiefly the flowering twigs of these two willows which, under the name of palms or palm branches, are gathered by country folk for the Palm Sunday decoration of churches.

As a rule, the sallows differ in having shorter and thicker twigs and larger and rounder buds. The leaves of the sallows, moreover, are broader and more egg-shaped than those of the large willow trees, and their upper surface usually has a distinctly wrinkled appearance. Sallows, too, are widely famous

WHITE WILLOW. *A graceful tree, found by most rivers, the white willow is valuable for its timber and bark, the latter being extensively used for tanning. Willows are often pollarded and the young shoots that appear afterwards are used by basket-makers.*

GOLDEN AND WEEPING WILLOWS. *The golden willow is a variation of the white willow, the difference being that the twigs of the former are yellow or reddish. The drooping branches of the weeping willow make it the most graceful of riverside trees.*

for their early flowering. They are often in full bloom before the end of the winter, and their flowers form the bees' first nectar-feast of the year.

If the sallows are watched during the weeks that follow their flowering period, it will be found that their leaves and their fruits reach maturity at about the same time. The male catkins wither and fall when their pollen has been shed, but the female ones remain attached to the tree, finally bursting into pure white masses of fluff which, along with the seeds attached to it, is scattered far and wide by the wind.

As a rule, the larger of these two sallows is the one known as the great sallow, or goat willow. The smaller is the grey sallow. The differences between the two, however, are slight, and the latter is often supposed to be merely a variety of the former. Nevertheless, the careful eye will detect distinctions.

Before leaving the willows entirely, a brief reference must be made to the common osier, because this species, although most familiar as a shrub with remarkably long and flexible branches, does sometimes develop into a small tree, reaching a height of twenty or thirty feet. It is much cultivated for the sake of its tough twigs (osiers), which are of great value for basket making and similar crafts.

The leaves of this species, as well as its twigs, are characteristically long and slender, their breadth being sometimes as much as twenty times less than their length. This character, together with their deep green colour above and their silvery-grey hairs below, forms an important aid to identification.

Leaving now the willows for the poplars, let us glance briefly at a few of

WHITE POPLAR. *Six types of poplar are to be found in Britain; the white poplar is an importation from Southern Europe. The leaves, which are shaped like those of the maple, are covered with a dense white down on the underside—a feature that gives the tree its name. This poplar bears catkins in March and April.*

the commonest kinds to be found in Britain, remembering that their love of the waterside is not nearly so marked as that of some of the willows, and that fine specimens can often be seen in the open countryside, or in parks and gardens where no water is apparent.

The white poplar is a native of southern Europe, but because of its great beauty it is often cultivated in Britain as an ornamental tree. Under favourable conditions it may reach a height of a hundred feet, with a broad oval crown, its most conspicuous feature being the almost snowy whiteness of the under surfaces of its leaves. A close inspection, however, will show that this whiteness varies a great deal, not only on the same individual tree, but even on the same branch of it, the leaves towards the tips of the twigs being much whiter than those that grow lower down.

It should be noticed also that the shape of the leaves varies in a similar way. Those toward the outer ends of the twigs are lobed almost like those of the sycamore, whereas those that grow lower down are roughly egg-shaped, with toothed margins.

A NATIVE POPLAR

Closely related to the white poplar, and often mistaken for it, is a species known as the grey poplar, which is, however, believed to be a native of Britain. It differs from the white poplar in a number of ways, but especially as is implied by its name, in the grey, instead of white, undersides of its leaves. Moreover, the lower leaves and often nearly all of those on old trees, may lack most of the hairs that should give them their distinguishing colour, and so appear chiefly green, or nearly so.

Belonging to the same group as the white and the grey species, though differing markedly from them in its appearance, is the aspen, or trembling poplar. It is not, of course, the only poplar whose leaves tremble in the breeze, for this in varying degrees is a characteristic of most of the poplars. The leaves of the aspen, however, have unusually long and slender stalks, much flattened at the sides, so that the lightest summer breeze is sufficient to set them quivering.

The leaves of the aspen are small in

size and more or less rounded in shape, with toothed margins. They are green above, but paler below, and when mature lack altogether the woolly covering that is so marked a feature of the two species just described.

BLACK POPLARS

Another interesting group of these trees is composed of the so-called black poplars, of which there are several different kinds. Only three of them, however, can be included here.

The true black poplar is one of our less common poplars, growing chiefly in the eastern and southern counties of England. When mature, its bark becomes dark in colour and deeply furrowed, and often bears a number of large, wrinkled protuberances or bosses. Its leaves are about four inches in length, roughly triangular in shape, and have long, hairy, flattened stalks.

It is important to remember that the tree most commonly spoken of as the black poplar, and which is far more abundant than any other poplar in Britain, is merely a hybrid. Its parents are our own black poplar and the American black poplar: in various ways it resembles both of these parents.

This hybrid black poplar bears the unfortunate name of black *Italian* poplar —a singularly inappropriate name in view of the fact that the tree appears to have nothing whatever to do with Italy. Its abundance in Britain is due to the fact that it is by far the most precious of all the poplars as a timber tree.

The black Italian poplar, however, differs from the true black poplar in a number of details. For example, its young twigs are smooth, not hairy, while its leaf-stalks are usually hairy, not smooth. Moreover, at the junction of the leaf-stalk and the leaf the black Italian poplar often bears one or two small glands—a character entirely lacking from the true black poplar in Britain.

The third member of the black poplar group is the so-called Lombardy poplar, said to have originated in northern Italy in the eighteenth century. There is, however, considerable doubt about this. The tree appears to be closely related to our own black poplar, though differing widely from it in its habit of growth. Its branches are all slender, and instead of spreading broadly they rise almost vertically, close to the trunk.

THE ALDER

So far as this chapter is concerned, the last tree on our list is the alder—as true a lover of the waterside as any tree in this country, and as truly British also. Although growing quite commonly in practically every part of the British Isles, it is relatively little known, perhaps partly because of its sombre and inconspicuous appearance, and partly because our poets and artists have taken little notice of it. Nevertheless, the alder has a number of distinctive features. It is, for example, one of the very few trees to have *stalked* buds—a character that affords a very useful guide to identification during the winter.

Its leaves, too, are quite unusual. They are usually more or less egg-shaped, but instead of tapering towards the tip, they are broader at that end than at the other. Their upper ends, in fact, are often indented instead of pointed, while their bases are distinctly wedge-shaped.

When, however, the alder begins to bear fruits, which it usually does at the age of about twenty years, it is these fruits that offer the readiest means of identification.

If the alders are watched when the woodcutters are at work, yet another of their distinctive features will be noted, for their wood, although conspicuously white when first cut, soon assumes a red colour when exposed to the air. It is not a very hard wood, but has many uses in industry, and is specially valued for its great durability under water.

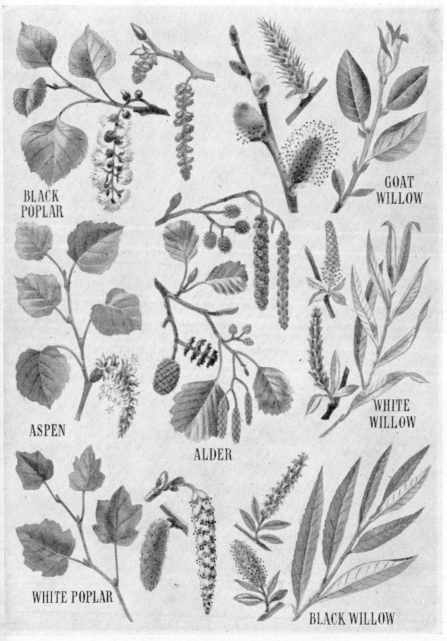

FLOWERS OF WILLOWS AND POPLARS. *Willows and poplars are catkin-bearing trees, the difference between them being that, with few exceptions, the catkins of the former are erect, while those of the latter are drooping. Male and female catkins are borne on different poplar trees, and the catkins appear before the leaves to facilitate pollination which is effected by the wind.*

SLOE BLOSSOM

WILD FRUIT TREES

by

CHARLES A. HALL, F.R.M.S.

STRICTLY speaking, all trees produce fruit of some sort. The cone of a pine is a fruit, as also is the "key" or samara of the ash. But in this chapter we are accepting the term fruit as commonly interpreted and are describing only those British trees which produce fruit reminding us of the fruit-shop. Actually, most of the fruits of trees to be described do not find their way into the fruit store, for, generally speaking, they are not of the quality to appeal to the palate, although some of them are used as edibles—most of them with the expenditure of much sugar.

Particularizing our fruit trees in this most unscientific way, we find our list a short one. There are only fourteen species, *viz.*, gean, bird-cherry, dwarf-cherry, sloe, bullace, crab apple, wild pear, rowan, medlar, whitebeam, wild service-tree, elder, mulberry, strawberry-tree. Of these, eleven, from the gean to the service-tree, are of the Rose family, although in general appearance they are quite different from the roses of cultivation. Membership of this family is determined, not by common features in the appearance of the plants, but mostly by the structure of the flowers. These usually have five petals, five sepals and numerous stamens. A feature is the union of the sepals at their base, forming a cuplet or little tube which usually adheres to the fruit: we see its withered remains at the dented apex of an apple. Another feature is the insertion of the petals and stamens at the tope of the cup formed by the union of the sepals, so that they are placed round the ovary and do not spring from below it.

Although all the trees mentioned are found in Britain and are commonly looked upon as British, some of them are doubtfully native. The mulberry is certainly an introduction, and the straw-berry-tree is considered to be indigenous only in the south-west of Ireland.

To take first the gean-tree: this cherry makes a fine flourish of flowers in woods and copses in May and June. It attains a height of ten to forty feet, its growth depending mainly upon its occurrence in a suitably nutrient soil. Once estab-lished, it grows rapidly, sending out short, stout branches which grow up-wards. The bark of these branches is of a satiny texture and peels. No suckers are produced from the roots. The white flowers are up to an inch and a half across and they occur in umbels, i.e., clusters in which the stalklets spring from a common point; but for a general explanation of botanical terms the reader is referred to the Flowers section of this book. The gean's flowers appear soon after the leaves have unfolded and almost obscure them. At its mouth the calyx-tube is contracted. The corolla opens widely and its petals are deeply notched, heart-shaped, limp in texture. Pistil and stamens mature together, so the flowers may be self-fertilized. Technically known as a drupe—it is fleshy and encloses a stone which is the seed—the fruit is heart-shaped, black or sometimes red, and may be bitter or sweet. The stone is large in proportion to the flesh, while the juice is not profuse and stains one's fingers.

When they first unfold the leaves of the gean have a bronze tint, but as they

mature they become pale green. The autumn tint may be yellow, reddish or brown. They range from two to five inches in length, with a breadth of one and three-quarters to two and a half inches, and are broadly oval, tapering gradually to a point; the leaf margin is acutely toothed. They are thin, limp and drooping, softly hairy underneath, with two glands at the base of each, and they have long, rather narrow foot-stalks.

Deemed to be a British native from Caithness southwards, this tree's wood is used in cabinet making and for tool-handles; it is of fine grain, tough texture, of a reddish tinge, and takes on a fine polish. Black-heart and Bigarreau cherries are supposed to have been developed from the gean, whose name is from the French *guigne* and appears to have been

cultivation it may assume the nature and dimensions of a tree, attaining a height of ten to thirty feet or more. Its bark is grey, smooth, astringent. The twigs are rigidly erect, smooth, reddish-brown, while the leaves, from two to four inches long, are thin, oval, slightly heart-shaped at the base, with the apex brought gradually to the point. The leaf-margin is doubly toothed, the teeth being finely-cut, and there are two glands on the leaf-stalk. Stipules—small leafy growths at the base of the leaf—are narrowly awl-shaped, serrated and glandular. In autumn the leaves turn from greenish-yellow to reddish.

This species' flowers are not clustered in umbels as in the case of the gean, but occur in loose hanging racemes from two to six inches long, proceeding from the axils of the leaves. Each flower has a stalklet about a quarter of an inch long and at first is erect, but as soon as it is fertilized it droops and quickly falls. A single flower has some resemblance to that of the blackthorn. It is white, from a half to three-quarters of an inch across. The petals are notched on their edges as though they had been bitten; and the stigma of the pistil is ripe before the anthers of the stamens, thus favouring cross-fertilization by the agency of insects. Inflorescence occurs on last year's wood, May and June being the flowering months. The fruit is a small drupe, ovoid or globular, about one-third of an inch diameter; it is black with a polished surface and a bitter taste. The juice is scanty and stains the fingers, and the stone is globular and wrinkled.

Wild or dwarf cherry is very often little more than a shrub up to eight feet high, producing numerous suckers from the root, but it is sometimes quite a tall tree, thirty feet or more in height. It is

adopted from common Scots usage.

The bird-cherry occurs in thickets, woods and hedges, and is native in various localities in Britain, though not in the south. It is found as far north as Caithness and extends southwards to South Wales and Leicestershire. In Yorkshire it has been recorded at 1,500 feet above sea-level. As a wildling it is seldom more than a shrub, but under found in a wild state from Yorkshire southwards, in woods, copses and hedges. Rather spare of foliage, in autumn it assumes a crimson hue pleasing to the eye, and in May and June its clusters of white cup-shaped flowers are very attractive.

The wild cherry's bark is reddish, and its drooping, slender branches are red. Its pendant twigs are also slender and smooth; the leaf-buds are small and protected by brown scales. Used for turnery and for smokers' pipes, the wood is reddish, fine-grained and polishes easily. Brown scales protect the flower-buds, the inner scales being frequently leafy. Resembling those of the black-thorn, the flowers are white and appear before the leaves unfold; they occur in umbels of two or three, or more, each flower having a stalklet about one to two inches long. The calyx-tube is not

WILD PEAR. *Very like the flowers of the wild rose in shape, the blossoms of the wild pear are pure white.*

contracted at its mouth and its lobes are scalloped. The corolla is more cuplike than in the two species of cherry so far described ; its five petals are oval, of firm texture and only slightly notched. Quite juicy with an acid flavour, the fruit is a red or black globular drupe; the juice does not stain. This species is considered to be the parent of our morello and Kentish cherries.

Dark blue-green in colour, the leaves are smooth, egg-shaped, or oblong egg-shaped, with short stalks, two to four inches long. They taper to a point, are toothed and scalloped on their margins, and of a leathery texture, growing alternately and not drooping. As a general rule there are one or two glands at the base of the leaf-blade or at the top of the leaf-stalk.

BLACKTHORN AND BULLACE

A species of plum, supposed to be the parent of cultivated damsons, the black-thorn or sloe can hardly be called a tree rather should it be classed as a shrub which loses its leaves in autumn (deciduous). It abounds in copses and hedges and produces its snow-white flowers before its leaves have properly unfolded. These flowers are in full bloom in March and April and are very welcome so early in the year. Often they are so numerous as to give the shrub the appearance of being covered with snow. Much branched, the plant has tough branches and rigid spines. The bark is black—hence blackthorn—and is a good foil to the white blossoms. The stems make good walking-sticks; and the twigs are rigid and branched, at first reddish-brown, but becoming black. Up to slightly more than two inches long by more than one inch broad, the leaves are stalked, finely toothed, usually smooth, various in outline, sometimes egg-shaped, at others oblong, with pointed or rounded tips. Reddish or yellowish is the autumn tint.

LOSSOMS OF BIRD-CHERRY. *The blossoms of the bird-cherry differ from those f the gean and dwarf-cherry in that they grow in spikes rather than in flat clusters. he trees flower from April to May and the fruit they bear later in the year is small, lack and very bitter to taste. Bird-cherry is found chiefly in the north of England.*

CRAB APPLE

BULLACE

WHITE BEAM

CHERRY

Wild Fruits

MEDLAR

WILD PLUMS

Occurring singly or two together on short smooth stalks, the flowers are from a half to three-quarters of an inch across. Their five white petals are inversely egg-shaped. The stigmas ripen before the anthers produce pollen, thus avoiding self-fertilization; and the damson-like erect fruits are globular, about half an inch in diameter, almost black with a bluish waxy bloom and a very harsh taste. This taste is softened when the fruit becomes over-ripe. The sloe is used in making sloe-gin, and a delicious jelly with a fine piquancy can be made with it in combination with apples. It is said that tea, when more costly than now, was often adulterated with dried blackthorn leaves.

Some botanists consider the bullace to be a variety or sub-species of the blackthorn, whilst others give it full specific rank. It occurs in hedges, woods and copses from Lanarkshire in Scotland, southwards, but is a doubtful native. In some cases it may be an escape from cultivation, and its habit marks it as a shrub rather than a tree. Like the sloe, it flowers early—March and April—but it differs in that the blooms appear with the leaves. The flower-stalks are softly hairy. The white petals are broader than in the sloe and the fruit is larger, from three-quarters to one inch diameter. It has a drooping habit and in this respect is unlike the sloe, which has erect fruit. In shape the fruit is globular and in colour either red or black.

Not black as in the sloe, the bark is brown and the branches are only slightly spinous. The pale green leaves are egg-shaped or broadly lance-shaped, with down underneath; they are up to two and a half inches long by one and a quarter inches broad.

WILD PLUM

Also considered to be a sub-species of the sloe or blackthorn, the wild plum is found in hedges and copses, flowering in March and April; it is definitely a tree. The blackthorn-like flowers appear with the leaves, which are downy only on the ribs underneath and tend to roll up. The branches are straight and produce no spines. Pendent, the fruit is oblong about an inch or an inch and a half in diameter, varying in form and colour. Although found growing wild, this sub species is not a native of Britain; its real home is said to be in western Asia.

Crab apple is the only species of apple native to Britain. It grows wild in hedgerows and woods from Perthshire and the Clyde southwards, and in May and June its white flowers streaked with pink delight the eye. It can hardly be claimed that the resultant fruits are pleasant to the taste, for they are exceedingly sour; none but a hungry and venturesome child would persist in

ELDER BERRIES. *The purple-black berries of the elder are used in this country for making wine and jelly*

eating them after the first bite. This does not mean that the fruit is entirely worthless, for pigs eat it with relish and jelly made from it has a piquancy that pleases the human palate.

Moreover, a tree laden with the yellow and red apples is a very agreeable sight. These apples are about an inch in diameter, indented top and bottom, and the pips are contained in five cells. The tree attains a height of twenty to thirty feet. Whilst it is young the branches spread, but later they droop, with the result that the head is rounded, almost hemispherical; indeed, the head's diameter may be greater than the height of the whole tree. The trunk lacks symmetry, the bark is rugged, the twigs are rounded, reddish-brown and shining. Tinged slightly with brown and of fine grain, the wood is of a hard, heavy quality. The leaves are of the characteristic apple type, shortly stalked, oblong egg-shaped, brought to a point, with toothed margins, smooth on the upper surface, usually downy beneath when young, and from one to two inches long. The flowers are about one and a half inches across, and occur five or six in an umbel. They are pollinated by insects, the stigmas maturing before the anthers shed their pollen. The styles of the pistil are joined at the base.

"Crab" refers to the acidity of the fruit, which abounds in malic acid: it has been applied to cantankerous humans, and the tree has given rise to the surname Crabtree, probably used originally to designate a person who lived near a crabtree, or had a conspicuous one growing in his garden.

The wild pear is said to be the original of the hundreds of varieties of pears which we cultivate, but there seem to be differences of view as to whether the tree is a British native, or whether it has been introduced and has reverted to a wild state. In any case, it is found growing as a wildling from Yorkshire southwards, occurring in hedgerows and woods. Being harsh and gritty, the fruit does not commend itself to the palate. About two inches long, characteristically pear-shaped, not, as the apple, indented at the base, it is green until November; then it becomes yellow. In spring, from April to May, it makes a brave show of its flowers, which are about an inch to an inch and a half across and have five white petals, an urn-shaped, five-lobed calyx, and numerous stamens with purple anthers turning black as they age; they occur in clusters of five to ten on

229

wood of the previous year's growth. The stigmas mature before the anthers and flies are attracted to act as pollinating agents. The tree, which may become as high as sixty feet, although it is often much less, assumes a shape which may be described as pyramidal. It has rough bark. The twigs which droop, as well as dwarf shoots, are often thorny. Of rough texture, fine-grained, tinted with red, the wood is used in turnery and cabinet work. When stained black it resembles ebony. The leaves on last year's wood occur in little bundles or clusters, whilst those growing on new shoots are arranged alternately. They are about an inch to an inch and a half long, stalked, egg-shaped or inversely egg-shaped, bluntly toothed, pointed at the apex, smooth, though slightly downy at first. Their autumn tint is yellow and when dead they become black. The pear is a long-lived tree and some well-known cultivated varieties have survived through centuries.

A variety of wild pear, regarded by some botanists as a definite species, is found in Cornwall and Devon. The leaves are more nearly oval than those of the familiar wild pear, and are heart-shaped at the base. The fruit is much smaller and although usually pear-shaped in some instances it is quite globular.

The rowan or mountain ash has been described elsewhere (p. 176). It is mentioned here as a native fruit tree, although perhaps the majority of our people do not regard it as such. Generally it is esteemed for its graceful leaves, its creamy - white clustered flowers and showy orange-yellow or coral fruits which please the eye rather than the palate. But thrushes and finches appreciate the fruit, and seeds pass unscathed through their digestive systems becoming scattered far and wide and accounting for the appearance of saplings in unexpected places. Moreover, there

FROM FLOWER TO FRUIT FORMATION of APPLE

BUDS & OPENING FLOWERS

UNRIPE FRUIT

REMAINS of CALYX and STAMENS

RIPENED APPLE

PETALS

SEPAL

OVARY

RECEPTACLE

SECTION THROUGH BLOSSOM, SHOWING APPLE FORMING AS PETALS FALL.

THE GROWTH OF AN APPLE. *The drawing shows how an apple is formed after the pink-streaked blossoms have been pollinated. It will be noted that the calyx and stamens remain after the petals have fallen and leave a scar on the mature apple.*

ROWAN BERRIES. *Known by a variety of names, the mountain-ash or rowan tree is found at its best in Scotland. The feathery leaves are divided into leaflets; the dense clusters of creamy-white blossoms give way in the autumn to scarlet berries, such as those seen above, which may be used in jelly-making.*

are still in our countryside housewives who have inherited the art of using wild fruit, and such use the fruits of the rowan in jelly-making. Rowans, as the Scots call the fruits, add a very fine tang to apple jelly. John Evelyn, in his *Sylva*, said, "Some highly commend the juice of the berries, which, fermenting of itself, if well preserved, makes an excellent drink against the spleen and the scurvy. Ale and beer brewed when these berries are ripe is an incomparable drink." The name "rowan" is from the Norse *runa*, a charm, and the superstitious folk of old times used the tree or parts of it as an antidote to witchcraft. Indeed, the tree has quite a prominent place in folklore. Fruit and bark are still used in herbal practice; they have an astringent action.

It is doubtful if the medlar is a native of Britain, but it is naturalized in some districts and grows wild in southern England, probably only as an escape from cultivation. It also occurs in the Midlands and the Channel Islands. Occasionally the fruits are offered for sale in fruit shops; they are not ripe until October and November, and are unpalatable until they become vinous as decay sets in; before that stage the flesh is harsh and distasteful. The medlar is found as a shrub or a small much-branched tree up to twenty feet high in thickets, hedges and gardens. In its wild condition the branches are more or less thorny, but in cultivation, where the conditions favour rich growth, the thorns do not appear. The rather large, almost stalkless

leaves are lance-shaped or oblong, finely
toothed, undivided, downy on the under
surface. Their autumn tint runs the
gamut of yellow, orange, russet and red.
The flowers appear in May and June;
they are white, about an inch and a half
across, and occur singly, stalkless or
with very short stalks, on short leafy
branches. The calyx has five woolly,
leafy lobes which persist; the corolla has
five petals and there are numerous
stamens. Usually the pistil has five styles
which are distinct and smooth. Something like a small russet apple, the fruit
is from a half to one inch in diameter; it
is almost spherical and easily distinguished
by a large concave or depressed area at
the apex surrounded by a hairy disc of
the persisting lobes of the calyx. The
tree is found as a native in Greece
Asia Minor and Persia.

NATIVE WHITE BEAM

Occurring as a tree in favourable
situations, or as a bush when exposed to
rough conditions, the white beam is no
too well known. A genuine British
native, it is found locally in woods and
margins of forests from Sutherland i
the far north to Kent and Devon in th
south. It is sometimes cultivated i
gardens and is common on chalky soils
flowering in May and June. The whit
flowers, about half an inch across, occu
in loose flattened clusters terminatin
short leafy branches; they are somewha
larger than those of the rowan to whic
the species is related. The inflorescenc
is covered with a white mealy down. Th
calyx-tube has five lobes, there are fiv
petals and the numerous stamens hav
white anthers. Usually the pistil has thre
styles which are hairy at the base. Th
leaves vary in form; they are two to si
inches long, egg-shaped or inverse
egg-shaped, stalked, often lobed, irreg
larly toothed. Above, they are smoot
and of a bright green colour; undernea
they are white and covered with whi

BERRY FRUITS. *Above are seen the
fruits of the mulberry, the wild service-
tree and the hawthorn, or May tree.*

woolly down, as also are the young shoots. It is the appearance of this white down which has given the tree its common name, which is literally "white-tree," the word "beam" being Anglo-Saxon for tree. As a bush, the species is hardly more than four or five feet high, but as a tree it rises to a height of twenty to forty feet, with branches tending upwards and a pyramidal form. The bark is smooth, of reddish-brown hue. The wood, which is hard, white and of small grain, is particularly useful in turnery and small cabinet work.

Like a small apple, about half an inch diameter, almost globular, of a red colour dotted with brown, with orange flesh, the fruit ripens in September. In Lancashire the fruits are known as chess-apples; they are highly appreciated by birds and squirrels. To human taste they are hardly acceptable until they are in a state of incipient decay, by which time their extreme harshness has been tempered. There are certain variations of the tree which are sometimes regarded as sub-species.

WILD SERVICE-TREE

The wild service-tree is native in southern and central England, but does not extend its range north of Lancashire. It has resemblance to the white beam. Some specimens are said to be many centuries old. It is of slow growth, attaining a height of forty to fifty feet, and occurs in hedges and woods, having a preference for clay soil. Flowers are produced in April and May. They are white, about half an inch across, and are numerous in flattened clusters terminating short leafy branches. In its early development the inflorescence is clad with loose down. The calyx is softly hairy and has triangular teeth; the anthers of the stamens are white, and the styles of the pistil, usually two in number, are partly united. Having toothed margins, the leaves are from two

FLOWERS OF TREES. *The flowers of the wild service-tree* (*top*), *the rowan or mountain-ash* (*centre*) *and the elder* (*bottom*) *are seen below.*

WHORTLEBERRY

BLACKBERRY

HAWS OF MAY

HIPS OF
WILD ROSE

WILD FRUITS. *The drawing above shows berries of blackberry, hawthorn, wild rose and whortleberry, the latter also being known as the bilberry.*

to four inches long, about three inches broad, in outline heart-shaped or oblong egg-shaped, with from six to ten pointed triangular lobes, smooth above and below except in early development, when they are downy. The leaf stalks are slender; the bark is greyish and smooth. A large head is formed by the spreading branches. Of a reddish tint and of fine grain, the wood is used in turnery and cabinet work.

Either pear-shaped or almost globular and of a greenish-brown colour, the fruits are small, about one-third of an inch diameter. They ripen in November and are practically juiceless. After being frosted, they become palatable, then the flesh turns brown and mealy.

ELDER TREES

As already indicated, all the trees so far described in this chapter belong to the Rose family. The elder, now to have our attention, is of the natural order Caprifoliaceae, which includes the honeysuckles, the guelder rose, snowberry and laurustinus, as well as such a tiny herb as the moschatel. The elder may be shrubby or a small tree up to twenty or more feet high. It is among our most familiar hedgerow growths and is found also in woods, coppices and on waste ground. It also appears in gardens, especially old ones, and its presence there is probably due to the ancient superstition that it is a powerful antidote to witchcraft and wards off evil spirits. Anciently, it was considered that elder-trees planted at the entrance to a garden or, better still, a complete hedge of elder, ensured full protection against the wiles of the evil ones. He who broke a twig or a branch from the tree would be unlucky. In some parts of the Continent he who wished to prune an elder first asked its permission. No answer was deemed to be consent, but before getting on with his work the pruner spat three times. In Scotland, where the species is called the bour-tree, it was held unlucky to put even a small piece of it in the fire. An old tradition has it that Judas Iscariot hanged himself on an elder-tree.

At first the elder grows with great rapidity and even a small piece of its living wood planted in the ground roots readily. The green shoots soon harden into hard tubes with a core of abundant pith. Extracting the pith, the small boy soon has a pea-shooter or a whistle. The tubes have been used as musical pipes from remote times; the generic name *Sambucus* is from Greek *sambyke*, a musical instrument. The pith is used in electrical experiments and has other scientific uses. Sometimes used in turneries, the old wood is hard and heavy; while the bark is grey, corky and rough. Unpleasant smelling, the leaves are stalked and divided into from five to nine egg-shaped, toothed, pointed leaflets from one to three inches long. The creamy-white flowers are borne in much-branched flat clusters about six inches across. In these clusters there are five primary branches, and these are branched and yet again branched. The corolla is flattened, five-lobed, with a short tube. Five stamens spring from the base of the corolla which is about a quarter of an inch across. The fruits are small, globular, aromatic, juicy, purplish-black berries. Country folk make wine of them and when dried in the sun they are quite passable substitutes for the dried currants used in cookery. Bark, flowers and berries are used in herbal medicine.

COMMON MULBERRY

The common or black mulberry is not British native, although we like to claim it as British. It was introduced into Britain in 1548, and since that date has been planted in gardens in various parts of the country. By tradition, Shakespeare, with his own hands, planted a mulberry-tree in his orchard at New Place, Stratford-on-Avon, and was the first to introduce the tree among his townsfolk. Later, in 1742, Garrick, Macklin, and others, were entertained under it. In 1765 it was cut down by a parson named Gastrel, who at that time was the owner of the property. Many relics—real or supposititious—exist of it.

At first the mulberry is a shrub, but as it matures it becomes an imposing ornamental tree, twenty to thirty feet high, with a large rounded head, and the wood is sometimes used in cabinet work. The leaves are about four inches by four inches, egg-shaped or heart-shaped, with three to five lobes, irregularly toothed and pointed; they are dark-green and on their upper surface rough with bristly hairs; in autumn they turn yellow. Appearing in June and July, the flowers occur in catkin-like spikes of clusters. They are pollinated by the agency of wind. The fruit is an oblong cluster of false drupes made up of parts of the flower become succulent. In appearance it is like a very large juicy blackberry. Developing from green to crimson and finally becoming reddish-black, it is mature in August and makes quite a good jam; it is also used in herbal practice. The mulberry is of the nettle family, which includes the elm, and other plants as well as the stinging-nettles. In China the larvae of the silkworm are fed on the leaves of the white mulberry; but they can be induced to eat the leaves of the species described here.

The strawberry-tree is native in the south-west of Ireland, where it may be as high as forty feet. It is an introduction elsewhere in Britain and has been planted in parks and gardens where it occurs mostly as an evergreen shrub from ten to fifteen feet high, or occasionally as a small tree. It is very attractive when laden with its waxy bell-shaped creamy-white flowers, often flushed with pink. The corolla, about one-third of an inch across, has five lobes; the five sepals are small. There are ten stamens which

HAWTHORN BLOSSOM. *Hawthorn is one of the commonest trees in the Britis Isles, being much used for hedging. In spring, the masses of white blossom are familiar sight in the country, but varieties of pink-blossomed hawthorn have bee developed. Both types stand up well to cultivation in towns.*

are inserted below the pistil; they have short filaments with velvety hairs at the base; their anthers are awned and have two pores at the tip. These flowers, with short stalklets, occur in a loose drooping cluster (panicle). They are followed by fruits which are five-celled, spherical, granulated berries which are orange or scarlet and have a resemblance to strawberries. They are about three-quarters of an inch diameter and take more than a year to ripen. Because of this, fresh flowers and fruits from last year's flowers may be seen together. The fruits may resemble strawberries but they certainly have not their lusciousness, for, in Britain at any rate, they are dry and flavourless. In a better climate they are of more attractive quality; in Asia Minor they are marketed, and in the island of Corsica a wine is made from them.

About two or three inches long, the pointed leaves are leathery, glossy, very dark-green, shortly-stalked, egg-shaped or oblong lance-shaped. They are alternately arranged on the shoots, yet from a distance appear as if clustered to form rosettes. This tree is of the Heath family (Ericaceae). Its specific name, *unedo*, is said to be a contraction of the phrase *unum edo*, i.e., "one I eat," implying that to eat one suffices.

The whortleberry, a drawing of which may be seen on p. 234, is a dwarf shrub and is also allied to the Heath family. Whortleberries grow best on fairly rich soil, and are found chiefly on heaths and in mountain woods. Common in northern Europe they are found in abundance in Scotland; they are also known under the names of bilberries and blaeberries. The fruits are dark blue-black berries.

CRAB APPLES. *The wild apple, or crab, as it is more familiarly known, is common throughout Britain. In spring the blossoms, which are rose-pink in colour and very fragrant, appear before the leaves ; the yellowish fruits (below) are very bitter to the taste in their raw state, though a palatable jelly may be made from them.*

HAZELS AND BEECH. *Hazels very rarely grow beyond the size of a large bush, and though their timber is useless the rods are pliant enough to be used for hoops in cask-making. Beech, seen on the right of the picture, is frequently used for hedging.*

HEDGEROW, HEATH AND COMMON TREES

by

CHARLES A. HALL, F.R.M.S.

HEDGEROWS are obviously planted by man; their formation is not natural in the sense of their having happened by an unexploited development of nature. They have been planted by human beings to define the limits of estates, to divide land into fields and pastures, and as boundaries between private ground and public roads. They serve not only to enclose land but as wind-screens and shelters for cattle, which also they prevent from straying. They certainly provide an attractive and interesting feature of the British scene. In exposed parts of the country, particularly in the north, the place of the hedge is often taken by the dry-stone dyke or wall.

In planting his hedgerows, man has used bushes and trees of various kinds. Trees of towering height have often been planted at intervals in the line of shrubs or bushes. The plant material of the hedgerow is generally such as is easily available locally and hence tends to vary with the locality. It is clear that no single hedgerow is likely to contain all the species of trees and bushes that will be mentioned in this chapter. Some will be found in one hedge, others in another. Careful landowners and farmers keep their hedges well pruned, but although the carefully trimmed hedge provides phenomena of interest to the botanist, what delights him most is the hedge which for years has had no acquaintance with the hedge-knife and has been allowed its head. The delight is in seeing bushes and trees developing more or less as they do in a wild state. And there is the further delight of ob-serving the plants which scramble over the hedge and use it as a support in their upward quest for light and air, for the display of their flowers and fruits. I refer to the honeysuckle, the roses and brambles, the clematis and bittersweet, the black and white bryony.

Most hedges are composed of mixed material, but here and there we find the material practically to be of one kind. Thus, we see hedges of beech in which the plants have been developed as bushes by pruning and have not been permitted to grow into stately beeches such as are seen in the woodlands. Unless allowed to develop naturally, even the sturdy oak is bushlike in the hedgerow. Holly, when allowed to have its head, may be a tree up to fifty feet high, but in the trimmed hedge is simply a bush, seldom displaying its red berries in winter.

Beech and oak in the trimmed hedge-row are interesting in that many of their dried leaves do not fall in autumn, but remain attached to the plants through the winter, thus adding colour to the scene when the prospect may be drear. Particu-larly is this so with the beech; its fiery-brown dried leaves caught in sunlight, or even on a dull day, are a delightful manifestation of nature's superb artistry. Equally cheering are the bright green, long, cone-shaped, pointed leaf-buds appearing in spring, often against the background of still unfallen dried brown leaves. Privet is frequently used as hedge material, particularly in gardens. It is a matter of common observation that when a privet hedge is well pruned, it remains green through the winter, last

WAYSIDE OAKS

FLOWERS OF THE WAYFARING TREE. *Found chiefly where the soil is dry, and most abundantly where the soil is chalky, the wayfaring tree never grows much beyond the size of a large bush. The branches grow in pairs on opposite sides of the stem, and the leaves show a similar formation in growth. The wood is extremely pliable and because of this is frequently used instead of withy (crack willow) for binding bundles of vegetables and sticks. The white flowers (seen on the left) appear in June; they are borne in clusters, each blossom in the cluster being the same size. In autumn these blossoms are succeeded by coral berries, which may be seen in the picture on the opposite page.*

year's leaves functioning until new leaves unfold in the spring.

Privet is native in south Ireland and the Channel Islands. A relative of the ash-tree, it grows as a wildling in various parts of Britain, particularly in the south of England, where it shows a preference for chalk soils. In the trimmed hedge it has little chance to show its flowers and fruits, but when it is allowed to grow naturally it produces slender panicles of fragrant white flowers which turn from white to a reddish-brown. Later, clusters of purplish-black berries develop from the small flowers. These berries are globular, about one-third of an inch in diameter, with oily flesh; they ripen in November and persist through the winter. An oil from them has been used for culinary purposes in Germany; they

also yield a red dye. Many trees which tower above the low growth of the hedgerow and certainly have been planted in it by man, may occur at more or less regular intervals.

Among them we see the elm, hornbeam, sycamore, horse-chestnut, oak, ash, lime, poplar, willow, beech and common maple. All these have been described in former chapters of this book. Sometimes an impressive row of Lombardy poplars is planted, growing erect like sentinels at attention. Willows, except the sallow or goat willow, thrive best in damp soil. Some of our wild fruit trees already described appear in hedges, among them bird-cherry, wild cherry, bullace, wild plum, crab apple, wild pear, elder and white beam—the last named being common in chalk districts. But we should not conclude hastily that all trees in the hedgerow have been planted deliberately by human agency; some have developed from seeds blown by wind or carried by birds. Ash and sycamore saplings are often seen, but the hedger seldom allows them to grow to full stature. The common or field maple grows treelike, when not cut back, to a height of twenty to thirty feet, but in the trimmed hedge it can be no more than a bush; it occurs wild from Durham southwards and naturalized in Scotland. It is always interesting with its deeply-fissured corky bark and five-lobed leaves with red stalks. In autumn these leaves become red, golden-brown or a rich yellow. A fuller description of this tree is given on p. 176.

The blackthorn or sloe (p. 224) occurs commonly in hedges and if not severely pruned makes a fine show of its starry white flowers in March and April—months when such fine flourish is particularly welcome. Presumably, it is named blackthorn on account of its black bark, so excellent a foil to its snow-white flowers, and also to contrast it with the whitethorn, hawthorn or may, which has dull-grey bark.

Hawthorn, of the Rose family, is undoubtedly the commonest and, in many respects, the most satisfactory of British hedgerow plants. It is long-lived and its growth forms a dense network. Its thorns are a menace to any man or beast who would break through. Here we have a true British native, abounding throughout the British Isles, and no plant could be handier or more satisfactory for the man who would make a hedge that will be a hedge indeed and

BERRIES OF THE WAYFARING TREE. *The wayfaring tree is known by a variety of names, among them, mealy-tree and cotton-tree. These are suggested by the fine white hairs which cover the wrinkled, heart-shaped leaves and which give the tree a perpetually dusty appearance. In winter, the buds of the leaves are protected by rough hairs against frost. The coral berries appear in the late summer, but as autumn progresses they change to black. Mention has been made of this tree's supple branches; on the Continent, the year-old shoots are used for basket-making, and when a little more mature, for pipe-stems. By reason of its pliability the wayfaring tree is sometimes known as twist-wood, lithe-wort or whip-crop.*

endure for very many years. When the hawthorn hedge is not severely pruned, or when it has been allowed to become ragged, the display of its flowers in May and June is a sight that pleases. Probably there is no more popular tree or shrub in the land. The flowers borne in flattish clusters are white, occasionally pink, fragrant, about three-quarters of an inch diameter. The stigma of the pistil is ripe before the anthers of the stamens are ready to shed pollen and flies are attracted to act as pollinating agents. Popularly called haws, the fruits are spherical or ovoid, dark-red and much appreciated by birds in early winter. The flesh of the haw is mealy, not unpleasant to the taste; it encloses a one- or two-celled nut, a single seed in each cell. Birds help to scatter the seeds which, even if swallowed, pass through the digestive canal unscathed and are deposited with excrement, thus accounting for the wide distribution of the species. The young leaves are not unpleasant to human taste and browsing animals eat them voraciously; but their voracity is curbed and they are prevented by the abounding thorns from doing too much injury to the tree or bush.

HAWTHORNS

The uncut hawthorn develops into a small tree from ten to forty feet high. Often we find it as a tree in the hedgerow and are thankful for it. The grey, smooth bark tends to flake in old trees. The tough, hard wood is used in cabinet work and turnery, and also in place of boxwood in wood engraving.

There is a sub-species of hawthorn which has more deeply lobed leaves, and the flower-stalks and lobes of the calyx are softly hairy. The flowers and fruits are smaller than those of the common species and appear later. A variety, the Glastonbury thorn, flowers in mid-winter. Legend has it that it was produced from the staff of Joseph of Arimathaea.

The old saying, "Cast not a clout till may is out" has much less reference to the month of May than to the hawthorn which is popularly called may. It was formerly held to be safe to set aside heavy winter clothing by the time the tree was in flower. The name may was given on account of its association with May-day celebrations, and the month in which it blooms.

SPINDLE-TREES

The spindle-tree is a British native distributed from Roxburgh southwards; it is rare in Scotland. We may see it in the form of a shrub in the hedgerow; in other situations, such as in copses and shrubberies, it may be a tree twenty feet high. As a hedgerow shrub it has a somewhat straggling habit. Grey and smooth is the bark; the green twigs are square, occurring in pairs opposite one to another on the branches, and the leaves, also growing in opposite pairs, are egg-shaped or oblong-lance-shaped, shortly-stalked, smooth, tapering to a point. Stipules—small leafy growths at the base of the leaf—are small and fall off before the flowers open. In length, the leaves vary from just over an inch to five inches. They have finely toothed margins. When crushed they give out an offensive smell. The small yellowish-white flowers, about one-third of an inch across, occur in loose clusters springing from the axils of the leaves. Each bearing from three to five flowers, the flower-stalks are about one to two inches long. The calyx is four-cleft; the corolla consists of four petals overlapping each other in bud; the anthers of the stamens mature before the four-lobed stigma is ready to receive pollen—hence fertilization depends upon visiting insects.

Early in the year this tree or shrub may not be recognized easily, but in autumn it stands out conspicuously on account of the crimson and gold autumn tinting of the leaves. Moreover, the fruits,

HAZEL CATKINS. *The long, swaying catkins of the hazel, often known as lamb's tails, are the male flowers; the female flowers are like small buds with crimson threads.*

which ripen in October, are outstanding. Each fruit is a four-lobed, pale crimson fleshy capsule about one-third of an inch across, with deep grooves between the lobes. Each lobe of the fruit is a seed-cell and when, on maturity, it bursts, the seed is displayed covered with a bright orange coat, technically called an aril.

There are folk who call this species dogwood, but it is of quite a different family from the dogwood soon to be described. Another local name is skewer-wood, due to the fact that the wood of the tree is tough and hard, highly suitable for making skewers. Pegwood is another name, obviously given from use in making pegs, and spindle takes us back to the days when spinning and weaving was a domestic occupation and the wood was used for spindles. Fine charcoal for artists' use is made from the wood, and formerly, if not now, the charcoal was used in the manufacture of gunpowder.

Dogwood, or cornel, is a British native

WILLOWS IN WINTER. *Coated with hoar-frost, the branches of the willows form a delicate tracery.*

egg-shaped with uncut but often wavy edges. At first they are silky or hoary, but later they became smooth, turning, as already noted, from green to red in autumn. They unfold about the end of April or beginning of May. Flowers are fully open in June and July. Individually they are small, about one-third of an inch across, creamy-white with a small four-toothed downy calyx, four lance-shaped petals and four stamens alternating with the petals. Massed as they are in dense, almost globular clusters at the ends of new shoots, they make quite a brave show. These flowers are rather short-lived; they produce fruit in the form of small berries, green at first, but by September very dark purple, approaching black. Small beetles and flies are attracted to the flowers by their odour which, if pleasing to certain insects, is offensive to human nostrils. The bark of the shrub also smells unpleasantly when crushed. In France, oil from the berries was used for soap-making, and it has been made to serve for lamp oil in Britain.

The guelder rose, often found in copses, flourishes in some hedges providing the soil is sufficiently moist. The hedgerow is brightened in autumn by its foliage which at that time is crimson, and also by its translucent red berries. It is of the same family as the elder and is sometimes called dog elder or water elder.

Nearly related to the guelder rose, the wayfaring tree occurs in hedges and copses from Yorkshire southwards, and is an unchallenged British native. It flourishes in a drier soil than that demanded by its relative, favouring limestone or chalk. Usually its form is that of a shrub, but now and then it is found as a tree ten to twenty feet high. The branches grow opposite one to another and are very pliant. Their pliancy and

found in hedges and woods, from Westmorland southwards; rarely in Ireland. It is a small shrub from five to eight feet high. It has no association with dogs; more properly should it be called dagwood, because its branches were used to make what the country folk called dags—skewers or pegs. Anciently they were used for arrow-shafts.

The short-stalked leaves, which are two to three inches long and pointed, grow in opposite pairs; they are broadly elasticity are exploited in the countryside, where they are used for binding bundles of faggots, etc., and are often called twistwood. The bark is greyish-brown and fissured. At the base heart-shaped, at the apex bluntly rounded, the leaves, three to five inches long, are dull-green, egg-shaped, stalked, devoid of stipules. An outstanding feature of the leaf is its soft, velvety upper surface, whilst the under surface is covered with white-star-shaped hairs. In their embryonic state the leaves are not packed in close, scale-covered buds as is general in trees, their nakedness being covered by a protective coating of down. Fresh shoots producing leaves are also downy, and we need not be surprised that with so much down about parts of the tree, giving it the appearance of being covered with white dust, it has been called cotton-tree, white-wood or mealy-tree.

PRIVET. *Largely used for hedging, privet (below) bears sprays of creamy flowers, succeeded by black berries.*

In May the flower buds begin to open. At first we see a densely packed cluster of little green buds which later become white flowers, each about a quarter of an inch across. There is a five-toothed calyx and a five-lobed corolla. The stamens are five in number; the pistil has three stigmas without styles; and the flower-cluster is conspicuous, about two or three inches across, and flattened. Clusters of berries (more correctly drupes) follow the flowers. Each drupe is about one-third of an inch diameter, somewhat oblong and flattened; it passes from coral-red to purple-black and is fully ripe about the end of August.

TYPES OF BUCKTHORN

Two species of buckthorn, both British natives, occur in hedgerows, although they are generally found in woods and thickets. Purging buckthorn appears from Westmorland southwards, showing preference for chalky soils. It is a shrub five to ten feet high, losing its leaves in winter. "Purging" obviously refers to its medicinal use as a purgative; indeed, the berries have a most drastic purging action and should not be used in their native state. Herbalists prepare a syrup from them in which form their violence is considerably modified.

The shrub has a rigid habit. The branches are spreading, growing opposite one to another, the smaller ones terminating in thorns. In winter one has to be careful not to confuse the species with the blackthorn, for the bark is black, but the thorns are not nearly so numerous. The buds occur in almost opposite pairs along the shoots and at the end of each shoot there is usually a pair of buds with a thorn between them. These buds are dark brown or blackish, pointed egg-shaped. The wood is hard, the sapwood yellowish white, whilst the heart-wood is reddish yellow.

About one to two inches long, the leaves are oblong or egg-shaped, shortly-

OAK TREE. *The valuable timber of the oak comes from its massive trunk. The bark, deeply furrowed in a network pattern, is the hiding-place of many insects, but the oak is able to resist their attacks and the wood does not appear to suffer damage.*

stalked, pointed at the apex. Their veins are prominent. They are bright-green and smooth above, somewhat paler underneath where, when young, they are downy. They occur in bundles at the ends of shoots and grow almost opposite one to another lower down. Stipules at the base of the leaf-stalk are awl-shaped. The leaf-margin is very finely toothed.

It is in April that the leaves unfold and in May and June the small yellowish-green flowers, about one-fifth of an inch diameter, appear singly or in clusters in the axils of leaves on last year's wood. Male and female flowers occur separately, and usually on separate trees. The male flowers have a bell-shaped four-cleft calyx, four pointed petals and four stamens opposite to them, whereas the calyx of the female is cup-like and the flower has four stigmas. Pollination is effected by insects. The berries are ripe in September when they are blue-black, globular, about a quarter of an inch diameter. Their juice provides the sap-green pigment used by artists, and the bark yields a yellow dye. The seed is curved like a horse-shoe.

Breaking or alder buckthorn, a shrub five to ten feet high, differs from purging buckthorn in that it produces no thorns, has more slender branches, leaves with parallel veins, and produces rather larger fruits, about half an inch in diameter, which pass from green to red and finally to dark purple—not blue-black. The flowers, also, are greenish white, not yellow-green. Moreover, whereas the parts of the flowers in purging buckthorn are in fours, those of the alder buckthorn run in fives and all flowers have both stamens and pistils, the former maturing before the latter. They occur with rather long stalks in clusters of two or three in the axils of the leaves. It should also be noted that the inversely egg-shaped or oval shortly-stalked leaves are arranged alternately and their margins are entire, i.e., not

toothed or cut in any fashion. Often called black dogwood, the wood of this shrub is used in the manufacture of gun-powder. It is not hard like that of purging buckthorn, but soft and spongy. The species prefers damp soil. Flowering time is May-July. Green dye is made from the unripe fruits. This shrub has a more northerly range than its so near relative; it is common in England and is found as far north as Moray and Ayr in Scotland; in Ireland it is very rare.

GOAT WILLOW

Almost too well-known to need minute description for identification, common sallow or goat willow occurs in hedgerows mostly as a bushy shrub, although in other situations it may become a tree up to thirty feet high. This is the earliest flowering British willow, its conspicuous catkins being in full flourish in April and May. Male and female catkins are borne on separate plants. The almost ovoid male catkins are conspicuous on account of their golden prominent stamens and great silkiness. The females, which have a nodding habit and lengthen to about three inches, are hardly less conspicuous, but lack gaiety of colour. This is the willow whose twigs and branches bearing catkins are gathered in this country for Palm Sunday celebrations and the said branches are commonly described as "palms." Some folk name the species "pussy willow"—this from the catkins which, when they begin to develop, have a furry appearance and feel. The sallow thrives on drier soil than that usually demanded by various species of willow. When its catkins are in full bloom it is visited by bees which highly appreciate the nectar and pollen, and moths are also attracted. It should be noted that the catkins are in full development before the leaves appear.

Last, but by no means least, in our catalogue of hedgerow trees, is the hazel

HEATHLAND. *Scots pines, silver birches and gorse bushes with their brilliant yellow flowers are to be seen in this typical stretch of sandy heathland.*

MOUNTAIN ASH AND BEECH. *A mountain ash seldom grows to any height in a wood, where it is liable to be choked by trees of stronger growth; but on a bare hillside, as in the picture above, it reaches full stature. A young beech is seen in the distance.*

llowed its head, which seldom happens, becomes a tree up to thirty feet high. There are few matured hedgerows in which it does not appear. The nature lover always experiences pleasure on seeing its pendulous, loose male catkins very early in the year—possibly by the end of January, but certainly in February. Called lambs' tails by country folk and children, they are all the more conspicuous because they appear before the leaves unfold. This is an arrangement which favours distribution of the abundant pollen by wind, for were the leaves expanded at the same time as the catkins are mature, they would catch most of the pollen intended to reach the female catkins which are on the same bush or shrub. The female catkins are so small that they are easily overlooked; they are like small buds, but are distinguished from leaf-buds by the crimson stigmas which protrude. The fruit ensuing from fertilization is the familiar hazel-nut enclosed in a jagged leafy cup. Filbert and cob nuts are cultivated varieties.

HAZEL TREES

The male catkins are made up of numerous small flowers each having eight stamens. A great quantity of pollen is produced. In outline, the leaves are nearly round; they are from two to four inches long, pointed, heart-shaped at the base, and rather coarse in texture when fully grown. The edge of the leaf is doubly toothed. The wood is soft and elastic and its elasticity renders the shoots useful for hurdle-making and for hoops or crates, and walking-sticks are also made from the shoots.

Heaths occur on poor sandy soils in which there is a deficiency of lime and of those nutritive salts essential for the vigorous health of many plants. They are well developed in the south-east of England, but also occur in the north and on dry hillsides. Some heathlands now existing may have persisted from very early times, but many have developed from woodlands cleared of timber. Again, some woodlands have apparently degenerated into heathlands under natural influences.

HEATHLAND TREES

The trees commonly found on heathlands are oaks, birches, beeches and hawthorn. Of the hawthorn, the sub-species already mentioned seems to be most abundant. Holly also occurs, sometimes plentifully. We also frequently see the rowan or mountain ash, and crab apple, white beam and wild or dwarf cherry occur occasionally. The Scots pine is often seen, but probably it is an invader. The box-tree, whose wood is used for wood-engravings, is found mainly on chalk downs, where it is a British native. Box Hill, the well-known beauty spot near Dorking in Surrey, has its name from the box-trees with which it is practically covered.

Amidst cultivated areas, we have in our country stretches of wilderness or waste land generally described as commons. The soil where they exist is dry and lacking in nutritive quality. Often these commons are cultivated lands gone to waste owing to the fact that the cultivator has despaired of getting any profitable return from them. They are left to nature's tender mercies and in them we see what nature untamed can do when it has a free hand. Bracken fern abounds, its russet autumn tint giving warmth to the prospect in the declining year. Gorse flaunts its golden glory early and late and broom adds its distinction. Of larger growth there is blackthorn or sloe, and hawthorn. Trees scattered over the wilderness are chiefly oaks and birches, and it seems possible that if they are left to their own devices they may so increase and extend as eventually to turn the wilderness into woodland—actually a reversion to what was most probably the primitive state of such areas.

FOXGLOVE

THE LIVING PLANT

by

F. MARTIN DUNCAN, F.R.M.S., F.R.P.S., F.Z.S.

BRITISH wild flowers possess a delicate grace and beauty that have aroused and inspired admiration throughout the centuries. Even the great Linnaeus, who devoted long years of his life to the study of rare and wonderful plants collected from all parts of the world, was so thrilled by the fragile beauty of some of our native flowers that he knelt down among them where they were growing and gave thanks to God for the vision of such pure and fragrant beauty.

The spring, when the leaves unfold and take all sorts of strange forms—star-shaped, heart-shaped, spear-shaped, arrow-shaped, fretted, fringed, furrowed, serrated, never the same from foot of stalk to blossom—is the best time to begin a study of our native wild flowers. We must never forget that even the humblest wayside weed is a living entity relatively as sensitive and as responsive as ourselves to surrounding conditions; to sunshine and darkness, to heat and cold, to prosperity and poverty. Only so may we arrive at a proper understanding of their true significance, how they live, put forth their leaves, feed, store up reserves to tide over hard times, mate, and provide for the effective protection and dispersal of their offspring and thereby for the continuation of their species. Nor should it be forgotten that we, in company with all forms of animal life, would soon perish if vegetation disappeared from the surface of the earth; for it is plant life alone which makes possible our earthly existence.

The leaf is not only the most distinctive but also in many ways the most essential part of the plant for it has many important functions to perform. The leaves are the principal organs by which plants breathe, and it is also by the aid of the radiant energy of sunlight passing through their green colouring matter, or chlorophyll, that plants are able to absorb carbon dioxide from the atmosphere and set free the oxygen. The leaves are also chiefly responsible for the processes involved in transpiration, or the giving off of surplus moisture, and the formation of food reserves. The leaves of the majority of plants absorb carbon dioxide from the surrounding atmosphere chiefly through their under surface, the rate of absorption depending upon the available amount of daylight falling upon the upper surface of the leaves, and the temperature of the air. In the absence of light the leaf cannot do this, and it is only when exposed to daylight that the living leaf can accomplish this delicate chemical reaction by the aid of its green colouring matter or chlorophyll, which acting as a reducing mechanism returns the oxygen to the air. By a reducing mechanism, as applied to the physiology of plant life, is meant a mechanism which wholly or partially deprives certain oxygen-containing compounds of their oxygen.

What is the significance, the vital importance of this intake of carbon dioxide from the atmosphere, on the part of the plant? Well, there are three very important organic compounds that are universally present in plants, without which growth and the continuation of life would be impossible, and for the building up of all three, carbon is absolutely necessary. These three important compounds are called proteids, carbo-hydrates and fats. Now proteids are very complex compounds and there is one substance that is mainly composed of them and is the most important part of any plant or animal, in fact, it is the only *living* part of either, and is protoplasm— it is the substance which forms the physical basis of life. Carbohydrates are simpler bodies than proteids and partially go to the building up of tissues and food reserves; sugars and starch are familiar forms, while the solid framework or skeleton of the stem and leaves is mainly composed of a substance called cellulose, which, under certain chemical reactions can be converted into sugars. Certain salts in very weak solutions are taken up by the roots from the soil and conveyed through definite tubular vessels up the stem and branches to the leaves, where they are worked up or combined to form carbohydrates, later to pass out of the leaf through another series of downcast pipes, in the form of soluble sugars to that part of the plant where food reserves are being stored, and there once more changed into starch. In this way the proteids, starch, and fats (vegetable oils) are stored up either in the seeds as foods reserves to be used later on by the developing seedling, or in the thickened underground stems (rhizomes), roots, or bulbs, there to be held in reserve until the following spring for building up the tissues of the growing plant.

SEASONAL CHANGES

All through the long summer days this complex work of building up and assimilation goes on within the tissues of the living leaves; then as the hours of daylight shorten and the temperature falls these processes cease, the remaining starchy products, transformed into sugars in solution, pass out through the veins into the body of the parent plant, the green of the leaf changes to russet or gold, and finally, the dry, withered leaf

falls or is carried away by a gust o autumn wind. All that remains to indicate the position once occupied by the leaf is a little corky scab marking the point of attachment of the leaf-stalk to the parent stem. This scab has been forming gradually, as autumn drew on to sever the leaf-stalk and plug the wound. If you will look at a young branch of a horse-chestnut in late autumn or winter, you will find the little horse shoe shaped scars from which the tree has gained its popular name and which are the scars left by the detached leaf stalks. You will find at the base of each little next year's leaf-bud, which ha already begun to form, and if examine with your pocket magnifying glass, then will be clearly seen the so-called nails c the tiny horse-shoe which are really th sealed off ends of the pipes—vascula bundles as the botanist calls them— through which the interchange of fluid between leaf and stem took place.

TRANSPIRATION OF PLANTS

We must now just briefly trace anothe function of the leaf, the process of trans piration. Go out into the fields and lane quite early on a summer morning an see pearl-like drops of water glistenin on the leaves of many plants. Note ho they are often lodged between th serrated edges of the leaves of th buttercups, wild strawberry, crane's-bi geranium and daisies. Though usuall described as dew-drops, such descriptio is frequently incorrect, for they hav been pumped out from the leaves in mo instances, rather than deposited on the surface by condensation from the chil moisture-laden air. This process transpiration confers two importar benefits upon the plant. First, the wate transpired brings with it salts in solutio required for the building up of foc supplies, while in the second place causes the root to absorb fluids mo quickly and easily.

COMMON WOODLAND FLOWERS

bove are honeysuckle (I); *wild strawberry* (II); *wood sorrel* (III); *and bluebell* (IV).

LADIES' BEDSTRAW AND GREAT BURNE

Ladies' bedstraw (left), which flowe
throughout the summer, grows in patch
on dry banks and downs. Small yellow flowe
are massed in numerous small dense cluster
the leaves are needle-shaped. The flowe
were formerly used for curdling milk j
cheese-making—hence the plant's nicknar
of cheese rennet. The great burnet (above
which may be found in moist meadov
has crimson or purple flowers arrang
in a roundish head, and toothed leafle

Why should the plant take all the trouble of drawing up so much water through its roots and carrying it up the stem into the leaves only to throw most of it away? It must be remembered that the salts required are only present in the soil in very weak solutions, and even if they were there in strong concentrated form the roots could not absorb them. Consequently the plant is obliged to take in large quantities of weak solutions to acquire the necessary amount of salts. Having travelled up to the leaves, the water has performed its carrying work and some of it must now be thrown away or transpired so as to make room for the arrival of fresh supplies of salt-solution. Most of the process of transpiration takes place through some of the tiny apertures on the under surface of the leaf, called the stomata. They are very numerous, often several hundreds to the inch, and are virtually restricted to the under surface of the leaf; in the aquatic plants, like the water lilies, for instance, with floating leaves, we must naturally look for them where alone they could be of use—on the upper surface. They are so small that all their structure can only be seen with the help of a microscope; then it is possible to see that each aperture is bounded by two special, somewhat kidney-shaped cells of the epidermis, called guard-cells, which, unlike most of the cells forming the surface skin or epidermis, are green and therefore capable of forming starch. Moreover they are so disposed that when they are filled with water—that is, swollen—the aperture or stoma as it is called, between them is opened; but when, for the time being, these guard-cells contain less water and contract, their walls are applied to one another and the stoma is closed. The state of water-tension in the plant depends upon the relation between the water within the plant and the external conditions of drought or humidity. Thus during dry weather when the plant is losing much water to the air, the leaves tend to droop, the water-tension of the guard-cells is lessened, and the stomata automatically partially or entirely close, and thus retard the drying up of the plant. But this is not quite all the story, for light plays a more important part in the movement of the guard-cells than drought or humidity of the atmosphere, for they tend to open in sunshine and close in darkness, their chlorophyll enabling them to form starch and grape-sugar (glucose) under daylight, while the neighbouring epidermal cells, destitute of chlorophyll, cannot do so. When the guard-cells are assimilating vigorously, their glucose draws water from the neighbouring epidermal cells and becoming turgid, opens the stoma slit aperture between them; while when the light fails, their activity and water content decreases, causing them to close. In addition, light also appears to exert a direct influence upon the state of water-tension within the neighbouring epidermal cells. Thus the stomata which have especially to do with regulating the transpiration of water vapour from the leaf, may be said to act as automatic ventilators.

IMPORTANCE OF OXYGEN

Free oxygen is as essential to maintain the active life of the plant as it is for the continuance of our own lives, and laboratory experiments demonstrate that oxygen is absorbed by the plant, that it is absolutely indispensable, and that the process of respiration is continuous through the life of the plant. The process is not entirely confined to the leaf stomata, for all active parts of the plant may be said to participate, as the oxygen is extracted from the water taken up by the roots, as well as from the atmosphere by the leaves.

We can better appreciate how the leaf performs these functions of absorption, transpiration and respiration if we call

WHITE WATER-LILIES. *White water-lilies are fairly common in some parts of Great Britain, and are among the most attractive of the country's water-plants. Unlike yellow water-lilies (see p. 308) the leafless flower stalks do not appear above the water.*

SNOWDROPS. *Although the snowdrop is probably not a native plant of Great Britain it is found growing wild in copses and meadows, its pure white flowers usually appearing as early as January. The sepals and petals bear patches of green near the upper edge.*

FLIES CAUGHT BY SUNDEW. *Hairs on the sundew plant, which may be found growing on peat bogs, or moist sandy heaths, are connected with glands which exude a sticky substance, and this effectively captures any insect which may settle. The body of the insect is dissolved and the plant absorbs the nitrogenous juices.*

in the aid of a microscope, for then if we look at a thin vertical section of a leaf we can see the different kinds of cells which take part in these life-sustaining processes. The cells immediately beneath and forming part of the upper surface skin, or epidermis, will be seen to have their walls slightly thickened and to contain no green colouring matter, or chlorophyll. Immediately below them is a layer of chlorophyll, containing cells of oblong shape that seem to be arranged on end and so closely packed together as to give the appearance of a fence or palisade. This palisade parenchyma (as it is called) is the chief laboratory of the plant, and it is there that the radiant energy of the sun, streaming through the green colouring matter or chlorophyll, is utilized by the living protoplasm of the cells in the splitting up of the carbon dioxide absorbed from the atmosphere, the liberation of the oxygen, and the building up of proteids and carbohydrates, those complex chemical materials required in the growth of the plant and the building up of food reserves. Below the palisade cells are layers of loosely arranged cells of varying size and containing chlorophyll, called from their appearance the spongy parenchyma, which also play their part in the processes of assimilation. Finally, below the spongy parenchyma we come to the layer of cells forming the cuticle, or skin, of the under surface of the leaf, and with which are mingled the cells forming the stomata, easily distinguished by their shape position and chlorophyll.

It is obvious that the leaf, if it is to be healthy and active so that it may perform the maximum amount of work, must receive its full share of sunlight and air and in that fact is found the reason for the

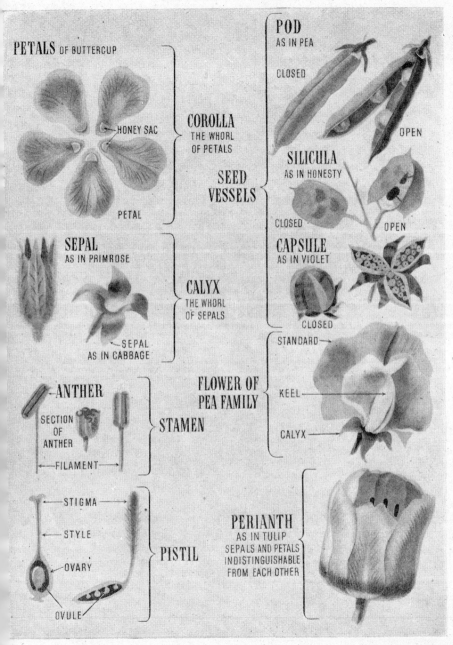

BOTANICAL DETAILS AND TERMS. *The drawings above are designed to explain some of the principal terms employed in botany, giving examples of their use (see also pp. 266, 267 and 270). Pollen from the anther fertilizes the ovule at the base of the stigma and seed is formed, borne in cases such as those seen in the right top corner. These show a wide range of variety in type, three examples of which are given.*

BLADDER PLANTS. *Sticky hairs on the stems of bladder campion (left) prevent crawling insects robbing the flowers of nectar. Bladderwort (below) captures small water insects with its bladders.*

varied shapes and positions of leaves on stem and branch. The competition for light and air is terrific, and the means by which the different kinds of plants win through are amazing. The struggle is particularly intense in the summer but is countered by more wonderful and beautiful adaptations of stem, branch and leaf to meet the changing environment. The time of prostrate or semi-prostrate leaves has gone; stems now grow stouter and rise higher, giving off branches at regular intervals, the larger free-growing plants which obtain unobstructed light most frequently bearing simple or slightly lobed leaves, while the smaller plants of lesser growth generally bear leaves that are either long and narrow, as in the grasses and reeds, or much indented, compound, and with small leaflets capable of seizing as many as possible of the broken sunbeams which have not been intercepted by the loftier plants, while casting as little shade as may be upon each other. Plants of straggling growth by means of tendrils, and leaf-stalks adapted for the purpose, hoist themselves upon the shoulders of plants of sturdier growth, and so climb to the top of the hedge from which to hang in graceful sprays. Many of these climbers grow their leaves so that they form beautiful mosaics, each leaf ranged side by side so as to cast no shadow upon its neighbour. Familiar examples of such leaf-mosaics are to be seen in black bryony, white bryony and ivy.

Leaves have to protect themselves from many foes, both insects and browsing mammals, as well as from extremes of climate and temperature. The sharp spiny armature of thistle leaves, the spiny leaves on the lower branches of the holly,

BLACK BRYONY AND IVY. *Bryony (right) and ivy (below) are plants whose strong clinging tendrils enable them to climb over other woodland plants to reach light and air.*

the spines of the gorse, and the stinging hairs of the nettle must suffice as familiar examples of protection against browsing animals; while the different kinds of hairs that clothe the stem, branches, and leaves in varying degrees of density and complexity of form, play their part not only in arresting the progress of creeping insects, but, where heavily developed on leaves, render them unpalatable and also constitute an effective protection against excessive transpiration, heat and cold. Some plant hairs are connected at their base to glandular bodies and exude sticky substances which effectively prevent small marauding insects like ants from climbing up to the flowers to rob them of their nectar; others are highly complex and actually play a part in the capture of insects and the subsequent absorption of the nitrogenous juices dissolved from the bodies of their prey, as in the common sundew and narrow-leaved sundew, often to be found growing together on peat bogs and damp sandy heaths, and the butterwort, also a dweller on moist heaths and marshy places. In the case of the bladderwort, the third of the so-called insectivorous plants, the small "bladders" are really modified leaves adapted for the capture of tiny aquatic insects and crustaceans popularly called water-fleas; and these bladders, when examined under the microscope, are seen to possess minute glandular hairs. The sundews and butterwort grow on poor, damp, peaty soil and have relatively feebly developed roots, while the bladderwort has no root at all, but floats in the waters of moorland pools and ditches; all are situations relatively poor in nitrogenous matter, and the specialized leaves and glandular hairs of these plants

are an adaptation for the provision of additional nitrogenous material by the capture of small insects and the breaking down of the soluble parts of their bodies.

DIVISIONS OF PLANT WORLD

Before going on to consider the part which the flowers play, and the vital function of seed production in the life of the plant, it is necessary briefly to state the manner in which botanists arrange the plant world into two principal groups, and how each of these primary groups are again sub-divided. All the true flowering, seed-bearing plants constitute the first great division of the plant world, called the Phanerogams— from two Greek words meaning visible mating—while all the non-flowering or seedless plants are gathered into the second great division called the Cryptogams—from two Greek words meaning hidden or unseen mating. The Phanerogams are again sub-divided by botanists under two headings: (1) the Angiosperms —from two Greek words meaning having seeds enclosed in a case, and (2) the Gymnosperms—from two Greek words meaning having seeds not enclosed in a case, naked-seeded; these are the cone-bearing plants or conifers of which the Scotch pine and the yew are famous British examples.

The second great division of the plant world, which comprises the Cryptogams or seedless plants is sub-divided under the following headings: (1) the Pterido- phytes (from the Greek *pteris*, a fern; *phyton*, plant), to which belong all the ferns, horse-tails and club mosses, plants possessing true stems and roots, and therefore spoken of as vascular Crypto- gams; (2) the Bryophytes (literally moss- plants), the true mosses and liverworts which possess no true roots; (3) the Thallophytes (literally a plant not differ- entiated into stem and root), in which are incorporated all the seaweeds, the lichens, and the fungi. The Thallophytes are all relatively simple in structure with no true differentiation into root and stem, and for this reason the plant body is known as a thallus (from the Greek *thallos*, a young shoot), though often in its entirety very diverse in shape. The seaweeds differ from the fungi in possess- ing chlorophyll and consequently are able to utilize the free carbonic acid gas of the atmosphere in the manufacture of their carbohydrates; while the fungi being destitute of chlorophyll are obliged to live either as true parasites upon other living organisms, plant or animal, or to grow upon decaying animal and vegetable matter.

EVOLUTION OF WILD FLOWERS

None of the Cryptogams or seedless plants produces true flowers, and in their higher forms, the ferns and horse-tails for instance, their life-history is marked by a regular alternation of sexual and asexual reproduction; while in the simplest forms, such as the microscopic algae and the bacteria, no sharply marked distinction of sex exists, multiplication taking place by fission of the parent cell and the perpetuation of the species is often carried on by the formation of special resting cells, or spores.

The intense study and comparison of the structure and development of the re- productive organs of Cryptogams and Phanerogams has thrown considerable light upon the probable evolution of the latter, and in conjunction with the study of available fossil remains, has demon- strated that the Phanerogams or flowering plants have descended from cryptogamic or flowerless ancestors.

From their perishable nature, the remains of plants as fossils are scanty often imperfect, and therefore difficult of interpretation. Small wonder then that the complete story of the evolution of the flowering plants remains an unsolved problem. The evidence is meagre, and the investigation of such data as can be

SPRINGTIME AT KEW

SECTION OF TYPICAL COMPOSITE FLOWER

PINNATE LEAF OF ROWAN

RAY & DISC FLORETS

BRACT RECEPTACLE

INVOLUCRE OF BRACTS

BUD IN AXIL OF LEAF

BIPINNATE LEAF OF ACACIA

TENDRILS

STIPULE

ENLARGED RAY FLORET

DISC FLORETS ENLARGED & IN SECTION

PAPPUS

SEED OF DANDELION

SEED OF THISTLE

NODE

INTERNODE

NODE

LEAF OF PEA

STIPULES

BRACTS

UMBEL OF COWSLIP

SET

POTATO TUBERS

BOTANICAL DETAILS AND TERMS. *In the drawing above may be seen an analysis of a typical flower of the Composite family, which includes knapweed, corn-marigold and the daisy. Examples of the different types of leaves—simple, pinnate and bipinnate—are also shown. In the cowslip (bottom left-hand corner), one of the primula family, the flowers arise as a group, or umbel, from the terminal axis of the stem.*

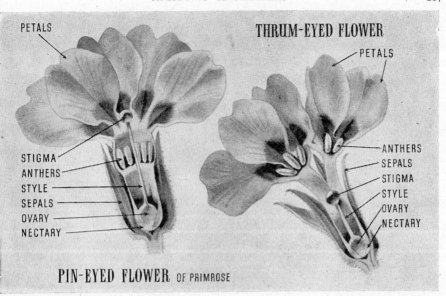

PETALS

THRUM-EYED FLOWER

PETALS

STIGMA
ANTHERS
STYLE
SEPALS
OVARY
NECTARY

ANTHERS
SEPALS
STIGMA
STYLE
OVARY
NECTARY

PIN-EYED FLOWER OF PRIMROSE

PIN-EYED AND THRUM-EYED FLOWERS. *Two types of primrose, illustrated above, are to be found; the pin-eyed, in which the stigma is placed above the anthers, thus preventing self-pollination; and the thrum-eyed, in which the stigma is not seen above the corolla tube. Both types are easily recognizable.*

gleaned from available fossil remains makes it abundantly clear that much has been completely lost in the mists of palaeozoic antiquity, so that only in broken outlines can the history of plant life through the ages be traced.

As with the account of the foliage leaves, so now in dealing with the flower, detailed anatomical descriptions will be deliberately avoided. It is far more important first to gain some knowledge of life and function through first-hand observations in the field. For our present purpose therefore let us consider a flower as simply consisting of four series of highly specialized leaves encircling at regular intervals the tip of the flower-stem. The outer circle, sometimes green, sometimes coloured, are called the sepals, and are principally connected with the protection of the flower bud during its growth. Next come the petals, sometimes pure white, usually of most lovely colour, often with spots

or blotches of stronger tint to guide and attract desirable winged insect visitors. Within the circle of the petals we find the stamens, not so easily recognized as leaves, for each stamen consists of a stalk and a head, or anther, in which the pollen grains are formed. The anthers are the male sexual organs of the plant, and when ripe, open and discharge their pollen. At the very heart of the flower, within the circle of the stamens, are one or more carpels, the number differing in the various families of flowering plants. Each carpel at its summit terminates in a stigma, while its more or less swollen base, called the ovary, forms a closed chamber containing a minute egg-shaped body, the ovule, which, after fertilization by the nucleus of a pollen cell, develops into a seed. The carpels represent the female sex-organs in the plant. Such in brief outline are the salient features of the flower of any plant belonging to the Angiosperms, or true flowering plants

HEMLOCK. *Above may be seen a typical example of a plant of the umbelliferous family, the small white blossoms on separate stalks being attached to a sturdier stalk which, in turn, joins the main stem. Hemlock, like wild carrot and hedge parsley, both of the same family, is found in hedgerows and waste places.*

with seeds enclosed in a chamber or fruit.

Let us take the Scotch pine for our example of the second division of the flowering, seed-bearing plants, the Gymnosperms of the botanist. It bears two kinds of cone-shaped flowers, one developing stamens only, the other carpels. The male or stamen-bearing flowers are yellow cones clustered together on the branch, each cone representing a single flower, and from its scale-like stamens producing large quantities of dry powdery pollen. The carpel-bearing, or female cones at first have the appearance of erect reddish buds, each really consisting of a single axis with spirally arranged carpels, somewhat complex in structure, each carpel consisting of a small scale from the upper face of which a larger scale protrudes and which, in

268

PRIMROSES. *The creamy flowers have pink-tinged stalks ; the leaves are wrinkled and covered with a soft down on the underside. Primroses bloom in April and May.*

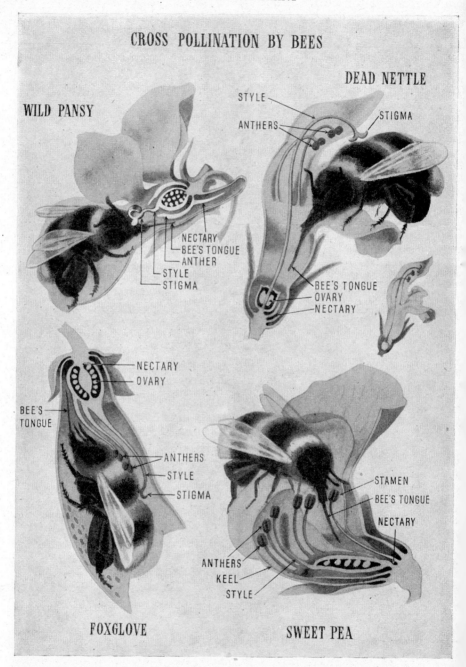

HOW BEES EXTRACT HONEY. *Above are seen detailed drawings of bees visiting different types of flowers. Pollen from stigmas and anthers is carried on the hairy bodies of the bees from one flower to another and cross-pollination is thus effected.*

turn, has attached to its upper surface two ovules. Pine trees depend for pollination upon the agency of the wind, a very uncertain and wasteful method, which accounts for the great quantity of light powdery pollen produced. In May, when ready for pollination, the carpellary cone stands erect upon the branch, and elongating in growth, causes the carpel-scales slightly to separate outwards. The ripe pollen grains, shaken out of the staminate cones by the swaying of the branches, are blown by the wind against the female cone and naturally fall into the crevices between the slightly opened carpels, and rolling down the carpellary scale come into contact with the integument of the ovules. After pollination, the carpels again close together and the cone becomes hard, green and woody, and gradually bends over until it finally points downward, its closely closed scales becoming brown in hue. Finally the scales separate at their tips and permit the seeds to be set free. The escape of the seed, however, does not usually take place until more than a year after pollination. Each seed is furnished with a separable wing-scale which acts as a sail and enables the seed to be carried by the wind for a considerable distance before falling to the ground. In addition, the dry cones when they fall from the parent tree are blown along the ground shedding any remaining seeds they may contain, and thus a double provision is made for the successful dispersal of the seed. The reader should examine the cones of the larch which are very similar to those of the Scotch pine, and also look for the staminate and carpellary cones of the yew, the seeds of which possess a special accessory, fleshy envelope, called an aril. This is of a lovely red colour, attractive to birds.

The varied shapes, scents, and colours of flowers have chiefly originated through the intimate partnership that exists between flowering plants and certain insects: a relationship of far greater importance to mankind than most people have realized. But for the presence of certain species of winged insects many of our crops could set no seed, while the bulk of our country and garden flowers would, in the course of a few years, cease to exist, so absolutely dependent are these plants upon their insect visitors for the successful pollination and subsequent development of their seed. Everything depends upon the successful pollination of the flower if the plant is to perpetuate its species, for without the fertilizing influence of the pollen grain content upon the ovule, the latter cannot become a fertile seed.

CROSS-POLLINATION

The simplest method of pollination is brought about by the transfer of the pollen from the anther to the stigma of the same flower, and if the flower does not depend upon the visits of insects, then it is said to be self-pollinated. When the stigma of a flower receives pollen from the flower of another individual plant of the same species, as for example from one foxglove to another, it is said to be cross-pollinated. Finally we have the case of those plants in which the pollen may be transferred from one flower to the stigma of another flower growing upon the same individual plant, which obviously represents a half-way stage between self- and cross-fertilization. It has been proved beyond all doubt, that in many plants the act of cross-pollination has a greater stimulating effect upon the ovules, resulting in the production of larger numbers of seeds, or seeds of better germinating quality.

The various means by which plants hinder, or actually prevent, self-pollination may be briefly grouped under four headings: (1) The stamens and stigmas do not occur on the same flower, but stamen-bearing and stigma- or carpellary-bearing flowers may be present on the same individual plant, as for example in the hazel, oak, and pine; or the two kinds of flowers may be borne on different individual plants, as in the willow and the yew. (2) The stamens and carpels in a single flower may ripen at different times; consequently the pollen and the stigmas are not ready simultaneously for the work of pollination. In such cases the stamens may mature first and shed their pollen before the stigma is in the receptive condition, or the stigma may be the first to mature. (3) The pollen from the same flower may have no fertilizing effect upon the ovules, in which case, should the stigma receive pollen from the same individual flower of which it forms a part, no seeds will be formed. (4) The relative arrangement of the parts of the flower may be such as effectually to prevent the pollen reaching the stigma of the same flower. A beautiful example of this method is to be seen in the so-called pin-eyed form of primrose flowers. Finally, there is the marked difference in the form and character of the pollen and flowers existing between plants which depend upon the wind for the transference of their pollen, and those regularly visited by winged insects. In the former the flowers are usually inconspicuous, unscented and possessing no honey nectaries, produce large quantities of dry powdery pollen, while their well-developed stigmas are so shaped as to expose their maximum surface to the wind-borne pollen. Where cross-pollination is effected through the visits of insects, the flowers are usually conspicuous, often brightly coloured, scented and possess nectar glands secreting sweet fluids for which the insects visit them; while in the majority the pollen grains, instead of being dry and powdery, are slightly sticky and readily adhere to the head, body, or limbs of the visiting insect. Moreover, the anthers are in such a position in the flower that their pollen

will adhere to that part of the insect which will be brought into contact with the receptive surface of the stigma of the next flower of the same species visited; thus insuring effective cross-pollination. Of course there are exceptions, and some insect-pollinated flowers are not only small and inconspicuous, but apparently scentless.

The different species of bees are perhaps the most important and highly specialized flower-frequenting insects, their long tongues and hairy bodies and legs having become perfectly adapted for the collection of nectar, and at the same time, for the transference of pollen from one flower to another. In many flower-frequenting butterflies and moths the tongue, or proboscis, is of such length as to reach the nectar gland at the bottom of long, tubular flowers, such as those of the convolvulus and the honey-suckle, which are quite inaccessible to all other insects. Though tubular, the flowers of the foxglove, on the other hand, are specially adapted for, and entirely dependent upon, the visits of humble-bees for cross-pollination, and the same applies to many of the pea-flowered plants. Indeed this intimate association between flower and insect is one of the most fascinating and important features of plant life that the reader may profitably seek to observe in the course of his country rambles.

Finally, we come to the means of perpetuation of the species through the effective protection and dispersal of the seed. Seeds are the offspring of the plant, and the fleshy fruit of cherry, plum and apple, the red berries of the holly and the hips-and-haws of the wild rose, along with the hard shell of the hazel-nut and the walnut, have all been evolved as effective means of protection and dispersal, while thistle-down and dandelion "clocks" and the tufted seeds of rose-bay willow-herb are familiar examples of seed dispersal by the help of the wind.

COWGRASS

A name for the common red or purple clover, seen in fields throughout Britain.

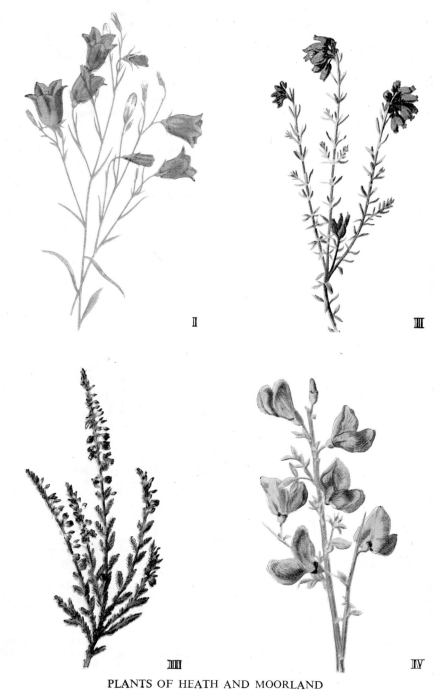

II

III

IIII

IV

PLANTS OF HEATH AND MOORLAND

Flowers seen here are harebell (I); *cross-leaved heath* (II); *ling* (III); *and broom* (IV)

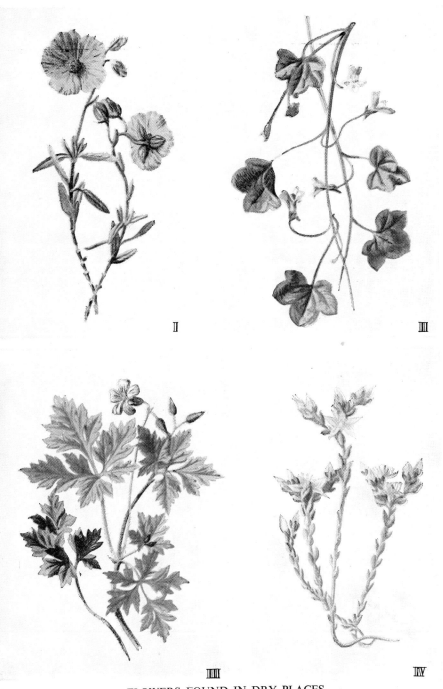

II

III

III

IV

FLOWERS FOUND IN DRY PLACES

Rock-rose (I); *ivy-leaved toad-flax* (II); *herb Robert* (III); *and stone-crop* (IV).

KNAPWEED

Flowering all summer in waste places, this plant is also known as hardheads.

WAYSIDE FLOWERS

by

ELEANOR VACHELL, F.L.S

As the broad highway that connects one city with another differs from the winding road that wanders across bleak mountain passes and through fertile vales, so too, wayside plants differ according to their environment, in different parts of the British Isles. Unlike woodland perennials that grow unmolested from generation to generation and increase by means of underground stems, bulbs and tubers, well stocked with food-stuffs, many of the wayside plants grow on hedgebanks, stone walls, and grass verges where they have to contend with dust and tar, steam-roller, scythe and billhook.

Plants that flourish in such situations belong to a somewhat cosmopolitan community made up of hardy perennials, small annuals, flowering shrubs, denizens that look native but are doubtfully indigenous, and naturalized aliens that have made their way inland from docks and ballast dumps and have become completely at home in the soil and climate of the land of their adoption.

Perhaps one of the most striking features of the British landscape and one that appeals specially to visitors from abroad is the prevalence of well-grown hawthorn hedges which seem to have been in use in this country since the time of the Romans.

Hedge-banks are the home of hundreds of different species and are gay with flowers during the spring and summer months. Usually the first flowers to appear are those of the barren strawberry, true harbinger of spring, that often opens its pure white blossoms before the end of December as if wishful to be in time to greet the New Year. Closely resembling the wild strawberry in its petals and shape of its leaves, it is often confused with its more useful namesake, but its receptacle remains hard and dry when the tiny achenes which are the true fruits are ripe, and never becomes swollen and luscious and scarlet.

EARLY SPRING FLOWERS

Towards the end of January a few early blossoms of the lesser celandine appear as if by magic in the hedgerows, for Dame Nature carefully saves the shining gold with which she paints the narrow petals for their inner side, which is visible to insects on the wing, and the buds are therefore almost as green as the angular leaves until the sun shines and bids them open. Among the fibrous roots are numerous long tubers, while smaller ones resembling grains of wheat occur in the axils of the lower leaves in *var. bulbifera* which, when detached, form new plants.

In very sheltered situations ground ivy or alehoof blooms very early in the spring, the small purple-blue flowers of variable size with under lips variegated with white and dark purple looking very attractive amongst a quantity of purplish-green leaves. The rootstock is perennial, the roundish leaves are often hairy, and the whole plant emits a very distinctive fragrance especially in warm sunshine. Each plant throws out numerous runners with threadlike internodes which soon perish, but as the buds formed on them quickly strike and grow, large areas are soon covered with a network of runners and young plants. Ground ivy is bitter and aromatic, and was once used for fermenting and clarifying beer.

Early in March sweet violets peep out from beneath a cluster of heart-shaped leaves. The plants increase by means of runners freely given off by the perennial rootstock, and the fragrant spurred blossoms of deep purple, pale reddish lilac, or pure white with purple spur, lightly poised on slender stalks, are visited by insects in search of honey. Both the flowers and leaves were formerly used to cure sleeplessness, quinsy, pleurisy, jaundice, etc., but their value was evidently overestimated.

When violets and their constant associates primroses and lesser celandines begin to lose their first glory, jack-by-the-hedge, known also as garlic mustard or sauce alone begins to monopolize the hedgerows. At first the coarse-looking plants with their broad crinkled heartshaped leaves and tiny snow-white flowers arranged in dense clusters are not very noticeable, but as time goes on th stiff stems lengthen, long narrow seed pods take the place of the inconspicuou flowers and the whole plant look untidy and unattractive. When bruise it emits a strong smell of garlic. Eve since the beginning of the year the fres young foliage of wild chervil or wil hedge parsley has enlivened the hedge rows, and when the first warm days com the tall flower-stalks suddenly appear i massed array and the terminal umbel hold up their heads and display their tin white flowers. So abundant is this plan in many parts of Britain that, during th month of May when the flowers are i perfection, the hedge-banks appear t be covered with a soft haze of white o either side of the roadway. Wild cherv can be distinguished from other closel allied white-flowered umbelliferous plan by its dainty feathery foliage and i

WILD STRAWBERRY. *Found on shady banks and woodland clearings, its trifoliat leaves and white flowers resemble the barren strawberry. The tiny achenes (or seec vessels) appearing in the pulpy red receptacle, are the true fruits.*

TANSY. *Tansy is a handsome plant of the Composite family, with bright yellow flowers and feathery, pinnate leaves. At one time, tansy was highly valued as a herb, and was frequently cultivated for culinary and medicinal purposes.*

DANDELION. *On the right are seen three stages in the growth of the dandelion, whose clocks are a familiar sight.*

long smooth shortly-beaked fruits.

Greater stitchwort was sometimes called White-Sunday because its pure white star-like flowers appeared in time to commemorate the festival of White or Low Sunday, six weeks before Whit-Sunday. The stems of this dainty perennial are angular and rough-edged, the narrow leaves taper to a long point and the snow-white petals are deeply cleft and are twice as long as the sepals. Closely allied to the greater stitchwort but not nearly as attractive is the common mouse-ear chickweed, a low-growing inconspicuous perennial with narrow undivided leaves and small uninteresting white flowers. It is very abundant by roadsides in waste places and in cultivated ground, and can be distinguished from other closely allied forms of mouse-ear chickweed by the absence of gland-tipped hairs.

When the flowers of wild chervil have faded and the tiny white petals have fallen, upright hedge parsley, another umbelliferous plant with tiny whitish flowers, appears in the hedgerows. It is shorter and stiffer and more wiry than its predecessor; the small blossoms show a faint tinge of pink on their petals, and the small fruits, instead of being long and narrow, are roundish and covered with short, hooked bristles.

Yet another umbelliferous plant with white flowers is common in hedges and by waysides during the summer months. Tall and graceful with finely-divided yellow-green leaves, hemlock can easily be identified by its smooth stems splotched with deep brown-purple. It is well that Nature has specially branded this plant with dark splotches of colour as a warning to men and animals, for it is very poisonous.

Abundant on grassy hedge banks throughout the summer months is bird's-foot trefoil. Its pretty little flowers arranged in a one-sided cluster eight to ten together at the top of the stem, vary from bright yellow to deep brownish orange; and the small trifoliate leaves though usually smooth are sometimes covered with long soft hairs. Creeping cinquefoil is abundant by roadsides and in waste places everywhere in Britain except in the extreme north. It is a small procumbent perennial with creeping stems, rooting freely at the nodes, stalked digitate leaves with finely serrated leaflets and rather handsome bright yellow flowers with five roundish petals. Owing to its astringent properties it was much valued by the ancients and was frequently administered as a cure for ague. Closely resembling the creeping cinquefoil in the size and colour of its blossoms silverweed is equally common in this country. The bright yellow five-petalled flowers are perhaps a little bit larger and richer in colour and its silvery-white

innate leaves with their six to ten pairs f lateral leaflets are very distinctive. Jnlike the creeping cinquefoil it prefers ɔ grow in lowly places by the wayside, ften selecting the edge of the roadway. Jumerous runners are produced that ɔot at the nodes so that the ground is uickly covered with a network of igorous young plants.

Composite flowers play a very im- ortant part in helping to beautify the edgerows, especially during the late ummer months. Each of these so-called flowers" is in reality a collection of mall florets growing together for their nutual good within a cup-like assem- lage of bracts called an involucre. This rouping of the florets into flowerheads as many advantages for they are able to nare the work of the flowerhead etween them: cross-pollination is more kely to be effected, and they are ren- ered more conspicuous to insects on ıe wing than if they grew singly on the tem. Knapweed or hardheads is a rather

tall tough-stemmed perennial with dull green entire or toothed leaves and numerous flowerheads of small dull rose-purple florets surrounded by an involucre of dark brown scales fringed with spreading bristles. It is a very variable plant and the flowerheads are sometimes with and sometimes without a row of showy ray-florets that possess neither stamens nor pistils and are only useful to attract insect guests.

Smooth hawk's-beard is another plant belonging to the natural order Com- positae that is common in grassy places by the roadsides throughout the British Isles. It produces an abundance of small flowerheads composed of yellow strap- shaped florets, and the smooth yellow- green leaves are mostly lobed, the upper ones being narrow and pointed, arrow- shaped at the base, and clasping the stem. It is a very variable species, usually with several stems that are almost leafless, at other times with single stout stems that are copiously leafy and tall. Nipple-

GREATER KNAPWEED. *The scaly flowerheads are crowned with purple ray-florets ; the stem is slightly branched and the leaves are deeply divided.*

wort is another wayside plant belonging to the same natural order. It is tall and leafy, with a stiff branched stem and numerous small flowerheads composed of yellow strap-shaped florets all possessing stamens and pistils. At one time was eaten as a salad and Julius Caesar army is said to have "sustained life for some time" by eating its roots.

DANDELIONS

Dandelions are too well known to require any detailed description. Because of their tiresome habit of appearing in places where they are not wanted they are ousted from lawns and paths, kitchen gardens and flower-beds, though if they were rare the handsome golden flower heads and jagged leaves would doubtless be very much admired. Dandelion "clocks" are marvellous examples of Nature's handiwork and when ripe the tiny fruits, wafted by the wind float away on their parachutes to find new home. In July and August ragwort is one of the most conspicuous wayside plants, for its stiff branched stem crowned by a mass of golden flower heads' and its glossy deeply-divided leaves, may be seen by nearly every road side especially on sandy soils. Artist delight in using it as a foreground for their pictures, but farmers do not welcome it on their land. Both the leaves and flowers yield useful dyes and it was formerly used as a cure for many ills, but its medicinal value was evidently much overrated. Yellow toadflax has stiff stems, clothed with narrow pointed leaves and surmounted by handsome spikes of yellow and orange long spurred flowers. Guided by the showy orange palate, bees alight in search of honey, their weight depressing the lower lip which affords an entrance to the nectar secreted in the spur. Before departing they repay their debt by brushing off the pollen from the stamens and carrying it to the stigma of another lower, so effecting cross-pollination. Though not as abundant as ragwort, tansy is nevertheless fairly common in many parts of the country. The stems are taller and stiffer, the leaves are deeply cut and jagged, and instead of growing singly the plants grow thickly massed together which greatly enhances their beauty. The plant is bitter, aromatic and tonic and has long been used in this country in cookery and as a cure for gout and dropsy. When the broad highway or the narrow lane is bordered by rough scrub or woodlands, the tall stiff stems and cylindrical flowerheads of the wild teasel are often conspicuous by the wayside. Arranged in pairs, the long narrow prickly leaves clasp the stem so tightly that they form a cup in which rain water collects. Numbers of small robber insects are drowned in these miniature ponds while attempting to reach the tiny mauve flowers closely packed together in the compound flowerheads.

In similar situations burdock is usually to be found. Its tall stout stems and large broad heart-shaped lower leaves are very characteristic and easily distinguish it from other species. The flowerheads are arranged in terminal panicles and consist of tiny purple florets half hidden by a nearly globular involucre or "bur" that catches in anything it touches by the hooked points of its numerous bracts.

In clearings where trees have been felled the tall showy flowerheads of rosebay willow herb are conspicuous everywhere, decking the countryside during the summer months with a blaze of deep-rose-purple. Known also as fire-weed, this handsome perennial appears in great profusion after forest fires. Its rapid increase in disturbed ground is due to its creeping rootstock and to its numerous tiny seeds contained in long narrow capsules. Each of these small seeds, very tightly packed end to end in four straight rows, is equipped with its own parachute of soft silky hairs, with the help of which,

WOOLLY-HEADED THISTLE. *The purple florets are succeeded by small seed-vessels (or achenes) which, when ripe, are crowned with long feathery hairs.*

A NARROW LANE IN MIDSUMMER. *The country lane is rich in the variety*
plants it shelters at all seasons of the year. In this picture are seen the jagg.

...eaves of bracken and nettle, growing in the shadow of the wayside oak; while in the ...awthorn thickets the bramble and the wild rose trail their tenacious, prickly branches.

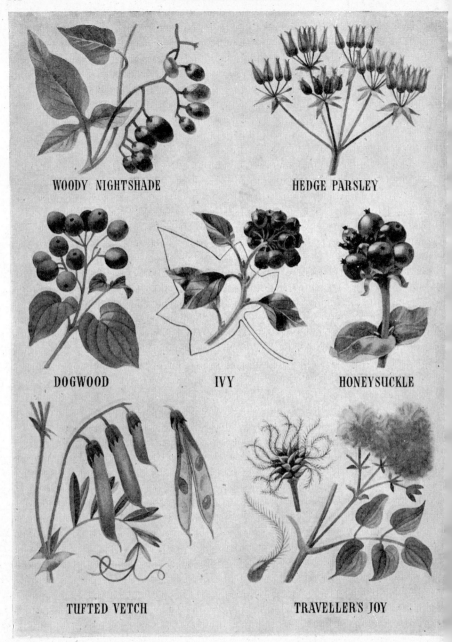

WOODY NIGHTSHADE   HEDGE PARSLEY

DOGWOOD   IVY   HONEYSUCKLE

TUFTED VETCH   TRAVELLER'S JOY

FRUITS OF WILD FLOWERS. *Above are seen fruits of different types of wild plants. The berries of woody nightshade and honeysuckle are scarlet, while those of dogwood and ivy are black; the fruit of the vetch is a pod containing several seeds, similar to that of a pea; the achenes of traveller's joy have bearded styles enabling them to be wind-borne; hedge-parsley seeds are smooth and oval.*

when liberated by the elastic movements of the ripening capsule, it sails off, airborne, to find a suitable home. The showy petals, spreading from the base, and the long narrow leaves, distinguish t at once from other species. Much less attractive is the broad-leaved willow herb. The rose-coloured flowers are smaller and fewer in number, the leaves are broad and toothed, and the style is divided at the top into four spreading lobes.

While passing through the outskirts of woods and copses, especially if the ground is rough or slightly rocky, isolated clumps of gromwell may possibly be seen. Its rootstock is perennial; the stems are tall and stiff and very leafy, the small yellowish-white corollas have spreading five-lobed limbs and the tiny nuts are hard and white and very smooth and shining. In similar situations the field forget-me-not or field scorpion-grass is often abundant, blooming continuously throughout the summer and autumn months. It has the hairy foliage and deeply cleft calyx of the wood forget-me-not, but the paler blue flowers are smaller and much less attractive. Calamint, a tall aromatic branched perennial plant with mauve flowers, also occurs in bushy places.

WILD ROSES

Leaving for awhile the broad highway to explore a narrow winding lane, we immediately notice the beauty of the uncut hedgerows, especially during the month of June, when dog roses are in perfection. The long trailing stems armed with straight or hooked prickles, the pretty pinnate leaves, the exquisite pink petals surrounding a mass of golden stamens, and later in the year the scarlet hips are all too well known to need any further description for the rose has long been regarded as England's national flower and its delicious fragrance has made it a general favourite. The genus Rosa includes a number of well-defined species of interest to botanists, some of which are rare while others are extremely common. The pulpy part of the so-called "fruit" or hip, which is really only the enlarged calyx that encloses the true nut-like fruits, is now largely employed in the manufacture of rose-hip syrup, rich in vitamin C.

CLIMBING PLANTS

Brambles and briars in the hedgerows help to support the weak-stemmed climbing plants that deck the lanes with bright patches of colour. Of these none is more gay than the tufted vetch that climbs over the hedges by means of its delicate leaf-tendrils and adorns them with one-sided spikes of purplish-blue flowers. Another common climbing plant that possesses no tendrils but succeeds in reaching its goal by the help of the short stiff reversed bristles on the edge of its stems and leaves is goose-grass or cleavers, an inconspicuous plant with small whitish flowers and narrow pointed leaves. Nobody can fail to recognize this tiresome plant because its rough stems and leaves cling to any obstacle in their way and its globular seed-vessels disperse themselves by getting entangled in the fur of animals or the clothing of anyone who happens to pass by. Black bryony employs another means of reaching the top of the hedgerows. Its long twining stems coil and twist amongst the shrubs and bushes producing at intervals numerous shining heart-shaped leaves and clusters of small inconspicuous green flowers which late in the autumn give place to very decorative scarlet berries. Yet another climbing plant deserves mention on account of its handsome white trumpet-shaped flowers. Great bindweed is common in hedgerows, strangling with its twining stems the plants amongst which it grows.

Returning once more to the main road as it approaches the outskirts of a city,

NETTLES. *Left are seen the branched spikes of the small green flowers of the common stinging nettle; below are seen the two-lipped corollas of the white dead nettle. The plants are not related*

bright colours disappear, their place being taken by the dull shades so prevalent amongst weeds of allotments and waste and cultivated ground. Good King Henry once cultivated as a pot-herb still lingers, often as an introduced species only, in the vicinity of old dwellings. It is easily distinguished from other species by its perennial rootstock, which is thick and fleshy, by its dark green triangular leaves, and by its clustered spikes of tiny green flowers forming narrow terminal panicles. White goosefoot or fat hen is a common weed of cultivated land. Like Good King Henry, it is wind-pollinated and having therefore no need of gaily coloured petals, its small green blossoms clustered together in dense spikes, are very inconspicuous. The pale green entire leaves are often covered with a whitish mealy powder.

Docks, thistles and nettles abound by the wayside in similar situations. Like the goosefoots the common nettle being wind-pollinated has small inconspicuous green flowers clustered together in long branched spreading spikes, the male and female blossoms being on different plants. The stinging powers of the nettle are very well known but many of the uses to which it has been put may easily be forgotten. Not only were the leaves considered an excellent pot-herb but before the introduction of flax and hemp nettles were used for making cloth and provided the thread used for sewing. Docks, on the other hand, have proved of little value to mankind. The British species are all tall perennials with numerous small inconspicuous flowers arranged in whorl-like clusters in terminal flowering-spikes. The broad dock differs from the curled dock in its broader eaves, in its looser whorls of flowers and especially in its perianth-segments bordered by a few small teeth. A tall stout plant is the woolly-headed thistle, with divided prickly leaves white and cottony underneath, and rather large ovoid flowerheads of purple florets surrounded by pointed cottony bracts ending in a stiff spreading prickle. The creeping thistle differs in its smaller, narrower, very prickly leaves, and smaller and more numerous flowerheads composed of pale purple florets. The cotton thistle, a tall stout branched plant with loose cottony wool, is possibly native though usually an immigrant to Britain. Though probably not wild in Scotland, it is generally selected to represent the Scottish thistle depicted in heraldry.

Two species of mallow occur abundantly on waste ground by the wayside. The common mallow is a stout biennial with large downy root-leaves, roundish in shape and acutely lobed, ascending stems and showy purple flowers. The plant contains a large amount of mucilage and the curiously-shaped roundish seed-vessels when unripe, are known by children as "cheeses." The dwarf mallow is much smaller than the common mallow; from which is can be distinguished by its prostrate stem, shallow-lobed leaves and small pale lilac flowers.

Easily recognized by their cruciform flowers, four plants belonging to the natural order Cruciferæ are abundant in

EASELS. *Wild teasels are common in copses, hedgerows and waste places in the southern and midland counties of Britain. During the first year of its growth the plant has no flowers; the leaves lie close to the ground in the form of a rosette. In the second year it bears flowers on tough, piny stalks that may grow as high as six feet. The flowerheads are cylindrical and spiny, with involucres of long, sharp bracts and the florets have purplish corolla tubes with unequal lobes. The leaves grow opposite each other, joining at the stem and thus forming a deep cup which collects rain and dew. In this cup many insects are caught and drowned, and the dissolved bodies are then absorbed by the plant. The wild teasel is generally found flowering in the latter part of the summer.*

ROSE-BAY WILLOW HERB. *A plant which spreads rapidly because of its wind-borne tufted seeds, the rose-bay willow herb has large rosy-purple four-petalled flowers arranged in spiky clusters known as racemes. The alternate leaves are lance-shaped.*

RED CAMPION. *Flower-ing from June to Sep-tember red campion is a biennial, generally found in moist shady woods and on hedge-banks. It is a handsome plant with rosy-pink scentless flowers, each of the five petals being deeply cleft; the calyx is a deeper colour. The stalks are reddish-brown and faintly hairy. The lower leaves of the plant are egg-shaped, but those on the main stem tend to be narrower. The flowers, as a rule, are uni-sexual, and conse-quently the fertilization of the seeds has to be effected by the transfer of pollen from one plant to another. The tiny kidney-shaped seeds are contained in a roundish capsule, toothed at the opening. Red campion belongs to the same family as a number of other familiar wild flowers such as bladder-campion (see page 262), corn-cockle, ragged robin, greater stitchwort and mouse-ear chickweed.*

similar conditions. Hedge mustard is an unattractive annual with very stiff spread-ing branches. The lower leaves are deeply divided, the small flowers are all yellow and the long seed-pods are closely pressed against the stem in elongated racemes. Usually the whole plant looks dirty and dusty. Yellow rocket or wintercress, on the other hand, always fresh and clean, as if it had recently been washed by a refreshing shower. The bright green leaves are deeply divided, the flowers are bright yellow, and the numerous seed-pods are crowded together in a long dense spike. Both hairy bittercress and shepherd's purse have small white flowers and deeply divided or compound leaves, but the shape of their seed vessels is totally different, for those of the hairy bittercress are long and narrow whilst those of shepherd's purse are short, flat and wedge-shaped and supposed to resemble a purse. This ubiquitous annual is in blossom all the year round. Very often allotments are divided from the roadway by iron railings or a rough untidy hedge. Through the railings it is easy to get a good view of the weeds that spring up all too quickly between the rows of onions and cabbages, and it is very apparent that most of them have un-attractive flowers. Commonest by far is chickweed, a very variable plant which, as it never ceases to blossom, can produce several successive crops in a year. It has been used as a vegetable and is said to resemble spinach, but many of the virtues it was supposed to possess were quite imaginary. To the same natural order belongs the white campion, a rather tall perennial locally abundant in hedgerows and cultivated ground. The leaves are opposite and entire and the five showy white petals are deeply cleft into two broadly oblong lobes. Like several other white flowers that are easily visible in the fading light, they emit their fragrance in the evening to attract night-flying insects on which they rely for the transference of their pollen.

Common sowthistle is a glabrous annual with a rather thick, hollow stem and rather small flowerheads composed of yellow strap-shaped florets arranged in a flat-topped panicle. The leaves are exceedingly variable and may be either deeply divided or entire, almost smooth or very prickly.

Scentless mayweed, a spreading branched annual with dissected leaves and rather large flowerheads, somewhat resembling those of a daisy, has a very long blossoming season. It is an untidy-looking plant and the flowers are not attractive. Petty spurge is another common weed of waste and cultivated ground that blooms throughout the year. A small erect annual with rounded yellow-green leaves, its tiny flowerheads consisting of one female and several male flowers are arranged in umbels of forked rays with a pair of floral leaves at each fork.

A ditch is likely to border the allotments on one side or the other. If so, persicaria may be looked for near the water. The dense oblong spikes of small reddish-green flowers and the broadish pointed leaves with a dark spot in the centre make it difficult to believe that this tall plant is closely allied to the knotgrass, a branched wiry annual that usually grows prostrate on the ground. Instead of being rather broad, the leaves are usually narrow; the flowers are not arranged in a showy spike but are small and inconspicuous and grow in tiny clusters in the axils of the leaves.

HEDGE-BANK FLOWERS

Before we enter the town, the rough untidy hedge-bank previously mentioned must be examined. Selfheal is sure to be there for it is exceedingly common, and the rich purple of its tiny blossoms and the reddish-brown of its oddly shaped bracts are familiar to most people. Exceedingly hardy, it blooms tirelessly over a long flowering period and the small flowers arranged in short dense heads are visited by bees in search of honey. It was formerly credited with wonderful curative powers and was used to heal all manner of ills. White deadnettle, a coarse hairy perennial, is probably not far away, covering bare patches of ground with its branching stems and whorls of white flowers. The corolla tube is curved upwards and the upper lip is long and arched. Very hardy, it too has a very long flowering season. Similar conditions suit the requirements of hedge woundwort, a tall coarsely hairy perennial with a strong disagreeable smell. The dark green ovate leaves are toothed and pointed and the deep reddish purple blossoms are arranged in whorls forming long terminal spikes.

Near-by three species of speedwell may be looked for. Procumbent speedwell and thyme-leaved speedwell both have inconspicuous flowers, but germander speedwell, sometimes erroneously called "eyebright," is one of the loveliest of all British flowers. Its dainty creeping stems and its skyblue blossoms veined with darker blue have inspired many poets to sing its praises, and it has ever been referred to as the "loveliest flower that grew in flower-loved England."

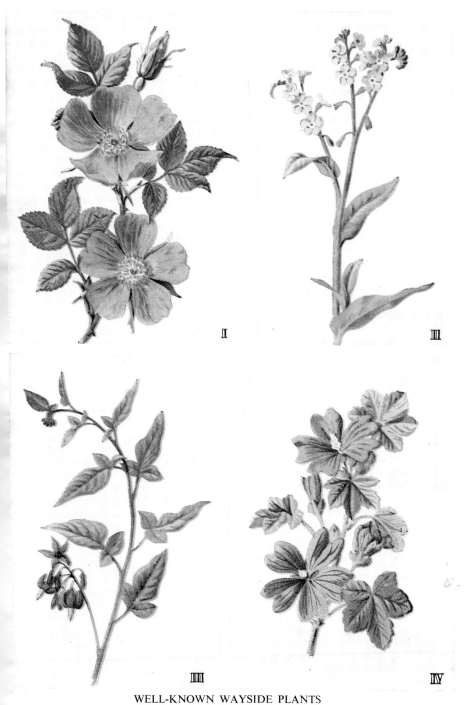

WELL-KNOWN WAYSIDE PLANTS

Dog-rose (I); *forget-me-not* (II); *woody nightshade* (III); *and common mallow* (IV).

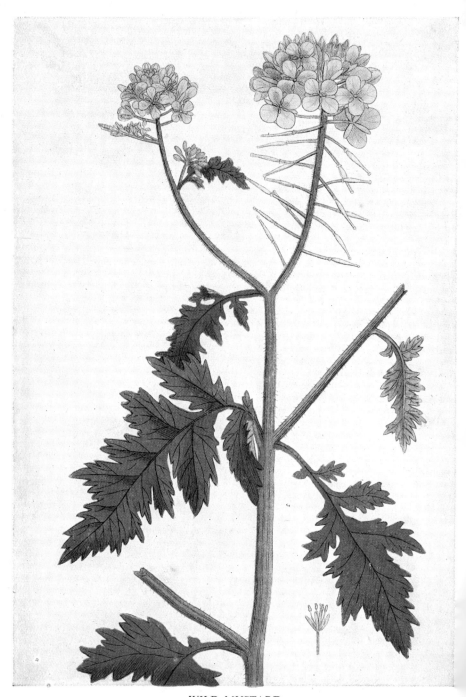

WILD MUSTARD
Commonly known as charlock this plant is a troublesome weed on cultivated ground

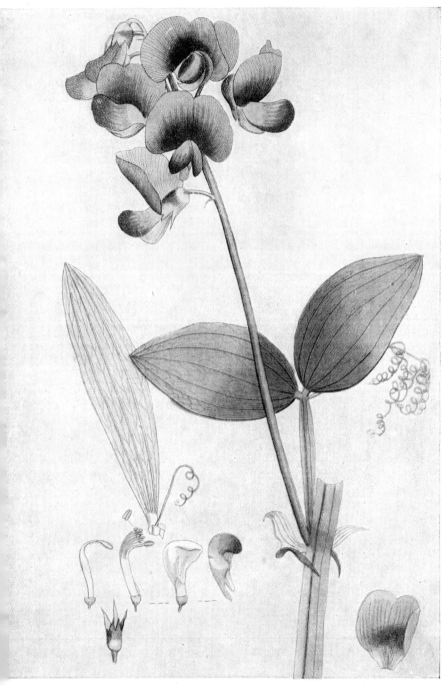

BROAD-LEAVED EVERLASTING PEA

escape from cultivation, this plant is sometimes found growing in waste places.

FIELD AND MEADOW PLANTS

Above are seen field scabious (I); *poppy* (II); *cornflower* (III); *and groundsel* (I

FIELD AND MEADOW FLOWERS

by

CHARLES A. HALL, F.R.M.S.

"FIELD" as used here describes an area of cultivated ground in which corn, root-crops or other crops are grown. The meadow is an area of grass-land used for cattle-grazing or in production of hay. Pastures are meadows entirely used for cattle-grazing.

In cultivated ground, man tries to get rid of vegetation he does not want in order to provide for growth of plants of economic value. The native plants he tries to annihilate and calls weeds are not too easily disposed of; they stage some sort of come-back, trying to reoccupy the ground from which they have been ousted. Thus some weeds of cultivated fields are species trying to reoccupy lost territory. But many of the weeds of cultivation are aliens, having followed man in the wake of his agriculture. So long have many of them been with us that they are frequently looked upon as natives but sometimes they have been introduced with seed from overseas. Most of these weeds of cultivation are annuals completing the cycle of their existence in a single season and depending upon production of seed for their continuance. There is an old saying, 'One year's seeding, seven years' weeding". Perennial plants have little chance in cultivated fields, for the plough plays havoc with their rootstocks from which new growth emerges year by year. The smaller weeds of the field usually get to work early in the season, before they are likely to be overshadowed and choked by the growing crops. Those of taller growth can afford to be later in their activities, being able to compete with the growing crops in the fierce and perpetual struggle for light and air.

An alien weed of cultivation long established in this country is corn marigold. The specific name *segetum* means "sown" and indicates a weed of cultivated fields. The species has not extended its range beyond the corn field or nearby ground. It is an attractive plant bearing compound flowerheads of many small florets closely compacted on one level—flowers of the Daisy order, Compositae. Two kinds of florets occur in each head, all golden yellow. In the centre are tubular florets with male and female organs forming the disk; around this are spreading ray florets, strap-shaped, minus stamens. The complete head is about one and a half inches across. The stem is twelve to eighteen inches high, branched, with oblong undivided leaves above and deeply-lobed stalked leaves below: leaves smooth, with a bluish-green (glaucous) hue. This species is an annual, flowering June-October, in some seasons more common than in others. It is easily recognized as it resembles a single chrysanthemum. The ox-eyed daisy, otherwise moon daisy, horse-gowan, dog-daisy or marguerite, is a closely related species. It is a common, conspicuous perennial able to flourish on very poor soil and often invades cultivated fields. The flowering season is from June-August, flowerheads being up to two inches across, with central tubular disk florets and strap-shaped white rays. The stem is usually about two feet high, although the height varies according to soil and situation, and the leaves are dark-green.

Another Composite abounding in cornfields is corn sow-thistle. It competes with corn in height, for it may reach anything from eighteen inches to four or five feet. The yellow, quite handsome flowerheads, perhaps two inches across, occur in clusters terminating the stems; they consist entirely of strap-shaped florets (like the dandelion), each complete with stamens and pistils. The stem is angled and hollow, and the leaves are toothed and wavy, those lowest on the stem lance-shaped, sometimes lobed, the upper ones clasping the stem at their bases. The seeds are crowned with silky hairs (a pappus), and are readily dispersed by wind. This species is perennial, flowering August-September.

In flower practically all the year, groundsel is one of the commonest weeds of cultivated ground. It hardly needs description, but we should note that it is a Composite with flowerheads loosely clustered at the ends of the stem and branches. The head consists mainly of tubular disk florets, those of the ray are short and often absent. The seed i crowned with a pappus, and is dispersed by the wind.

Coltsfoot sometimes invades fields and meadows, although it abounds mostly on waste ground and banks where the soi is poor and heavy. Once established, it i difficult to get rid of, for it has vigorou underground stems so deeply set tha the ploughshare generally misses them and a small bit of a stem left in the ground is able to produce a strong plant Its flower-bearing stalks emerge from rooting nodes of the underground stem as early as February or March. A pecu liarity of this species is that its flower appear before its leaves. This is for tunate, for the later canopy of rathe large leaves would smother any flower

COLTSFOOT. *A plant o the Composite family coltsfoot is a perennia with a thick and tenaciou rootstock from whic leaves and flowers spring The former are broadl heart-shaped with out standing veins, and ar leathery on the uppe surface and downy on th under surface. The stem supporting the flowers ar covered with small bu elongated scales; th flower itself is brigh yellow. The seeds ar crowned with down an are wind-borne. A featur of this plant is that it flowers appear, in the earl spring months, before th leaves. At one time, colts foot was believed to hav curative powers in ches complaints and was use in medicine; herbalist still employ it for thi purpose, and the plant i also used in the manu facture of herbal tobaccos*

OX-EYE DAISY

POPPIES. *Abundant in cornfields, the scarlet flowers of the wild poppy are borne on slender, bristly stalks; the grey-green leaves are deeply divided.*

appearing at the same time. The bright-yellow flowerheads, about an inch across, are attractive, each consisting of tubular disk florets with pollen-bearing stamens and many strap-shaped ray florets in several rows, with pistils only. The seed is crowned with a hairy pappus. The flowerstalk is seldom more than eight inches high, lengthening and becoming slender as seeds are matured. On their undersides the leaves are covered with woolly hairs which used to be employed as tinder, and a tobacco was made from the leaves. Coltsfoot is esteemed by herbalists as a remedy for lung troubles. Another Composite of cultivated fields is stinking mayweed, an annual flowering June-September, from six to twelve inches high. The leaves are doubly pinnate, deeply cut with narrow segments, and *smooth*. The daisy-like flowerheads, about an inch across, have yellow disk florets and white, neuter, strap-shaped rays. The receptacle, something resembling a pincushion, to which the florets are attached, is convex, lengthening as the head develops. The smell is offensive. This plant is common in the south, it thins out to the north, and is rare in Scotland.

PINK FAMILY

Growing to a height of one or two feet or more, the corn cockle competes with growing corn without being smothered. It is an alien annual, of the Pink family, flowering July-August, more frequent in some seasons than in others. An attractive plant of erect growth, it has long, narrow, opposite leaves and solitary flowers, from one and a half to two inches across, on long leafless stalks. The five woolly calyx teeth protrude beyond the five reddish-purple petals.

Also of the Pink family, seen in flowe from June to August in fields, pasture and waste places, is bladder campion o white-bottle. This is a native, one t three feet high, with stem branched nea the base, swollen at the nodes, an opposite oblong pointed leaves covere with bluish bloom. There are clusters c many white flowers, about three-quarte of an inch across, sweet-scented at nigh

alyx is five-cleft with network of veins, inflated; petals (five) are deeply notched.

Lesser bindweed or field convolvulus is an easily identified troublesome weed of the fields. It is perennial, with slender creeping roots difficult to eradicate, and twining stems apt to weaken or destroy other plants in their stranglehold. The leaves are arrow-shaped at base, egg-shaped, pointed. The flowers are about one and one-eighth inches across, trumpet-like, light-pink or whitish. This species is common in England, particularly in the south but rarely found in many parts of Scotland.

To the artist's eye, the rich scarlet of poppies mingled with yellowing corn is a rich feast, but the farmer abhors them. Poppies are easily recognized, yet those of the field are aliens. Two species are common with us, both annuals flowering through the summer. First we have the field or common red poppy. This species attains a height of one or two feet and is covered with stiff hairs. The scarlet flowers have a dark eye: the seed vessel is *globular* and smooth. This occurs commonly in England and Ireland, but is local in Scotland where it seems mainly to be replaced by the long-headed poppy, which is usually more slender with more deeply-cut leaves and smaller flowers. It is readily known by its *oblong* seed vessel.

Another alien weed of cultivation established in Britain, but rare in the far north of Scotland, is fool's parsley. It is poisonous, and its common name suggests that only a fool would eat it. This is an umbellate plant, of the Parsley family, bearing small flowers on stalks rising from a common centre like the supporting ribs of an umbrella. It is a leafy annual, erect, one to two feet high; the leaves are two or three times pinnate with slender segments; bright-green, their stalks sheath the stem. The inflorescence is a compound umbel of eight to ten rays on long stalks, each ray bearing umbel of white flowers, with two or three linear drooping bracts on the outside of the cluster. These bracts are a feature, and also is the objectionable smell when the plant is crushed.

Plants of the order Cruciferae (literally "cross-bearers") have four sepals and four petals arranged after the manner of a Maltese cross. This extensive order includes valuable vegetables, such as cabbages, turnips, water-cress, etc. As weeds of cultivation we have field cabbage or navew and charlock or wild mustard. Possibly cultivated turnips and rape have been developed from varieties of field cabbage. It is an upright annual one to two feet high; the lower leaves are green with a slight bluish tinge (glaucous) more or less lobed or wavy with a large terminal lobe and rough hairs. The stem leaves are smooth, pointed, variable narrow-oblong, heart-shaped or lance shaped, always clasping the stem at their bases, which are eared. The flowers are yellow about half an inch across. Charlock is a pest—a coarse plant, one to two feet high with some stiff hairs on the branched stem. The lower leaves are rough with short hairs, generally with a large coarsely-toothed oval terminal segment and smaller lobes along the stalk. Upper leaves are stalked, oblong or lance-shaped. There are lemon-yellow flowers, over half an inch across. The seed pod is up to an inch and a half long ending in a stout beak one-third of its length. Another alien Crucifer found in fields and waste places is the intriguing penny cress named after its round flattened pods suggestive of a coin. These pods are about half an inch across the fruit of small white flowers occurring in clusters which lengthen as the fruit develops. The whole plant is smooth.

COWSLIP. *The drooping bell-shaped rich yellow flowers of the cowslip rise from wrinkled, pale-green leaves*

FIELD CHAMOMILE

with a slight bluish bloom, one to two feet high. The stalked root-leaves soon perish; the stem leaves are oblong, those above clasp the stem and are eared at the base. Not common, the species is sometimes called mithridate mustard. It flowers in spring and summer.

The Borage family is known by its spirally-coiled or scorpoid inflorescence, with flowers usually blue; by its four-seed fruit, and unsegmented leaves and juicy stems covered with rough hairs. The leaves of borage are used for flavouring claret-cup, and from alkanet a dye is extracted. An outstanding, quite handsome species with us is viper's bugloss, with stout stems bristling with hairs, one to three feet high, and narrow tapering leaves with short and long bristles. The flowers are showy; first they are reddish, later becoming bright blue. The stamens protrude from the corolla tube, and at the base of each flower there is a bract. This plant is found in waste places, etc., especially on chalky soils; it is rare in north Scotland. A weed of cultivation in this family is field bugloss, an annual with angular branches, straggling bristly stem, four to fourteen or more inches high. The bright-blue flowers, about a quarter of an inch across, are funnel-shaped, the corolla being invariably bent or humped. This species flowers June-July. Forget-me-nots are of the same family, and as a weed of the field we have the yellow- and blue-forget-me-not, or scorpion grass. This is a small hairy plant flowering in the spring, distinguished from other forget-me-nots by its corolla which is

FORGET-ME-NOT. *This plant belongs to the Scorpion grass family—a name derived from the shape its flower stalks assume when the plant blossoms. The flowers, which appear in early summer, are light blue with a yellow eye; the leaves are smooth.*

pale yellow on expanding but later turns blue.

Fumitory, an annual flowering nearly all the year round, is a rather engaging weed of fields and waste places. At first it forms a tuft, later the stem reaches one to three feet, trailing on the ground or weakly climbing. It has much divided pale-green leaves, somewhat fernlike, and short racemes of small tubular rose-coloured flowers tipped with purple. There are two sepals, and six petals in unequal pairs; the five stamens occur in two equal bundles. Herbalists use the plant as a remedy for stomach disorders. The name is from *fumus*, the smoke of the burning plant being said by our superstitious forebears to drive out evil spirits.

DEAD NETTLES

Plants of the Labiate order have clear features—square stems and branches, opposite leaves, flowers with two-lipped corollas generally growing in whorls in the axils of the leaves, fruits of four little nuts. In cultivated ground we have a very common species, red deadnettle, a long-established alien flowering April-October. The flowers are dull rose colour, about three-quarters of an inch long, crowded in whorls at the top of the stem which has short-stalked egg-shaped or heart-shaped upper leaves suggesting those of nettles, but not stinging. The common hemp-nettle of the same family, is abundant in fields and waste-places—an annual flowering July-September, which may be quite dwarf, but if well-nourished may grow to about two feet. The stem breaks into spreading branches, all rough with stiff hairs, as are the egg-shaped toothed leaves. The flowers are two-lipped, pinkish or whitish in whorls, those at the top of the stem being crowded. There is a variety called *versicolor* with attractive yellow flowers which have a purple spot on the lower lip. Closely related is the red hemp-nettle, an annual not so common but frequent in

BINDWEED. *Bindweed climbs to light and air by twisting round other plants; flowers are white or tinged with pink.*

GOAT'S BEARD. *Goat's beard (left) which belongs to the Composite family, is found fairly commonly in meadows and waste open spaces in England, though more rarely in Scotland and Ireland. Its curious name is suggested by the stiff, hairy head crowning each seed; but it is also known as "John-go-to-bed-at-noon" because the flowers are in the habit of closing about midday. Goat's beard is a biennial and has a rootstock similar to that of a parsnip. The long, curling leaves, somewhat like grass in appearance, have no stalks, and at the base of the plant clasp the main stem. Each flower is borne on a separate, slender stalk; the involucre bracts show distinctly, being larger than the yellow ray florets. The flowering season is in the months of June and July.*

southern England. It is not as robust as the common hemp-nettle, nor as hairy: the flowers are purple, six or more occurring in close whorls in the leaf axils of the upper stem. Other Labiates of the field are corn mint and corn woundwort. Corn mint is a rather variable perennial flowering July-September. Annual stems grow from a creeping rootstock to six or twelve inches. The habit of the plant is usually low and spreading. Lilac flowers are densely clustered in the axils of the leaves, and unlike other species of mint, the terminal leaves have no or very few flowers in their axils. The odour is unpleasing. Corn woundwort is a weed of cultivation, fairly common in England, but rare

in Scotland. The weak stem is prostrate, but produces erect flower spikes. Small pinkish and white-spotted two-lipped flowers occur two to six in the axils of the leaves. This is a humble relative of the unpleasantly smelling hedge woundwort conspicuous in waste places, hedges and woods.

The buttercup thriving best in cultivated ground is the creeping buttercup or crowfoot, easily identified by runners which root at every node, forming new plants. A native of the fields is the scarlet pimpernel, known by its little, attractive bright-red flowers which only expand in sunshine—hence a common name, "poor man's weather-glass". It is of the Primrose family. Field-madder, a member of the Bedstraw family, is also noted. Its numerous square hairy stems, three to six inches, bear narrow pointed hairy leaves in distinct whorls of four to six. The lilac flowers, about an eighth of an inch across, are stalkless and compacted into flat, round clusters. This plant is quite common, flowering May-October. Lastly, as a flower of the field, as well as of hill pastures, we have hearts-ease, or wild pansy, easily known by its pansy-like flowers. The numerous cultivated varieties of pansy are said to have been developed from this species, which is subject to much variation.

Turning particularly to the flora of meadows, we find this depends upon the nature of soil and subsoil, moisture and other conditions. We almost involuntarily associate buttercups and daisies with the meadow. The common daisy, literally day's-eye, is known to everyone. Flowering almost the year round it is most vigorous in spring, when it may carpet some meadows. It is a Composite with yellow disk florets and strap-like white rays, the latter red-tipped on their undersides. Two buttercups abound in meadows, bulbous buttercup, distinguished by a bulb-like thickening at its base and by its sepals which, when the flower is expanded, are turned back on

SCABIOUS. *Two types of scabious are to be found in Britain—field scabious and devil's bit scabious, illustrated on the right. The name refers to its short rootstock, which has the appearance of being bitten off short. This plant is found in pastures and on the light soil of heathland, and is generally quite prolific. The flowering season is from July to October, and the blooms are purplish-blue or, occasionally, white. The chief difference between the devil's bit scabious and the field scabious is that the flowers of the former are slightly domed, while those of the latter are flat. Both types of scabious mentioned already are of the Teasel family, but sheep's-bit scabious, which may also be found on heaths, is of the Campanula family.*

RED CLOVER. *Common red clover is found in meadows and pastures as a wild plant, but it is frequently grown as a fodder plant. The oval leaflets are marked by a distinctive crescent-shaped white band, while the purplish-red flowerheads are globular.*

the stalk; and the common meadow buttercup or crowfoot. The bulbous buttercup, with its furrowed stem, is seldom more than a foot high; but meadow crowfoot, in good soil, may be two to three feet high; its stems and stalks are hairy, but not furrowed. The bright yellow flowers are about one inch across, terminating stems and branches, and appearing in showy clusters which catch the eye. The creeping buttercup is also a meadow plant.

COWSLIPS

Cowslip or paigle is a primrose of sorts, flowering April-May. In some English meadows it is abundant, but it is localized and uncommon in Scotland. It is distinguished from the common primrose by its smaller and much less spreading flowers which occur in umbels with a drooping tendency. Yellow, they have an orange spot at the base of the corolla lobes, and are sweet-scented. The flowers are used for making wine, and herbalists say the plant is a remedy for insomnia.

Goat's-beard is a biennial Composite with large solitary heads of many yellow strap-shaped florets terminating stem and branches one to two feet high. The leaves are narrow, resembling grass; the stem yields a milky juice. Seeds are crowned with a pappus and the attractive seed-heads are about three inches across. The plant is said to close at noon —hence the popular name, Jack-go-to-bed-at-noon. The hawkbits are Composites with heads of yellow strap-shaped florets borne on leafless stalks rising from the root. The outer florets are often greenish or reddish underneath.

Rough hawkbit has solitary heads fully an inch across, with stalks woolly or hairy, six inches to more than a foot long. The leaves are deeply lobed, the lobes pointing to the base. This perennial flowers June-September. Flowering later (August-September), autumnal hawkbit is a common perennial with branched stalks, six to eighteen inches, bearing a number of heads erect in bud. The stalks are swollen under flowers and the leaves are either deeply segmented or simply toothed, slightly hairy on the undersides of the ribs. Another Composite of meadows is yarrow or milfoil, used by herbalists as a tonic and stimulant. The perennial rootstock produces barren leafy stems to about twelve inches, and other leafy flowering stems, with clustered heads of florets. The clusters are conspicuous, but a separated head is hardly more than a quarter of an inch across; it has pinkish or white tubular disk florets with yellow anthers and a few white or pink ray florets minus stamens. The leaves grow alternately and are feathery, deeply cut.

Scabiouses bear little flowers clustered in conspicuous heads. They are not, however, Composites, but of the Teasel family. Field scabious is handsome and might be mistaken for a cultivated variety. Flowering July-September, it thrives best on chalky soils, but is common elsewhere. Attractive lilac flowers form flattish heads up to an inch and a half across, the outer radiating flowers, with unequal corolla lobes, being the larger. In good soil the plant may be two or three feet high. Devil's-bit scabious, said to have had its rootstock bitten short spitefully by the devil, abounds in pastures and heaths, flowering July-October. Purplish-blue and occasionally white flowers form clustered *round* heads, about three-quarters of an inch across, terminating long stalks. The corolla lobes are *equal*.

Stitchworts, once supposed to cure the stitch, are of the Pink family, bearing

BUTTERFLY ORCHIS. *The flowers of this plant are white, tinged with green.*

star-like white flowers in forked clusters. They have five-pointed sepals, five deeply-cleft petals. A common meadow species is lesser stitchwort. The smooth four-angled stems, one to three feet long, bear narrow, smooth, stalkless, pointed leaves and produce numerous flowers about a quarter of an inch across. This is a perennial, flowering May-August.

In dry pastures we may see field gentian, not showy like some Alpine species, yet attractive—a little plant, three to ten inches high, with oblong-ovate, pointed, opposite leaves with uncut margins, and purplish-blue flowers about half an inch across, three-quarters of an inch long. The corolla is a four-cleft tube with a fringe of bluish hairs in its throat. The calyx is four-lobed, the two outer lobes being larger and broader than the two inner. This is an annual, flowering July-October.

PLANTS OF PEA FAMILY

Plants of the Pea family have seeds in pods and flowers with five irregular petals resembling a butterfly. The upper petal is the "standard", two side petals are the "wings", and the two lower petals are joined to form the "keel". In the meadow, frequent in England, especially on chalky soil, we have the horse-shoe vetch, flowering May-August. The pale-yellow flowers, about half an inch long, occur in umbels of five to ten. This species is distinguished from vetches in general by its seed-pods of several joints, each joint curved as a horse-shoe. Meadow pea, or vetchling, has weak, branched, smooth, angled stems which straggle or feebly climb. The leaves are divided into a pair of lance-shaped pointed leaflets and end in a simple or branched tendril. Bright yellow flowers borne on long stalks occur in clusters of three to ten. The seed-pods are rather long, flat, many-seeded. Black medick or nonsuch has dense heads of small yellow flowers and leaves split

into three leaflets. Resembling a small clover, it is identified by kidney-shaped one-seeded black pods. Hop trefoil is a slender prostrate plant rather like black medick; but clearly recognized by its head of withered flowers resembling hops. White or dutch clover has creeping stems rooting at the joints and long-stalked leaves split into three leaflets, often with a white band across them. The white or pinkish flowers are about half an inch long, and compacted in a dense head at end of a long stalk. Lesser yellow trefoil or clover resembles hop trefoil, but is a smaller, less robust plant. Its flowers are deep yellow, dark-brown when faded, occurring in heads of not more than twenty, often many less, the heads terminating long stalks. It is a common species, flowering June-August. Purple or red clover is the clover of the meadow, valuable in the hay crop. Purplish, sweet-scented flowers occur in roundish-oblong heads and produce abundant nectar much sought by bees. This is a robust species growing up to two feet high, and flowering all summer.

Vetches are of the Pea family. They have weak stems and often climb feebly by means of tendrils. The leaves are cut to the mid rib into leaflets and have partly arrow-shaped stipules at their bases. The common vetch is found wild as an escape from cultivation. The flowers are stalk-less, growing in pairs or solitary, about one inch long, with a lilac standard and purple wings. Spring vetch occurs in dry sites and is not common. Its stems are prostrate, spreading, about six inches long. The leaves are divided into two to four pairs of leaflets and the solitary, stalkless flowers, about a quarter of an inch long, are purple. This is an annual, flowering April-May.

In barren pastures or on sandy shores and heaths is found rest-harrow. It assumes various forms, sometimes erect, often a spreading undershrub, much branched, rooting at its nodes. The

FIELD OF PRIMROSES. *Primroses are found both on sheltered hedge-banks and in open fields. The flower stalks join a main stem hidden among the tufted leaves.*

leaves are split into three-toothed leaflets, often sticky. The pink flowers occur singly in the axils of the leaves. The pod is swollen, with two or three seeds, and the roots are long and tough. Rest-harrow is in flower .June-September.

Orchids are always interesting.

Tropical species grow on stems and branches of trees, but British species all root in the soil and produce small flowers in spikes. A feature of orchids is the pollen-mass which is detached when an insect visits a flower and becomes glued to its head. The insect carries it to another flower, effecting cross-pollination. The butterfly orchis is fairly common in moist meadows, flowering June-July. The stem may be a foot high; at its base it has two oblong leaves. The relatively large, white flowers, sometimes tinged with green, form a loose spike some inches long. Towards evening they emit a sweet fragrance. Spotted orchis is common, flowering in the spring and early summer. The root consists of flattened tubers divided into two or three finger-like lobes. The leaves, varying from lance- to egg-shaped are marked with dark spots. About twelve inches high, the flowering stem bears a dense spike of flowers about two or three inches long. The flowers vary in depth of colour, they may be lilac or white, with purple lines and spots.

PLANTAINS

Plantains abound in meadows, the most abundant being fibwort plantain called by children "cocks-and-hens". Everybody knows this plant with its long lance-shaped ribbed leaves and long angular stalks terminated by short, dense spikes of flowers with protruding stamens. A second species is greater plantain or waybread with broad leaves and long spikes of flowers producing seeds appreciated by canaries. The hoary plantain favours limestone and chalky soils, but appears elsewhere. Its egg-shaped unstalked leaves generally press, rosette-like on the ground. The long stalk bears a dense cylindrical spike of flowers, one to two inches long with the protruding pinkish or purple stamens. This, perhaps, is the most attractive of our plantains.

Common sorrel has leaves with a pleasant acid taste which adds piquancy to a salad. It is known in Scotland as sourocks. This is a plant of slender growth with stems up to two feet and spikes of small red-green flowers. Sheep's sorrel is a closely related plant, a few

inches to a foot high, with narrow lance-shaped leaves, most of them barbed at the base. It favours dry pastures, and becomes tinged with red as it matures.

Lady's mantle is of the Rose family but quite unlike the rose as usually thought of. It grows to about six inches high and has large, attractive soft leaves scalloped into several serrated lobes. Numerous small yellowish-green flowers occur in loose clusters. The old folk used to think the leaves resembled a suitable mantle for Our Lady.

UMBELLIFEROUS PLANTS

A conspicuous umbellate of the meadow is cow-parsnip. It is of stout growth, attaining a height from eighteen inches to upwards of six feet, according to nutrient conditions. The stem is furrowed, hollow, branched at the top. In the early stages of their growth, the flower buds are contained in a sheath at the base of the leaves. Small white flowers are clustered in spreading compound umbels. The plant is said by some to be poisonous, but rabbits enjoy it. An umbellate of lesser growth, common in dry pastures is burnet saxifrage—a slender perennial in season from July to September, with leaves rising from a stout rootstock. The leaves are cut to the midrib into four to eight opposite, roundish, toothed leaflets and there is one terminal leaflet. There are a few stem leaves. The height of the plant is from ten inches or so to two or three feet. There are compound umbels of white or pinkish flowers.

Yellow-rattle or cock's-comb is interesting because it has developed partial parasitism, securing some nourishment from roots of grasses. It is an erect, stiff plant with wiry four-sided stems, four to twelve inches high, and opposite toothed oblong pointed leaves. Yellow two-lipped flowers with inflated calyces terminate the stem in leafy clusters. The seeds rattle in their dry swollen capsule.

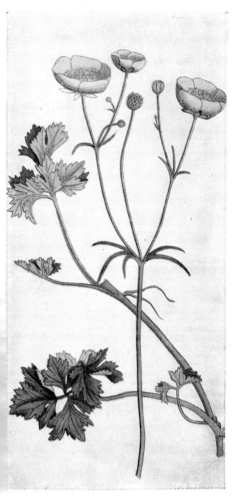

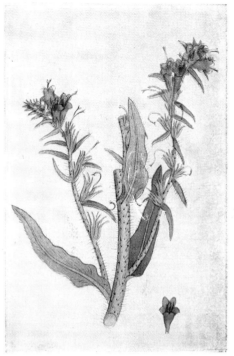

BUTTERCUP, VIPER'S BUGLOSS AND RED DEADNETTLE

One of the most familiar of all wild flowers the buttercup (above) grows on every type of soil. The variety illustrated is known as the creeping buttercup because it gives off runners which root at the nodes and develop into new plants. Red deadnettle (lower right) is also a common wild plant. Viper's bugloss (upper right), found on roadsides and waste places, is a plant with handsome purplish-blue flowers. Leaves and stem are covered with hairs.

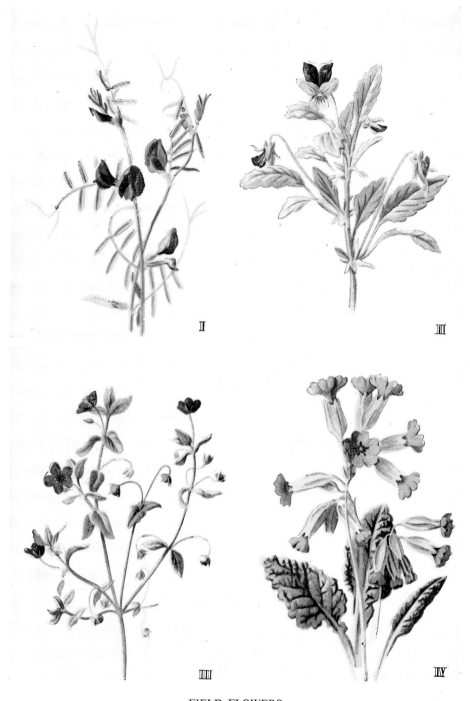

FIELD FLOWERS

Seen above are vetch (I)*; heartsease* (II)*; scarlet pimpernel* (III)*; and cowslip* (IV).

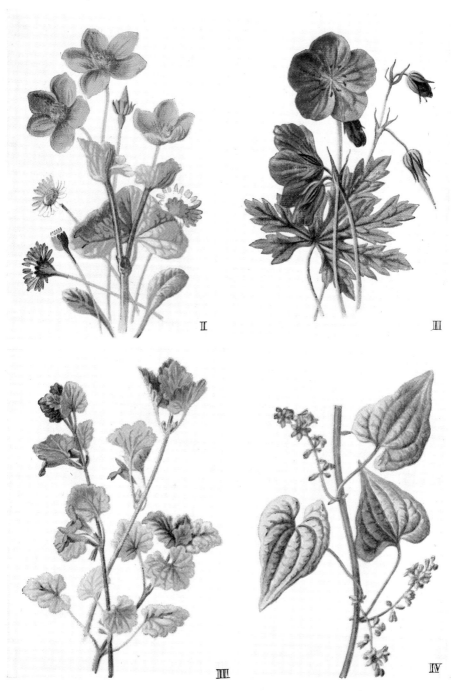

COMMON WILD FLOWERS

Marsh marigold and daisy (I); *crane's bill* (II); *ground ivy* (III); *black bryony* (IV).

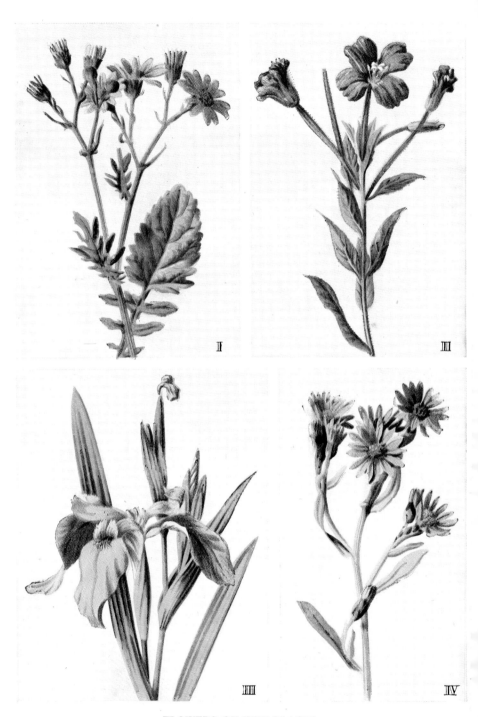

FLOWERS OF WET PLACES

Water ragwort (I); *great willow herb* (II); *yellow iris* (III); *and sea aster* (IV).

FLOWERS OF WET PLACES

by

F. MAKINS

IN wet places—about the only parts of Britain preserving their original character—plants form natural communities, which reach their climax without interference. Take, for instance, a vacant stretch of mud or silt and notice how it is gradually colonized by various species until saturation is reached.

Now lean over the parapet of a bridge and look into a river. One may see long green streamers waving with the current. The leaves are literally streamlined; they may be broad or thread-like, according to the species. The stems may be long thin cables to take the strain of the water, or may grow erect from the river bottom, swaying to and fro in the current. If, when pulled out of the water, the leaves have a greasy texture like oiled paper, the principal veins being prominent and hard, the plant probably belongs to the genus Potamogeton, or pondweed. The flowers of the pondweeds are not exciting. They are in small greenish clusters on the ends of stout stalks arising from the angles of the leaves with the stem and appear from June onward; in the centre are four seed-bodies called carpels, producing a fruit of four seed-like nuts.

Other entirely submerged plants are the Canadian pondweed, water milfoil and varieties of water starwort. The Canadian pondweed is not a native of Britain. It was first seen in 1847 in Yorkshire, Leicestershire and near Berwick-on-Tweed; since then it has spread all over the country and threatens to choke our waterways. The plant is anchored to the bottom by its roots and sends up masses of leafy stems, the leaves being small, narrow and crowded along the stem in pairs or threes. The flowers are peculiar. There are two kinds, male and female. Look at a colony in July and note the long white threads among the leaves. At the end of each is a minute transparent greenish purple flower. These are the females. The white thread is not a stalk but the elongated base of the flower. The males are without this long base and therefore less noticeable.

COMMON POND PLANTS

Water milfoil and starwort are closely related, though very different in appearance. Both are common in ponds, ditches and shallow slow-moving streams. Water milfoil consists of feathery tufts attached to long streamers. A close inspection of a tuft will show it to be made up of three to five leaves radiating from the stem and cut into fine segments. The flowers appear in June and continue till August. They are green and very small, arranged in clusters at regular intervals on a leafless stem projecting half out of the water; in fact, they occupy the position that the leaves would under the water.

As for water starwort, bright green masses of it can be seen in practically every pond and stream. The masses or tufts are made up of individual stems bearing small leaves in pairs. The leaves on or near the surface are broader and arranged in rosettes. These rosettes act as floating buoys supporting the submerged stems in an upright position. Some varieties are wholly submerged and do not end in floating rosettes. The flowers are of two sexes and very peculiar. The male consists of a single stamen at the end of a slender filament; the female of a stalkless four-angled seed body with two long appendages to catch the floating pollen. One variety sprawls over wet mud well out of the water.

Rather like water starwort from a short distance, but less common, is water blinks, which makes dense green masses in water or on wet mud. The surface leaves never make a rosette. The flowers are small and white, in the angles of the upper leaves; they have two sepals, five petals and three stamens, and are related to the garden Portulaca.

Everyone has noticed how in early spring the surface of so many rivers and ponds is starred with thousands of pretty white flowers. This is the water crowfoot. In it the difference between the floating and submerged leaves is greater than in water starwort. The floating leaves are divided into broad lobes, the submerged into narrow threads. In some varieties the floating leaves are absent. It is then possible to mistake the plant for a pond-weed—until it flowers.

The queen of all floating plants is the white water lily. Far commoner is the yellow water lily. The broad flat leaves floating on the surface of still water are well known. They are attached to rubbery stalks that wind about under the surface, allowing the leaves to rise or fall with changes in the water level. The flowers of the white kind float on the water; those of the yellow project some inches above it, on stiff stalks.

Floating or broad-leaved pondweed has the habit of a water lily, though the leaves are smaller and not so broad. They make a pretty mosaic on still water. Unlike the other pondweeds the leaves are thick and opaque. In summer, numerous spikes of small greenish flowers stick up between the leaves.

BOG PIMPERNEL. *Below are seen the starry flowers of the bog pimpernel. The petals are pale pink, and the flowers are borne on long, slender stalks. These in turn, rise from the creeping main stem which is crowded with small, circular leaves.*

YELLOW IRIS

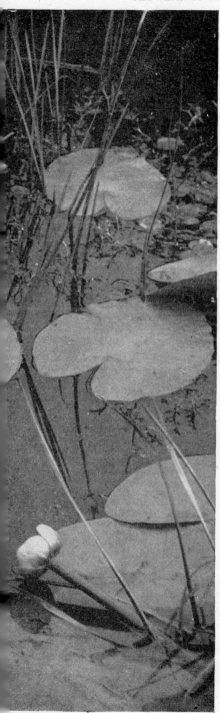

YELLOW WATER LILY. *Found on ponds and rivers, the heart-shaped floating leaves of this water-plant are thick and leathery; the flower sepals are yellow.*

Swans are fond of the roots and for that reason are often mistakenly given credit for keeping ponds and lakes free of weed growth.

Then there is the frogbit with leaves like those of a small water lily. The flowers have three semi-transparent petals like white tissue paper. It is locally common in water channels though not widely distributed. The floating leaves of persicaria are a good deal longer than broad, and shaped like spear-heads. In summer pink flower-spikes project above the water. A peculiarity of this plant is its ability to thrive equally well on land, when it becomes a troublesome weed in reclaimed alluvial soil.

INSECT-EATING PLANT

Anyone who is lucky enough to see a small cluster of rich yellow flowers sticking out of the water and rather like a snap-dragon in shape will have found one of the few insect-eating plants. The leaves are all submerged and finely divided. Attached to them are little bladders, provided with trap doors opening inwards. Small insects find their way in but cannot get out. They die inside the bladder, and are gradually absorbed by the plant. This is the bladderwort. It has no roots and so cannot absorb mineral salts from the soil; instead it gets them from the bodies of small insects and crustaceans. It is found in stagnant ditches and ponds, and flowers in July and August.

Despite its popular name, the water violet is not a violet, but related to the primulas. The leaves are all submerged and finely divided like the water milfoil. From April onward pale lilac flowers appear above the water in whorls on an erect leafless stem. If seeds are sown

WATER VIOLETS. *The water violet, despite its name, is related to the primula family. The finely-divided leaves are submerged, but in early spring leafless stalks bearing the delicate lilac-coloured flowers, appear above the water.*

when ripe in a pond, the new plants will rise above the water the following spring.

Though superficially resembling a green scum, the duckweeds are composed of countless small floating leaves, with root-like filaments hanging from the lower side. The duckweeds are the smallest plants with true flowers, which however, are rarely seen. They sometimes appear on the edge or upper side of the leaf; there are no petals, merely a single or at most two stamens and one seed body.

Having now dealt with practically all the submerged and floating plants likely to be recognized, let us turn our attention to those plants with the greater part of their structure above water-level. The bulrush has tall green leafless stems up to

eight feet high and crowned with clusters of dark brown inflorescences. Often mistakenly called bulrush, the reedmace or cat's-tail is the tall reed bearing the well-known velvety heads shaped like a narrow cylinder and ending in a point. The leaves can be used for making mats, baskets and chair seats. Bur-reed has erect sword-like leaves, with round prickly-looking heads of flowers or branched stalks. The leaves of the floating bur-reed are strap-shaped and often float on the surface; the flowering stem carrying the burrs is simple, not branched.

Next come three flowering plants of singular beauty and interest. First the flowering rush, about three feet high with long narrow leaves triangular in

UR-REED. *This water-plant has long, sword-shaped leaves. The round, prickly looking flowerheads are borne on branched stalks.*

section, and rose-pink flowers about an inch across borne in a cluster at the top of a leafless stem. Then the water plantain, which has large spear-shaped leaves and pinkish flowers about half an inch across; and third, the arrowhead with pure white flowers and arrow-shaped leaves. All three plants like to stand in water. Arrowhead's submerged leaves are reduced to a narrow strap, without the characteristic arrowhead at the end; the thick, almost bulbous, base of the stem is a favourite food of the Chinese, who cultivate the plant. They all belong to the same family, Alismaceac, which appears to be closely related to the buttercup family, Ranunculaceae. This is evident from the structure of the flowers. In the centre is a cluster of separate carpels, from underneath which the stamens spread out, while, as in the Ranunculaceae, the petals are quite separate from each other and easily detachable. Linnaeus, the great Swedish naturalist of the eighteenth century, had, in fact, given the name Alisma ranunculoides to the lesser water plantain. This differs from the commoner species in the shape of its leaves, which are much narrower—lance-heads rather than spear-heads—and is a smaller plant altogether; the flowers are large and pale purple, but fewer in number and arranged in a single cluster, not in a panicle.

Another plant which likes to stand in water is the water forget-me-not. It is hairy, but unlike the other forget-me-nots the hairs do not spread outwards but lie flat. The flowers are large for a forget-me-not and are bright blue with a yellow eye.

Water purslane creeps over wet mud

YELLOW IRIS. *Found on the banks of lakes and rivers, the yellow iris has stiff, sharp-edged leaves; two or three bright yellow flowers, which emerge from sheath-like bracts, are borne on the stalk and appear in spring and summer.*

YELLOW MONKEY MUSK

WATER PLANTAIN. *Belonging to a family which is related to that of the buttercup, the water plantain has large, spearhead-shaped leaves and pinkish flowers, arranged in panicles. Lesser water plantain has narrower leaves and purplish flowers.*

and is often found in water. Its leaves are pear-shaped, not more than half an inch long, and occur in pairs along the stem, while the minute pink flowers are tucked away in the angles of the leaves.

Watercress belongs to the cabbage family, so many of which are rich in vitamins and therefore anti-scorbutic. The thick succulent stems send out leaves alternate with each other, and each leaf is divided into about seven leaflets with toothed or wavy margins. The flowers are small, with four white petals; the pods are sausage-shaped. Sometimes confused with watercress is the marshwort, in which the leaflets are more sharply toothed. In watercress the leaflet at the end is usually larger than the others; in marshwort it is smaller.

The flowers have five petals and appear in summer along the stem and not at the end as in watercress.

Several of the speedwells take to water, best known being brooklime, the stem of which is thick and succulent, rooting in the mud as it grows. The leaves can be eaten as salad; they are oval, smooth and rather thick, in pairs along the stem; from the angles of the upper pairs groups of small but very pretty blue flowers appear in May and continue throughout the summer. Water speedwell is much the same except for its longer and narrower leaves. Marsh speedwell has still narrower leaves—almost grass-like —while the flowers are white or pink, in alternate clusters. All the speedwells have four petals, two stamens and flattish two-lobed seedpods.

Monkey musk, or monkey-flower, the seeds of which resemble the face of a grinning monkey, has showy yellow flowers, one in each of the upper leaf angles. They are two-lipped or personate, and the leaves are in opposite pairs, broadly oval and coarsely toothed.

The common rush indicates water-logged soils but is seldom found growing in water. Its leaves are reduced to a few brown scales at the base of the green stem. There are two well-marked varieties: in one the flowers are in tight globular clusters and in the other in open sprays. The green stems filled with solid pith were once used as wicks in rush-lights. The hard rush is harder and stiffer, with interrupted pith. Very common is the jointed rush, of which the flattened stem is hollow and divided by internal cross partitions. Toad rush is a small tufted plant often found in shallow rills, wet cart ruts and other damp places. The stems repeatedly fork, while the flowers are solitary in the forks or along the branches. These rushes are really degenerate lilies, the flowers being similar in structure to those of the lily family.

"Flag," says the dictionary, is "the popular name for many plants with sword-shaped leaves, mostly growing in moist situations." Sweet flag is un-fortunately not as common as it was, perhaps owing to the reclamation of

MARSH MARIGOLD. *Found in marshes and river-meadows, this plant, which is also known as kingcup, has broad, glossy heart-shaped leaves with toothed edges, which increase in size after the flowering season. The handsome flowers are bright yellow with a shining surface and appear during the spring months.*

marshes. Its leaves are crinkled on one edge and sweet-scented, which made it a favourite rush for covering and sweetening floors in the Middle Ages. The flowers are in a tight yellowish-green spike projecting from the side of a leaf. The well-known yellow flag is an iris.

REED-SWAMP COMMUNITIES

Reeds are a characteristic feature of swamps, often covering wide stretches and producing what is known as reed-swamp communities. Reedswamps are also formed by bullrushes and bur-reeds already described, and by other plants such as sedges—of which there are many species—outside the scope of this book. As deeper water is approached we may come to floating-leaf and submerged communities. An intelligent observer will soon discover for himself the nature and extent of the various communities and the conditions which produce them. The vegetation of a small pond, for instance, is particularly interesting; usually the different communities occupy concentric zones—from submerged through floating-leaf and reedswamp to marsh and land vegetation, though one or more may be absent.

When the water falls below the soil level we see a transition through marsh to terra firma. Characteristic marsh plants may spread on the one side into swamp and on the other to firm, though moist, land. Here any of the following plants may be found.

Meadow-rue grows about three feet tall and has quantities of small yellowish flowers, consisting mostly of stamens; the leaves are divided into wedge-shaped leaflets. The celery-leaved crowfoot is a buttercup with thick hollow stems. Another buttercup inhabiting wet places has narrow undivided leaves like spear-heads; this is the spearwort. The king of the marshes is the marsh marigold or king-cup. Its golden yellow flowers, like outsize buttercups, appear in March and

are over by June, though sometimes there is a second flowering in the autumn. A modest relative is the lesser celandine, common in hedgebanks in early spring. The dainty cuckoo-flower appears with the cuckoo; it is also called lady's smock and many other pretty names, and its pale lilac flowers and ladder-like leaves are familiar to everyone. Less well known is the marsh violet which has blunt sepals and round kidney-shaped leaves. Another herald of the cuckoo, the ragged robin, is a campion, belonging to the Pink family. It has pink deeply fringed petals and very narrow opposite leaves. All the campions have an urn-shaped calyx (the cup which holds the flower), five petals narrowed at the base to a claw, ten stamens and five long thread-like styles. Belonging to the same family are the stitchworts. Marsh stitchwort is a striking flower, pure white and not many on the plant; the leaves are long and narrow and covered with bluish-grey bloom. Much more common is the bog stitchwort with smaller and more numerous white flowers and shorter and broader leaves. In all the stitchworts each petal is divided almost into two so that at first it looks as if the flower had ten petals instead of five. Water stitchwort has broad leaves and five styles to its largish white flower, the others having only three styles. Rather like stitchworts are sandworts and pearlworts, but the petals are undivided; the former have three styles, the latter four or five.

ST. JOHN'S WORT

Two of the St. John's worts, related to the garden rose of Sharon, are fond of wet places. The square-stalked St. John's wort has many pretty yellow flowers on four-angled stems, each flower having a large bunch of stamens in the middle. Marsh St. John's wort grows in thick masses in standing water, often toppling over and becoming submerged; the leaves are woolly and almost circular;

MINT AND FIGWORT. *Water mint (right) has a distinctive mint smell and pale blue flowers. Water figwort (below) has small greenish-brown flowers.*

the few flowers pale yellow. Both species have their leaves dotted with transparent glands which can be seen by holding the leaves against the light.

The tall marsh mallow is first cousin to the hollyhock. The leaves are velvety and the flowers pale pink, like a single hollyhock. It is not a common plant, and favours brackish rather than fresh water.

The fragrant meadowsweet, with its panicles of creamy flowers, belongs to the Rose family, as also does the handsome water avens. Unlike the wood avens or herb bennet the flowers of the water avens droop, and are purplish and cup-shaped. Somewhat like it are the flowers of the marsh cinquefoil which, as the name indicates, has five leaflets to each leaf. Golden saxifrage is a curious little creeping plant with round leaves and greenish yellow saucer-shaped flowers. It carpets the edges of clear brooks and damp places in woods. The flowers appear very early in the year; they have four green sepals, no petals, and a ring of eight yellow stamens. In the Vosges mountains in France the plant is eaten as a salad under the name of *cresson de roche.*

The showy spikes of purple loosestrife, rising to a height of several feet, are a beautiful sight along river banks and in marshy land from July to September. The leaves are narrow, often in threes, while the flowers have four to six thin petals with a long style in the middle. Yellow loosestrife is not related; it has its narrow leaves in threes or fours but the flowers are arranged in a leafy panicle. Another showy plant of similar situations is the great hairy willow-herb or codlins-and-cream, rising sometimes to a height of six feet or more; the flowers are strikingly rose-red and have four petals, eight

BUR-MARIGOLD. *The bur-marigold is a handsome water-plant. The leaves grow from a strong, branched stem and are long, narrow and much-toothed. Their dark rich green sets off the greenish-yellow flowers which are framed in spreading bracts. A second type of bur-marigold has leaves which are divided into three.*

stamens, and a long narrow stalk-like ovary which bursts open late in the season to allow the escape of cottony seeds which are wafted away in the wind. A smaller plant altogether, with smaller flowers, is the square-stalked willow-herb; the little white stigma in the middle of the flower is club-shaped and undivided, whereas the small-flowered willow-herb has a stigma divided into a cross.

MARSH PENNYWORT

Though very common in squelchy ground, white-rot or marsh pennywort may easily escape notice, as the flowers are minute and hard to find. Its leaves are round, about the size of a penny, and borne at the end of slender stalks arising from creeping stems. As in the garden nasturtium, the stalks are attached to the middle of the underside of the leaf. This plant is sometimes unjustly blamed for causing liver-fluke in sheep.

One alone of the five common species of water dropwort deserves notice: the large hemlock water dropwort—a poisonous plant. Its flowers resemble the hemlock and wild parsley but the whole plant is stiffer and the seed-pods are different, being long and narrow and crowned below the two styles with the persistent sepals.

Water bedstraw has thin weak stems along which small narrow leaves are arranged mostly in fours. From the upper sets the tiny white flowers appear from June to August. It is a relative of the troublesome cleavers but its fruits are quite smooth.

Also called "all-heal" and yielding a valuable medicine, the great wild valerian is a tall plant that likes moist shady places. Its leaves are in opposite pairs and divided into two rows of narrow leaflets. Though the flowers are small, each being five-lobed, with three stamens, they are collected into a showy cluster at the top of the stem. The colour of these flowers is white or pinkish.

A stately plant is hemp agrimony, so called from the resemblance of its three-fingered leaves to those of the true hemp. Its heads of pink flowers, from which long hair-like stigmas protrude, appear in late summer. Related but very different is the humble marsh cudweed, often met with in muddy places. It is a low plant with narrow leaves covered with white cotton, and flowers, in yellowish-brown clusters.

Bur-marigolds have an indefinable grace of their own. The leaves are long, narrow and toothed, of a rich dark green, and the flowers are greenish-yellow, each head being framed in spreading bracts. There are two common kinds, one of which has the leaf divided into three.

Yellow fleabane is like a yellow daisy, of which the woolly stems and leaves— and especially the smoke from them when burnt—are said to drive away fleas and gnats. The flowers come in late summer. Water ragwort is like the common ragwort, except that the leaf has a somewhat top-heavy terminal lobe, while the seeds are all smooth.

THISTLES

Then come the thistles. Marsh thistle has tall winged stems and narrow leaves; both stem and leaves are very prickly. The small flower-heads in clusters at the top are deep crimson or white. Meadow thistle—rather a misleading name, as it is confined to really wet places—is a beautiful plant. Its bright crimson flower-head is solitary at the end of a long stalk. The leaves are not very thistle-like.

Hawk's beards usually grow in dry places, but one, the marsh hawk's beard, is not uncommon in moist shady places in the north. It resembles the dandelion but has leaves up the flowering stem.

Moneywort or creeping jenny is a fairly common inhabitant of marshy ground. It is related to the yellow loose-strife but creeps along the ground, and is often cultivated in hanging baskets. The yellow flowers appear in the angles of broadly oval leaves that are in opposite pairs along the stem.

Often seen in hedge-banks but liking wet places, comfrey has large leaves and drooping clusters of purple, yellow or white bell-shaped flowers.

Water figwort is a stiff plant with winged stems and small greenish-brown flowers with gaping mouths. The leaves are almost oblong, and blunt at the end; they have a rank smell like elder.

The pink snout-ended flowers of lousewort appear from May onwards in wet pastures and heaths, but have to be looked for as they keep close to the ground. The leaves are prettily divided. The name indicates an old superstition that sheep which fed much on the plant became verminous.

Water mint is easily known by its mint-like smell and round heads of pale blue flowers. Gipsywort is quite distinct, its leaves are deeply saw-toothed on both edges and the small whitish flowers appear in the angles of the upper leaves in late summer; like mint, it belongs to the Labiate family, in which it shares with salvia the distinction of having only two stamens; the plant gives a black dye with which gipsies are supposed to stain their skins. Skullcap is another distinct Labiate of wet places; the flowers are bright blue in the upper angles of stiff toothed leaves; a close examination of the calyx will reveal a knob on the back, giving a fanciful resemblance to a cup with its handle. Of the woundworts, marsh woundwort has labiate flowers which are reddish purple variegated with white and appear in late summer in erect spikes; when clapped on a wound the leaves are supposed to promote healing.

In wet and muddy places one often sees great quantities of water pepper, or biting persicaria, with bright green wavy-edged leaves and small greenish flowers in drooping spikes. If a bit of the leaf be placed on the tongue it leaves a very hot taste.

The early purple orchis is fairly common in damp fields and woods from April to June. It can be told from other common orchids by the flower spurs being all directed upwards. The leaves are often spotted. Marsh orchis has a hollow stem and long dense spikes of purple or flesh-coloured flowers; sometimes they are almost white.

Bogs, a word we have not so far used, are formed by the accumulation of water over lime-free rocks and sand. In bogs among heather and cotton-grass may usually be found the very interesting sundew, an insect-eating plant. Look for little rosettes of fleshy spoon-shaped leaves covered with crimson gland-topped tentacles, excreting a gummy fluid. An insect alighting on the leaf is held by the gum. The tentacles bend over and absorb the juices of the insect. Another insect-eating plant found in bogs is butterwort. Its succulent leaves form a rosette from the centre of which rises the violet flower which changes colour when held in the smoke of a pipe. Spread with gum, like butter on bread, the leaves act as a fly-paper. The margins curl inwards. Both these plants have small roots, out of reach of mineral salts which they get from the bodies of insects.

Bog asphodel is a small lily with yellow flowers, stiff grass-like leaves and long creeping roots. Cranberry is a frequent inhabitant of bogs, mostly in the north. It can be told by its small red berries and thin wiry stems. The flowers are pink with four spreading or turned-back petals and the edible fruits are delicious in tarts. A very pretty little plant is the bog pimpernel which has pale pink flower on long slender stalks arising from creeping stems crowded with tiny circular leaves. Often found with it is the lesser skullcap, its small pink flowers in pairs. But the chief glory of the bogs is the bog gentian—not a common plant—with its large trumpet-shaped flowers of deep blue streaked with green.

LADY'S SMOCK AND
LESSER CELANDINE

Found in moist meadows throughout Britain lady's smock (left) is also known as milk-maids and cuckoo flower. The delicate flowers, massed on the stem, are pale lilac or pink in colour. The stem leaves, divided into leaflets, are fairly long and slender, but the runners from the root-stock bear rounded leaves. The star-like yellow flowers of the celandine (above) appear on sunny banks and in hedgerows as early as February. The shining leaves assume a variety of forms; most usual is the heart-shaped.

FLAX, CLOVER AND
RIBWORT PLANTAIN

Common flax (above) when found growing wild is nearly always an escape from cultivation. The five-petalled flowers are a delicate blue, while the slender leaves are blue-green. In red clover (upper right) the flowers are borne in compact rounded heads at the base of which are two trifoliate leaves. Ribwort plantain (lower right) is found in dry pastures and waste places. The lance-shaped leaves are prominently ribbed.

FLOWERS OF DRY PLACES

by

CHARLES A. HALL, F.R.M.S.

How can plants thrive where water is scarce or in intermittent supply? In Britain there is no Sahara, yet in many places vegetation has to cope with desert conditions, as on sand-dunes and the sea-shore. Salt-marshes, whilst moist enough with brackish water, are physiologically dry wastes so far as land plants are concerned. These demand fresh water which is hard to come by in a terrain impregnated by salt. Chalk downs are dry places because, although subject to all weathers and normal rainfall, the chalk quickly absorbs water and drains off. Water conservation is the chief problem which plants occupying dry sites have to meet, and they have solved in several ways.

The normal plant absorbs water at the root and gets rid of excess in the form of vapour through pores (stomata) in the leaves. Indeed, it is by this process of transpiration that water, with its nutrient salts in solution, is kept in healthy circulation in the plant's tissues. But in dry places excessive evaporation of water has to be prevented and the life-sustaining fluid preserved. Conservation of water may be achieved by stunted growth, reduction of the number of stomata, by the edge of leaves being turned to fierce sunlight, by stems and leaves becoming succulent, by rolled leaves or leaves nestling in rosettes, by a screen of hair preventing wind from drying the leaf-surface, by a thickened epidermis, by a covering of waxy substance or bloom which hinders evaporation, and by other devices.

Stonecrops store water in fleshy leaves which are often small and so can carry on successfully in very dry situations.

They absorb water whilst the going is good and retain it even through long drought. A good example is biting stonecrop or wall-pepper, which can thrive happily on old walls, rocks and in other dry places. Its leaves are small, thick, sometimes nearly globular, and the cell-sap contains a sort of mucilage which helps to retain moisture. This species has prostrate leafy stems without flowers and flowering shoots one to three inches high. The starry yellow flowers occur in terminal clusters. The plant has an acrid taste, and is fairly common, flowering June-July.

STONECROP AND ORPINE

English stonecrop meets its problem in the same way as wall-pepper. Its succulent leaves are almost globular, crowding the prostrate barren stems. On the stems which bear flowers, the leaves are less numerous and scattered loosely. The star-like flowers are white, often spotted with pink. This plant, found in rocky and sandy places, generally near the sea, is more frequent on the west coast than on the east. Orpine, often seen in cottage gardens, clings to life so tenaciously that it is popularly called "live-long." It, too, is succulent, able to thrive on limestone rocks, but is usually found in the shade of dry hedgebanks. Its leaves are much larger than those of the two species already mentioned, the lower ones being up to two inches across. The thick perennial rootstock produces rigid annual leafy stems one to two feet high, these being terminated by dense clusters of purple flowers, July-August. Rose-root or midsummer-men is common in dry places on our mountains, but is also

GOLDEN STONECROP. *Sometimes called wall-pepper this plant grows in tufts in dry places and may be frequently found on walls and rocks. The main stem grows close to the ground. The flowers are bright yellow and star-shaped; the leaves are very fleshy, and on a barren stem are closely crowded.*

found on sea-cliffs in the west of Scotland. It is cultivated in rock gardens. The rootstock is stout, knotted, almost woody and rose-scented. The succulent leaves are crowded: a fleshy erect stem, six to twelve inches high, from June to August, is terminated by a compact cluster of small yellow, occasionally purplish flowers, the middle one opening first. Male and female flowers occur on separate plants.

Of the same family as the stonecrops, but of a different genus, is navelwort or pennywort, which favours old walls and rocks, particularly in the south and west of England and parts of the west of Scotland, flowering June-August. This species also conserves water in fleshy leaves. With its woody perennial rootstock firm in a crevice, the plant sends out annual stems and leaves, the leaves being mainly from the root. Their blades are round—hence pennywort—depressed in the middle, suggesting a navel, where on their undersides they are attached to their stalks. Loose, erect flowering spikes, six to twelve inches high, bear pendent yellowish-green tubular flowers with an insignificant calyx.

Ivy saves drafts on its resources by producing evergreen leaves which serve for an extended period and remove the necessity for the development of a full complement each year. This climber covers tree trunks and considerable areas of walls where it is subject to strong heat and light, cold, and drying winds. Water must be conserved, so exhausting evaporation is checked by the structure of the leaves, which are thick-skinned, glossy, leathery. Ivy clings to its support by claspers emerging from the stem; these excrescences do not penetrate the tissues of a tree or take any nourishment from it. But although the plant is not a parasite, it sometimes smothers the tree by which it climbs to secure light and air.

Some members of the pink family are able to thrive in dry places. Field mouse-

ORPINE. *A plant of the same family as stonecrop, orpine, or livelong, has handsome purple flowers and fleshy toothed leaves. It is often grown as a herbaceous plant in cottage gardens.*

SEA PURSLANE. *Flowering between the months of May and September, se purslane may be found on sandy or pebbly shores. The leaves are dark green wit a shining surface and are stalkless, while the small flowers are greenish-white an open only in the morning sun. They are bisexual, and the fruit is a large, roun vessel containing a few black pear-shaped seeds.*

ear chickweed gets on well in dry places, hilly fields, etc., but it is not common. Its stems, from six to ten inches high, are branched from the base and clothed with hairs which are sometimes tipped with glands. The oblong leaves grow opposite each other. Attractive white flowers, up to one inch across, are borne in loose clusters. There are five petals, each one notched, and five hairy sepals, half the length of the petals; sometimes the hairs are glandular. The pistils have five styles and there are ten stamens. Sand spurrey is adapted to dry, sandy places. It has prostrate stems, three to eight inches long, branched from the base and covered with glandular hairs. The fleshy leaves are almost thread-like, up to half an inch long, tapering to a

point. Rose-pink flowers, about quarter of an inch in diameter, occur i forked clusters. There are five unce petals, and five sepals with glandula hairs and membranous borders. Se purslane meets desert conditions of th sandy seashore by storing moisture i its numerous ovate fleshy leaves crowde on slightly branched succulent stems fou to eight inches high. Greenish-whi flowers about a quarter of an inch acros on short stalks, grow from the axils of the leaves. This is a deep-green, qui smooth, shining plant spreading on th shore in tangled masses, beginning flower in May and continuing throug the summer. Thyme-leaved sandwo flourishes on old walls and in stor places and reduces evaporation by pr ucing very small stalkless egg-shaped pointed leaves on branched, spreading, slender yet tough stems, two to ten inches long. There are forked clusters of numerous white flowers up to a quarter of an inch across. The five-pointed sepals have each three hairy veins and the five uncut petals are usually much shorter than the sepals. There are ten stamens and three styles. This is a common annual, particularly in the south, flowering June - August. Procumbent pearlwort occurs on heaths, in stony places and sandy marshes; it gets into garden paths, fills spaces in crazy paving and is a general nuisance to the gardener. The prostrate stems spreading from tiny tufts of root-leaves are from one to three inches long and much-branched. The leaves are awl-shaped, about a quarter of an inch long, and very small numerous white flowers are borne separately on thin delicate stalks.

Orache is of the Goosefoot family, in which we have such useful plants as beet, spinach and mangold wurzel. This particular species is a common weed which often invades cultivated ground, but is at home in waste places and on the seashore. It is an annual with a furrowed stem, prostrate or erect; sometimes the central branch is erect and the other branches bend to the ground. The whole plant is dark-green or more or less mealy-white. Leaves are all stalked, the lower ones being triangular and opposite, while the upper ones are lance-shaped and alternate. Flowers are small, some male, others female, all arranged in slender leafy spikes.

ROCK ROSE. *A common wild plant, the rock rose is found growing abundantly on dry chalk downs and gravelly soils. The plant is shrubby and the long stems trail on the ground. The slender oblong leaves have a hairy upper surface and the under surface is downy. The flowers are five-petalled, pale yellow and very fragile.*

ROSEROOT AND TOADFLAX. *Rose-root* (left) *is of stonecrop family. Ivy-leaved toadflax* (below) *takes its name from its five-lobed leaves.*

Common rock rose is of the Cistus family. Most of the cultivated rock roses have been developed from this species. It is adapted to dry meadows and pastures and particularly favours chalk areas. The much-branched stem is prostrate and shrubby, three to ten inches long. The opposite leaves, about one inch long, are from lance-shaped to egg-shaped, and are green above and white with downy hairs beneath. These hairs protect the stomata and reduce evaporation. The attractive yellow, rose-like flowers, up to an inch across, are stalked and occur in lengthened one-sided clusters. The five petals fall quickly. There are three large and two very small sepals and numerous stamens. This species flowers July-September.

A number of Composites—members of the Daisy family—do well in dry situations, being adapted to them by various devices. Six of them are here described. Slender thistle is not common but is seen in dry places, especially near the sea. According to nutrient conditions, it may be anything from a few inches to three or even four feet high. The stem and undersides of the leaves are covered with loose white cotton. The deeply-lobed leaves are prickly and run from joint to joint down the stem, giving it a winged appearance. The plant gets its name from its slender flower-heads, which are small and narrow, about three-quarters of an inch long and a quarter of an inch across. They are numerous in a cluster terminating the stem. The flowers are pale purplish-pink, the florets all being tubular. Cudweed, an annual, occurs in dry pastures and stony wastes. Its surface is protected from drying winds by a covering of cottony hairs. The stem is erect, up to twelve inches high, ending in dense

MUSK MALLOW AND CENTAURY.
*Musk mallow (right) is related to the
hollyhock. Centaury (below) has pink
flowers and stalkless leaves.*

round woolly clusters of flowerheads,
about half an inch across, each consti-
tuent head being about an eighth of an
inch across and consisting of twenty to
forty tubular yellowish florets. In this
species the branches overtop the main
stem, hence the old name of *Herba impia*
—undutiful plant—from the notion of
children disrespectfully dominating
parents. Mouse-ear hawkweed is found
on dry banks, roadsides, old wall tops
and in dry pastures. Tufts of leaves
spring from the perennial rootstock and
creeping leafy runners are produced.
These extend over the ground and root
at points, forming new plants. The leaves
are lance-shaped or oblong with uncut
margins and long, silky hairs; they are
green on top but the undersides are
white with stellate down. The flowerheads are about an inch across and consist of attractive lemon-yellow strap-like
florets, the outer ones with red streaks
underneath. These heads are after the
dandelion pattern, occurring solitarily
on leafless stalks proceeding from the
root. Wall hawkweed is an erect plant
with stem one to two feet high, terminated by stalked flowerheads, each
about an inch across, in compact clusters
of only a few or up to twenty or more.
At the base of the stem there is a tuft of
root-leaves which are oblong or egg-
shaped, stalked, hairy. The flower bracts
supporting the flowerhead, and the flower
stalks bear black glandular hairs. The
stem is smooth. The yellow florets are
strap-shaped. In identifying this plant it
has to be noted that it varies in the number
of flowerheads and stem leaves, as well
as in hairiness. It is found on old walls
and in other dry places. Narrow-leaved
hawkweed is common in dry woods and
rocky places. In addition to having the
characteristics of its genus, it is singular

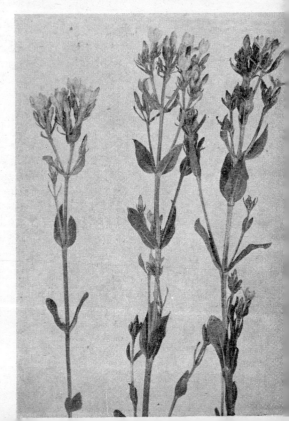

HERB ROBERT. *Found growing on most dry hedge banks, and especially common on stony waste ground. Herb Robert, which is a member of the geranium family, is a much branching plant, with brittle, hairy stems, and leaves which are divided into a number of leaflets. The five-petalled flowers, which are pink, are borne in small clusters.*

in having a rigid, erect stem, one to three feet, unbranched, with leaves confined to the stem. These leaves are stalkless, narrow, somewhat toothed. Another character is the almost umbellate dense cluster of large yellow flowerheads at the summit of the stem. Florets are all strap-shaped as in other species. Another interesting Composite of dry places is golden samphire, a rather rare species adapted to desert conditions such as obtain in salt-marshes, or on rocks and cliffs. It has narrow, thick, fleshy leaves which, at the flowering season, July-September, are dense at the top of the stem. The stem is from about six inches to three feet high, and the flowerheads are about one inch diameter, produced singly at the ends of

short branches. There are tubular disk florets with stamens and strap-shaped ray florets with pistils. All the florets are yellow, and the fruits are crowned with hairs, enabling them to be wind-borne.

In order to be at home in the arid conditions of sandy shore, sea bindweed or convolvulus has developed a slender root which penetrates the sand to a considerable length, and also small fleshy leaves which conserve moisture. The leaves are kidney-shaped or rounded, with lobes at their bases. It sometimes happens that the whole plant is covered with sand, only the handsome flowers being in evidence. The flowers are trumpet-shaped, about one and a half inches across, pale-rose, with red or yellow stripes. Although called bindweed, this species does not bind. It has sacrificed the twining habit of other bind-weeds and its stems are prostrate, often but a few inches long.

The rock cresses related to the Arabis of the garden are Crucifers, having the four petals arranged in the manner of a Maltese cross. Their root leaves form a rosette, the stem leaves being stalkless. The seed-pod is long, narrow, flattened. Thale cress or wall cress is common on dry banks and walls, growing to a height of six to twelve inches. The root leaves are oblong, toothed, spreading; the stem leaves few and small. The white flowers, each about an eighth of an inch across, are clustered, and the pods are spreading, about three-eighths of an inch long on stalks half their length. Hairy rock cress is an erect plant, about a foot high,

found on walls and dry banks. Its stems and leaves are rough with hairs. The inverted egg-shaped root leaves are dark green, and stalkless stem leaves half-clasp the stem. The small white flowers are in terminal clusters tending to droop, while the pods are slender, erect, one to two inches long. Northern rock cress is a rarity, found on rocks among the mountains of Scotland and Wales. Its stem, three to six inches high, is branched at the base. The flower is larger than those of the species already described—about a quarter of an inch across, and white or white tinged with purple.

Common whitlow grass is also a Crucifer. It grows on dry banks and walls and is often in flower as early as February. This is a small annual which perishes in a few weeks. All the leaves spring from

CRANE'S-BILL. *Crane's-bill of all species is of the geranium family. Seen below is bloody crane's-bill, so called because its five-petalled flowers are a deep rose colour. The rounded leaves are sharply divided, and the stalks are faintly hairy. This plant has always been popular for cultivation in garden borders.*

the root and form a rosette spreading on the ground. The flower-stalk has no leaves; it may be from one to six inches high and is terminated by a cluster of small white flowers, the petals of which are notched. As the fruit develops the cluster lengthens. The pods, which contain minute seeds, are elliptical, flattened, and at least twice as long as broad.

A plant of medicinal value, the common centaury, adds charm to dry pastures and meadows, especially on chalky soils, from July to September. This plant is of the Gentian order and is rather variable in its habit. Usually it is from two or three to eighteen inches high with an erect angular stem branched above and bearing strongly-ribbed oblong leaves opposing one another. The plant is crowned with numerous clusters of attractive rose-coloured flowers, three in each cluster, the central one opening first. The flowers open only in bright sunshine; they have a long, narrow corolla-tube which breaks into a five-cleft spreading limb.

GERANIUM FAMILY

Plants of the Geranium genus have beaked fruits with awns resembling a long bird's-bill. The name is from *geranos*, a crane, hence we have the English name crane's-bill. Several species are adapted to dry conditions. Herb Robert is very common in stony wastes, on old walls and hedge-banks. The brittle, hairy stem, six to eighteen inches, has a spreading habit; it is often strongly tinged with red, particularly when the plant is in a very dry situation. The leaves are divided into three palmate segments (ternate) and these are again cut into toothed lobes, presenting a fern-like appearance and becoming red in autumn. The attractive flowers are a bright pink, delicately veined, half an inch or more across. When bruised the plant has a disagreeable smell. Dove's-foot crane's-bill is common in waste-

places, by roadsides, etc. It is a much less conspicuous plant than herb-Robert. The stem is prostrate and spreading, up to twelve inches long, with soft hair and round leaves which are deeply lobed and soft with downy hairs. The flowers are less than half an inch across, light-purple, occurring two together. Shining crane's-bill is not common. Its prostrate stem, six to eight inches, and round, deeply-lobed leaves, tinged with red, are fleshy and shining. The flowers are borne two together; they are rose-coloured, up to three-eighths of an inch across. This delightful little plant is found in stony places and on old walls. Cut or jagged-leaved crane's-bill is common on waysides, in waste places and dry pastures. The spreading stem is hairy, one to two feet long. The leaves are hairy, no downy, round in outline, cut nearly to the base into narrow segments—hence "jagged." The flowers, up to half an inch across, grow two together and are bright red. The five sepals have abrupt point and the five petals are deeply notched and about the same length as the sepals

True rushes, whilst appearing to have grass- or sedge-like characters, technically have affinities with the Lily family. The usually have stiff stems and narrow o cylindrical leaves and produce small flowers in clusters: these are pollinated by wind. The floral envelope (perianth is like a calyx, its six segments being brownish-green, and dry. Usually there are six stamens. The pistil has three slender stigmas. The seed-capsule opens in three valves and the seeds are small. In the arid sands of our south coasts we may find the sharp rush, although it is far from being common. Its stems, growing in large tufts, are very rigid and may be up to four feet high. The leaves and outer bracts are cylindrical, rigid, and have prickly points. The seed-capsule is much longer than the perianth: this is distinguishing feature.

There are plants of the Pea family

PENNYWORT

which carry on successfully in dry places. Lady's fingers is found in dry pastures and stony places in most parts of Britain, flowering June-August. Stems, six to eighteen inches tall, rise from a perennial rootstock. The leaves are pinnate (cut to the mid-rib) into entire, narrow leaflets about half an inch long. The yellow to red stalkless pea-flowers, about three-eighths of an inch long, occur in two tufted heads at the ends of the branches, each head enclosed by a deeply-cut leafy bract. This ensemble gives the suggestion of a two-lobed kidney—hence the species is sometimes known as kidney vetch. Hare's-foot trefoil occurs in dry places. The stems are up to twelve inches high, and are slender, erect, branching. The leaves are split into three narrow leaflets. The stipules end in a bristle. The whole plant is softly hairy. Small flowers, first white, then pink, are borne in stalked heads which at first are almost globular, but later become oblong or cylindrical.

The flowers are almost hidden by th calyces which are longer than the coroll and covered with soft hairs. The in florescence has a fanciful resemblance t a hare's foot. Wood vetch, climbing ove shrubs or other vegetation, often to height of six feet or more, with its displa of purple-veined white flowers, is goo to behold. It occurs in hilly regions an rocky woods, most frequently in Scot land. The leaves are pinnate with six t ten pairs of abruptly pointed leaflets an a terminal branched tendril. The flower are borne at the end of long stalks in one sided drooping clusters of six to eightcer The pod is smooth, broad, pointed both ends, about one inch long.

On dry hedge banks and borders c fields we may see musk mallow—a sma relation of the hollyhock of the garde Its stem is erect, twelve to eightee inches high or more, single or slightl branched. The root leaves are kidne shaped, with three broad scalloped lobe

WALL SPEEDWELL. *Veronicas or speedwells are related to the same family c toadflaxes. Wall speedwell, found growing on walls and in dry fields, has egg-shape toothed leaves. The small, pale blue flowers, rather like those of the germand speedwell, or bird's eye, are clustered on a spike.*

WILD CARROT SEEDS. *Above, greatly magnified, may be seen the fruit of the wild carrot. The seed is deeply ridged, and four of these ridges bear long, curved spines. Wild carrot is an umbelliferous plant of the same family as hemlock and hedge parsley. The flowers are white and the leaves are fern-like, and deeply divided.*

The stem leaves are cut to the base into three divisions, and each division in its turn is cut into linear segments. The rose-pink or rarely white flowers are from one and a half to two and a half inches across and clustered at the tops of stems and branches. There are five sepals and five petals and many stamens. The whole plant is light-green, hairy, and when crushed, emits a slight musky odour.

Two of our native plantains occur in dry sites. Sea plantain, as its name implies, favours the coast, where it is found in salt-marshes and muddy places: it is also found on alpine heights in Scotland and Yorkshire. The plant has a distant likeness to ribwort plantain (p. 304), but the leaves are narrow, thick and fleshy, and only faintly ribbed. The flower-stalk is not furrowed. The woody rootstock is branched and crowned with tufted woolly hairs. The flower-spike is cylindrical, one to two inches long—not as

dense as in ribwort plantain. Buck's-horn plantain is our only plantain with divided leaves: these are narrow-linear, with one rib and once or twice lobed, more or less downy. They bear a fancied resemblance to a buck's horn and are generally prostrate. The flower stalk is not furrowed. This species occurs in dry gravelly or sandy places, and is most commonly found near the sea.

Wild mignonette, easily known by its likeness to the mignonette of gardens, is found commonly on dry limestone and chalky soil and waste places. The ascending stem is one to two feet high, stiff, branched. The leaves are variably deeply divided. The plant is bushy. Small greenish-yellow flowers form lengthy, thick terminal spikes. The stamens are yellow and numerous. Dyer's rocket or yellow-weed is also a mignonette of sorts, rather like the species just mentioned, but it has taller stems and long, narrow, blunt, shining undivided leaves. It also favours dry chalk or limestone soil.

Dewberry, a member of the Rose family, is a species of bramble or blackberry. It is not uncommon on dry hedgebanks, in thickets and on borders of fields. It differs from the ordinary blackberry in having only a few large black drupes combined in the fruit and these are covered with a blue bloom. The stems are roundish or slightly angled and prostrate. The flowers are rather large, and the fruit is partly enclosed by the calyx.

Rue-leaved or three-fingered saxifrage is a little plant which grows on old walls and cottage roofs. Seldom is it more than three inches high. The leaves are wedge-shaped, three-lobed, resembling those typical of the rues: they and the stem are sticky with glandular hairs. The whole plant is light-green tinged with red. There are small, numerous flowers which are white and borne on long stalks in loose clusters. There are five petals, five sepals, and ten stamens.

TOADFLAX AND SPEEDWELL

Ivy-leaved toadflax is common on old garden walls, worming its way into joints between stones or bricks. It is not a native plant but has made itself much at home throughout Britain and Ireland. The five lilac and yellow petals are joined into a tube, spurred at its base and at its mouth divided into two lips, the upper lip two-lobed, and the lower three-lobed. These flowers are about half an inch long and are borne singly on long stalks emerging from the axils of the fleshy leaves. The long, slender stems often root at their joints. This species flowers through the year: it may be a nuisance in gardens, because of its spreading habits.

The speedwells or veronicas belong to the same natural order as the toadflaxes. Wall speedwell grows on walls and in dry fields. The plant is downy and

collects dust. It is small, seldom six inches high. The leaves are egg-shaped, toothed, not lobed, the lower ones being stalked. The whole plant is yellowish-green. There are small pale-blue flowers which are numerous in a terminal, leafy, spike-like cluster. Ivy-leaved speedwell has leaves which are all stalked, at the base heart-shaped, and five- or seven-lobed, a stem prostrate and branched, and from the axil of each leaf a solitary stalked pale-blue flower emerges. The flower is small, about a quarter of an inch across. In the fruiting stage the flower-stalk is bent back. The whole plant is dull-green, with long jointed hairs. The species is very common in waste places and it often invades cultivated ground.

Wild carrot is an umbellate of the Parsley family. It has an erect tap-rooted stem, one to three feet high, with leaves so segmented as to appear fernlike. There are compound umbels of small white flowers, each about one-eighth of an inch in diameter. The umbels are about two inches across, and commonly in the centre of each there is a single bright-red flower, or partial umbel of such flowers. As it matures, the umbel becomes hollow in the centre and in the fruiting stage it is almost globular. This plant favours dry places, especially near the sea, and abounds on chalky soil.

Pellitory is of the Nettle family, but it does not look much like an ordinary nettle, nor does it sting. It grows on old walls and in stony and waste places: it is not common in the north. The stems ascend six to twelve inches high and are branched, brittle, hairy, red in colour. The oval leaves with uncut margins and slightly pointed, grow alternately, and the small pinkish flowers grow in clusters in their axils. This plant used to be cultivated in herb gardens, being valued as a medicine: indeed, it is still used by herbalists as a remedy for gravel and dropsy—generally in conjunction with wild carrot and parsley piert.

MALLOW AND MILFOIL. *Both mallow and milfoil are wild plants of field and meadow as well as of hedgerow and waste places. The flowers of the mallow, seen on the right of the picture, are pale purple, streaked with a darker shade of the same colour; the petals are heart-shaped. Yarrow, or milfoil, seen on the left, has white or pinkish flowers arranged in flat clusters. The long leaves have a feathery appearance.*

335

WILD DAFFODILS

WOODLAND FLOWERS

by

ELEANOR VACHELL, F.L.S.

PLANTS, like people, dwell together in communities—each community consisting of individuals that require the same conditions of soil and aspect, and flourish best at the same altitude and with the same amount of moisture, heat and light.

In Britain the species characteristic of closed woodland communities are nearly all perennials, most of which increase by means of underground shoots, runners, bulbs or tubers, instead of relying entirely on seeds for the perpetuation of their race. The roots, stems and leaves of these woodland perennials form a dense network through which young shoots and runners can easily force their way and flourish but which cannot be penetrated by newcomers, such as aliens or annuals, whose comparatively small seeds have little chance of gaining access to the soil.

These woodland species belong therefore to a somewhat exclusive community and rank amongst the aristocrats of the plant world. They are the descendants of generations of similar plants that have lived in the wood before them, each in turn contributing to the life of the community in its own particular way. Their existence is interdependent upon the lives of other inhabitants of the area, for most of them rely on insects for the transference of their pollen and on birds and animals for the dispersal of their seeds. By way of payment for these services rendered they give pollen and nectar, attracting their visitors by bright colours and sweet scent. The size, scent, colour, and shape of their blossoms, their time of opening and closing and even the length of their flowering-season

are the result of natural selection by the insects upon which they rely for assistance; their thorns and prickles are their weapons of defence against unwanted pilferers; and the tempting flavour of their nuts and berries is adapted to attract the taste of birds and animals that aid in the effective scattering of their fruits.

In life, then, these woodland plants contribute to the well-being of all around them, while after death their rotting stems and foliage form humus which in turn provides nourishment for bacteria, saprophytic plants that feed on decaying vegetable matter, and innumerable fungus forms. Oak woods, beech woods, pine woods and ash woods all have their own plant communities, and even these differ according to altitude and aspect, and the geological formation of the soil.

Having stored up a reserve of foodstuffs, chiefly sugar and starch, in their underground stems and tubers, many of these plants are ready at the approach of spring to put forth leaf-buds and flowers. Amongst the first to appear are the snowdrops, true harbingers of Spring, their pure white pendent blossoms lightly poised on slender stems and decked with honeyed grooves of green. These "fair maids of February", as they are sometimes called, though often abundant in woodlands and copses, are considered only doubtfully native in many parts of Britain.

Dog's mercury is also one of the earliest woodland species to start growth after the winter rest, and sometimes even before the end of January the young shoots arising from a long creeping

WINTER ACONITES

STINKING HELLEBORE. *This is an uncommon plant with large divided leaves and green, purple-tinged flowers.*

rootstock have pushed their way through the brown earth softened and soddened by past frosts, and with heads gradually straightening have begun to display their loose spikes of small inconspicuous green flowers. Relying on the wind to waft the pollen from the male to the female flowers on separate plants, dog's mercury has no need to allure insect guests and therefore dons no bright-coloured petals and provides no honey or sweet scent. The stems of this common plant, named after the heathen god Mercury, are simple, the jagged-edged leaves are shortly stalked and undivided, and the capsule is slightly rough and thickly clothed with bristly hairs.

Early in March the fragile pale green foliage and slender stems of moschatel appear in sheltered woods and on bare earthy patches in hedgerows. Growing from a creeping rootstock the stems, about four inches high, bear terminal globular heads of five small greenish flowers. Milton, describing the watchful cherubim in *Paradise Lost*, says: "Four faces each had, like a double Janus." These words might well be used to describe the alert-looking flowerhead of the moschatel, for the four tiny blossoms are set back to back on a common flower-stalk facing in different directions. As guardian of the ways the moschatel is superior even to a "double Janus" for it has a fifth flower that faces upwards and commands the sky. This fifth blossom, which is visible from above, must be very useful to a plant that depends on insects for the transference of its pollen.

SPRING FLOWERS

Wood spurge is another plant with inconspicuous blossoms, abundant in woods and copses in the early spring. Possessing neither petals nor sepals, the tiny flowers are combined into flower-like groups consisting of numerous tiny barren flowers and one stalked fertile flower surrounded by a bell-shaped involucre with crescent-shaped glands. Alone these small blossoms would hardly be noticed, but the tall flower-stems being branched above in a loose umbel are brightened and made attractive by the presence of a quantity of golden-yellow petal-like bracts. The reddish leafy stems are almost shrubby in appearance, the lower leaves looking dark and almost evergreen in contrast to the pale yellow green of the fresh young bracts.

After green and greenish-yellow—represented by the flowers of dog's mercury, moschatel, stinking hellebore and wood spurge—white and pale yellow are the prevailing shades in woods and copses in Britain, for both are easily visible to insects in search of honey and pollen in the dim light of early spring.

One of the daintiest plants that blossom during the first few months of the year is the broad-leaved garlic or ramsons, readily distinguished by its broad flat spreading leaves and its stiff flower-stalks bearing a loose umbel of about a dozen rather small, pure white star-like flowers.

In some parts of Britain the broad-leaved garlic is very abundant in woods and copses, literally covering the ground with an exquisite carpet of white. Though so beautiful to look at, its leaves when bruised emit a very strong odour of onions so it is wise to admire it and to leave it to decorate the woods. In Russia, where the plant grows abundantly, it is used in cooking and as a remedy for scurvy. In Britain, too, it was formerly held in high estimation, for an old couplet advises "Eat ramsons in May and all the year after physicians may play."

In March the exquisite white flowers of the wood anemone or wind flower appear above ground. They owe their attraction not to showy petals, but to six or more white oval petal-like sepals that are sometimes delicately tinted with pink. Each solitary blossom, surrounded by a frill of deeply divided leaves, is a natural barometer and only opens when the weather is fine; while the stem, firmly anchored to the ground by its creeping rootstock in which has been stored up sufficient foodstuffs for winter use, is so slender and pliable that it can withstand the full force of a March gale. According to Greek tradition, Anemos, the wind, employs his star-like namesakes as heralds of his coming in the early spring. Less prettily named, the pignut or earthnut, is another early white-flowered plant that occurs abundantly in open places in woods, in fields and in hilly pastures throughout almost the whole of Britain. In April or May a few dainty dissected leaves arise from the pignut's roundish chestnut-coloured tuber and push their

DOG'S MERCURY. *A common woodland plant, dog's mercury flowers in early spring before the leaves of many other plants have developed.*

WILD GARLIC

WOOD ANEMONES. *The pink-tinged white blossoms of this plant (left) appear in March.*

way through the soil. Soon the slender annual stem appears, bearing an umbel of tiny white flowers which in time give place to small, ribbed, oval-oblong fruits of a deep purple-brown hue. Children enjoy searching for the nuts or tubers, which, as their name implies, are rooted up and eaten by pigs. In some countries, too, they are considered a useful article of food, resembling chestnuts in flavour.

Flowering just a little later in the year, wood sanicle belongs to the same natural order (Umbelliferaceae) as the pignut. It is a perennial with a short, almost woody rootstock, and nearly leafless branched stems ending in a small head of tiny pinkish-white flowers. The dark-green leaves are divided into about five palmate segments and the fruits are covered with hooked prickles that, by getting entangled in the fur of passing animals or the clothing of human beings, are carried off to start life in a new home. This dainty little plant, often characteristic of chalk beechwood associations, though it also occurs in abundance in oakwoods on loam, was so greatly valued in the Middle Ages for its curative properties that an old herbalist stated that it would "make whole and sound all wounds and hurts both inward and outward." It is considered probable that it owes its name to St. Nicholas, who is said to have interceded with God for the lives of two children who were brutally murdered and obtained their restoration to life and health in answer to his prayer.

In May, growing abundantly in woods and shady places, wood sorrel may usually be found in bloom. An elegant little plant with delicate yellow-green clover-like leaves and white or lilac-veined

RED CAMPION. *The rose-pink petals of red campion (left) are deeply cleft.*

WOOD SORREL AND WOOD VIOLET. *Above may be seen wood sorrel, whose white flowers are faintly veined with pinkish-purple. The yellowish-green leaves are trifoliate. Wood violets (below) differ from sweet violets in having no perfume although their leaves and flowers are very similar in appearance.*

flowers, it is sometimes thought to be the true shamrock used by St. Patrick to illustrate the doctrine of the Trinity. Springing directly from the creeping rootstock, the trifoliate leaves are sometimes used as a salad on account of their pleasant acid taste. Being highly sensitive they fold together at night and during stormy weather. The fragile,

usually drooping flowers look almost bell-shaped, as the five white petals are often united at the base, and the seeds, which are contained in a capsule, are each equipped with an elastic coat which curls back when the fruit is ripe and ejects them with considerable force as though they had been shot from a catapult.

That well-known early spring flower,

BLUEBELLS. *Common in woods through-out Britain, bluebells are seen in early spring. The rootstock is bulbous.*

of its pale yellow flowers that spring from a loose rosette of crinkled leaves have endeared it to the hearts of all British people. If a number of blossoms be examined, it will be seen that in half of them the pistil is situated above the stamens in the corolla-tube. These are called pin-eyed flowers. In the other half, called thrum-eyed flowers, the stamens are above the pistil. By this arrangement, transference of pollen by insects is assured from the pin-eyed to the thrum-eyed forms and *vice versa.* The pale yellow colour of the flowers makes them clearly visible in the dim light of early spring and as they never close or hang their heads when the sun goes down, they are very conspicuous in the evening light. In the *Grete Herbale* the primrose is called "Pryme rolles of pryme tyme because it beareth the first floure in pryme tyme." This is explained in popular works as meaning the first flower or rose of spring, but in old books it is the daisy, not the primrose, that bears the name. As the days lengthen and the light gets stronger, pale yellow and white, no longer the prevailing colours in the woods, are superseded by the richer shades of summer.

In April or May, bluebells or wild hyacinths make their appearance in the woods. They, too, have stored up a supply of food-stuffs in their yellowish-white bulbs, deeply buried in the earth, and are ready to make early preparations for reproducing their race. The long, narrow, deeply channelled leaves appear first above ground, but they are soon over-topped by the tall stiff flower stems bearing a number of purplish-blue blossoms, each with its attendant purplish-blue bracts. The flowers are bell-shaped and drooping and when fully developed the tips of the perianth-

the primrose, is abundant in woods and copses, on sunny slopes and in sheltered glens, throughout Britain. Having stored up sufficient foodstuffs, chiefly sugar and starch, for winter use, in its thick fleshy rootstock, it is ready to start its blossoming season as soon as spring sunshine takes the place of frost and cold. Its sweet fragrance and the early appearance

SNOWDROPS

segments are partly rolled back. Blue-bells increase so rapidly by vegetative reproduction that they dominate large areas of woodland and by forming dense carpets, effectively prevent colonization by other herbaceous plants. Nearly everyone knows some wood where these favourite blossoms grow in profusion, and where a blue haze in the distance announces that they are once again in bloom.

So different in size and yet closely resembling bluebells in colour, pale wood violets may be found in woods and shady places about the same time of the year. Differing from ordinary wood violets in their paler, narrow petals, straight-veined lower lip, and in the shape and colour of their spur, they lack,

too, much of the beauty of sweet violets that are such universal favourites because of their delicious scent. Bees alighting on the lower petal, come in contact with, and shake, the stigma that partly bars the way to the honey-store. This movement releases the dry loose pollen, protected from rain by the drooping position of the flower. Besides the showy coloured flowers specially adapted for the reception of insects, most of the species have small inconspicuous, petalless flowers that appear later in the year and produce an abundance of seeds. These cleistogamous or self-pollinating flowers which are sufficient to reproduce the species, habitually fertilize themselves.

Another very attractive shade-loving plant is the lesser periwinkle, which has

CUCKOO-PINT. *This striking woodland flower is known by a variety of names, among them lords-and-ladies and wake-robin. It belongs to the arum family. The plant grows from a tuberous rootstock, and the distinctive arrow-shaped leaves, often marked with black or purple splotches, appear in March. From the centre of these leaves rises a flower-stalk bearing a large pale green leaf-like bract called a spathe. This gradually unfolds in a shape somewhat resembling a monk's cowl to reveal a purplish or pale yellow club-shaped spadix around the lower portion of which are arranged a number of stigmas and anthers. Pollination is effected by small insects.*

blue-purple flowers and blossoms during the months of May and June. Though it blooms profusely, it ripens comparatively few seeds, but spreads rapidly in woods and thickets in many districts by means of its long, thin, rooting stems. It is locally abundant in some parts of the country for its almost prostrate shoots form a dense network of undivided evergreen leaves that exclude other vegetation, but being a great favourite in rock-gardens and shrubberies, it is sometimes only a garden escape.

WOOD-RUSH AND CUCKOO-PINT

Two or three species of wood-rush are very characteristic of a woodland community in spring. The great wood-rush is locally abundant in woods and shady places, chiefly in hilly districts, but is seen to its best advantage on low cliffs and rock-ledges, where its light-green, grass-like leaves and tall brown flowering stems often form a very decorative fringe. The great wood-rush has a tufted perennial rootstock and somewhat resembles an ordinary rush, but differs in its softer grass-like leaves, often fringed with longish hairs. The tiny rush-like flowers are arranged in little clusters of two or three in a loose compound panicle. The stems are about eighteen inches high, and the leaves are broader than those of any other British species. Much more slender is the hairy woodrush. It, too, is rush-like in appearance, but differs from a rush in its narrow grass-like leaves. The small brown flowers, usually all distinct, are arranged in a small irregular terminal panicle. Though common in woods and shady places, it may escape observation.

Locally abundant on the borders of woods and on hedge-banks, lords and ladies, cuckoo-pint, wild arum, or wake robin is another shade species, with a tuberous root, that blossoms in April and May. The broad, arrow-shaped leaves of shining green start early to unfurl. They

CUCKOO-PINT BERRIES. *The bright red berries of the cuckoo-pint are seen above.*

are followed by a long purplish or pale yellow spike or spadix, bearing stamens and pistils, which is half concealed by an enveloping spathe. The cunning way in which these lords and ladies imprison their insect benefactors makes a curious story. When the pale green spathe gradually unfolds, revealing the bright-coloured club-shaped spadix, the midges and other small insects, attracted by its rich colour or the prospect of honey, settle upon it and climb down into the rounded cavity at its base. Without any difficulty they push their way past the fringe of stiff hairs encompassing the spike, where the enveloping spathe is

OLD MAN'S BEARD. *Also known as traveller's joy, this plant often entirely covers trees or shrubs, climbing by means of the leaf stalks, which have a powerful hold. The white flowers, which have a hawthorn-like odour, grow in loose clusters; while the seed-vessels with long bearded styles, give the plant its name.*

contracted, but as the hairs curve downwards, the insects, having once entered the cavity, are hopelessly entrapped. A delicious feast, however, awaits them, for the no-longer ripe stigmas secrete drops of honey: a repayment by the plant for their enforced captivity. Not until the anthers ripen and shed their pollen on the imprisoned guests, drowsy and stupid after their orgy of honey, does the barrier of hairs that barred their exit gradually shrivel and set them free to carry the pollen to other flowers. Sometimes dozens of midges can be counted at the base of a single spathe. When the berries become succulent and scarlet, birds play their part in helping to scatter the seeds.

Most widespread of all British St. John's worts, perforate St. John's wort is abundant in open woods and in scrub, and also on hillsides, especially on calcareous (lime-containing) soil. Its rootstock is perennial, with short runners; the stems are stiff and much branched, about fourteen inches high, and the small oblong leaves are marked with pellucid dots and appear to be perforated when held against the light. Like other flowers with golden sun-shaped disks, St. John's worts were once associated with the old Norse god,

HONEYSUCKLE. *A familiar plant in hedgerows and copses, honeysuckle has a powerful scent and is rich in nectar. The pink-tinged yellow flowers grow in clusters and the corolla tube is divided into five lobes. The egg-shaped leaves grow in pairs.*

BLACK HOREHOUND. *A woodland herb*
(left) whose juice is used to cure coughs

Baldur. In later times, through the
teaching of the Church, Baldur was
replaced by St. John the Baptist, whose
midsummer festival is marked by many
remains of sun worship. Because of their
resemblance to the sun's evil-dispelling
rays, their flowers were regarded as a
specially powerful antidote to the evil
practices of witchcraft.

Hairy St. John's wort is not as
common as the perforate St. John's
wort, and is usually found in fairly well
lighted spots at the edge of woods and
in scrub, especially on basic soils. A stiff
erect perennial, always more or less
downy, it has oblong leaves and
numerous pale yellow flowers arranged
in an oblong panicle. Bright and showy
the flowers secrete no honey. They are
however, visited by insects for their
pollen, and perhaps also because they
expect them to be honeyed.

Rather frequent in the southern part
of Britain, wild basil is a plant of hedge
rows and wood borders. It has softly
hairy branched stems that grow from a
shortly-creeping rootstock, and rose
purple irregular flowers forming compact
whorls or clusters in the axils of the
upper leaves or at the end of the branches
Though very different in appearance
wood sage belongs to the same family
Fairly common in woods, on heaths and
in hedgerows but chiefly on rocky
ground, it is a stiff erect plant with a
creeping rootstock, branched stems about
a foot high, toothed undivided leaves
that are wrinkled and downy, and small
pale yellow flowers arranged in pairs in a
one-sided spike. Leaves and flowers are
bitter in flavour owing to the presence
of a tonic principle, a certain amount of
which occurs in all labiate plants. It was

BUGLE. *A plant of the Labiate family*
bugle has spikes of bright blue flowers

WOOD ANEMONES. *Before the leaves appear on the trees in spring, wood anemones are seen, their white star-shaped blossoms being particularly noticeable in the absence of other flowers. The leaves are deeply lobed and coarsely toothed.*

therefore, used at one time as a tonic medicine, and sometimes takes the place of hops in brewing.

Wood betony also belongs to the same plant family, and should be looked for in July and August on the borders of woods and copses and on grassy places by the sea. The rootstock is perennial, and the flowering-stems which are stout and rigid, are usually about a foot high. The leaves are dark green with jagged edges, and the dark purple-red irregular flowers are arranged in a short dense spike at the top of the stems. Long ago this well-known plant was supposed to possess remarkable powers of healing and was therefore cultivated in physic gardens belonging to monastic buildings. "Sell your coat and buy betony" is an old saying well expressing the high esteem in which it was held.

Another plant belonging to the same family is the yellow archangel or weasel-snout, that occurs abundantly in woods and shady places and blooms freely during the summer months. Resembling the common white dead-nettle in habit, it has narrower leaves, long barren stems and handsome yellow two-lipped flowers blotched with red.

AVENS AND ANGELICA

Avens or herb bennet blooms freely through the summer months and is abundant on the borders of woods and in hedgerows throughout the British Isles. Its rootstock is perennial, with annual erect stems; the leaves are divided into very unequal segments and the small flowers have five yellow petals and numerous stamens.

Its three lobed leaves and five yellow petals were considered symbolical of the Holy Trinity and the five wounds of Our Lord, and for its supposed curative powers it was sometimes referred to as the blessed herb. Named after St Benedict (Benet), in olden days it was

WILD ANGELICA. *Angelica is a tall, stout plant, often attaining a height of four or five feet. Its white purple-tinged flowers are arranged in umbels, while the large, handsome leaves are pinnate with sharply-toothed segments.*

used as a remedy for every imaginable disease, and it was even stated that no venomous beast could harm a man who carried its root about with him. Each tiny fruit is provided with a hooked spine by means of which it attaches itself to the fur or hair of any animal that happens to pass by and so gets carried by short stages over large areas.

Wild angelica, a tall erect plant belonging to the natural order Umbelliferaceae, is abundant in damp woods, thickets and wet places. Its stout, smooth stems of soft light green suffused with pinkish-purple, and its large compound umbels of small pinkish-white flowers, are easy to recognize even from afar. Its divided leaves, the stalks of the upper ones dilated at the base into large bladder-like sheaths, are very characteristic, as are also the fruits, which are surrounded by a double wing. It blossoms from midsummer until cut down by the first autumn frost.

RED CAMPION

One of the commonest British plants, that flowers all through the summer, red campion often lends a bright touch of colour to wood-borders and hedgerows, preferring acid soils and good drainage. An ornamental plant with oblong tapering leaves, it stands about eighteen inches high, and has bright rose-coloured flowers. Broad-leaved helleborine is a fairly common and very attractive orchis that may be looked for in woods and shady places during the summer months. Usually about twelve inches high, the stems are slender and wiry, and the lower leaves are broad and oval, strongly veined, and tightly clasping the stem. The rather small flowers have pointed yellow-green perianth segments tinged with purple, and are arranged in a loose one-sided spike. Adapted for cross-pollination by insects, the flowers are visited exclusively by wasps. Tempted by the copious store of honey in the lip

cavity, the wasp, on alighting, licks up the nectar and, in so doing, attaches to itself two club-shaped pollen-masses. Having finished its feast, the wasp flies off with this grotesque head-dress, and visiting another flower, presses its forehead, with its club-shaped crest, against the stigma.

Wood crane's-bill, one of the largest-flowered and most attractive of all

ENCHANTER'S NIGHTSHADE. *This tall plant has clusters of pale pink flowers and faintly toothed leaves.*

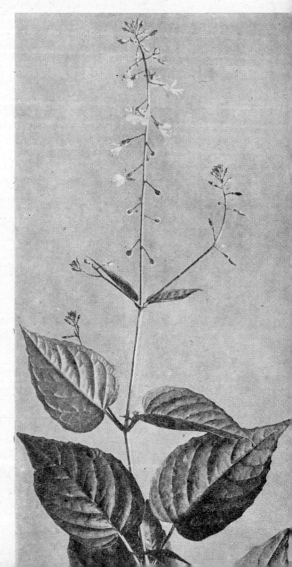

British crane's-bills, occurs in open woods, in scrub, in mountain pastures, and on river banks, during the summer months, thinning out in extreme north and in the south of England. The handsome flowers have five notched rose-purple petals and five sepals; the root-stock is perennial and the blossoms appear in June and July.

Blue is represented in summer in the woods by the common bugle, a low-growing perennial that increases rapidly by means of its creeping shoots, which literally take possession of the ground where it has established itself. The small blue flowers are whorled and crowded into a spike which is made more showy and attractive by the rich bluish-purple hue of the upper leaf-like bracts.

HONEYSUCKLE

That favourite twining shrub, honey-suckle or woodbine, one of the first to unfold its pale green leaves in early spring, is too well-known to need much description. Its long trumpet-shaped flowers of pale yellow suffused with red, emit a delicious fragrance and are visited by insects for the rich store of honey secreted in the narrow tube. Birds eagerly eat the clusters of bright red berries. Strawberries and raspberries also provide luscious fruits to tempt hungry birds to help them by scattering their seeds. The strawberry's fruit is not, however, a true fruit, but merely the succulent pulpy receptacle that bears the tiny fruits; whereas the fruit of the raspberry is composed of a number of succulent drupes placed upon a conical spongy receptacle. The strawberry increases by throwing out runners, while the rasp-berry produces a network of under-ground shoots. Both bloom early in the summer and are found in woods, hedge-banks and thickets.

Though very different in appearance, agrimony belongs to the same family as the strawberry and raspberry. It is a tall plant with deeply divided leaves and tiny yellow blossoms arranged in a narrow tapering spike. The calyx is covered with hooked bristles that catch easily in the clothing of passers-by and in the fur of browsing animals, thus ensuring that the seeds will be conveyed to a new home.

In deeper shade the common cow-wheat is often abundant in woods and thickets, the slender stems bearing narrow pointed leaves and long-tubed yellow flowers arranged in pairs, all turning one way and looking very attractive under the trees. In similar situations, especially if the ground be moist, the small white flowers of woodruff may be looked for in May and June. It is often cultivated in gardens for its fragrance. The bright-green leaves are arranged in whorls and the tiny flowers in stalked terminal panicles.

WINTERGREEN AND MAJORAM

Lesser wintergreen is perhaps one of the most lovely treasures that can be found in any wood in Britain. Each plant produces several roundish smooth leaves, and a flower-stalk bearing a terminal cluster of drooping creamy-white bell-shaped blossoms resembling those of the lily of the valley. In shady places, too, enchanter's nightshade is found, but unlike the lesser wintergreen, it is exceedingly common, literally covering the ground in places where it has established itself and increasing rapidly by means of its creeping roots. The dull green leaves are egg-shaped and tapering to a point, and the minute pinkish-white flowers are arranged in terminal clusters.

Before leaving the outskirts of the woods there is another plant to look for, where the light is strong and the ground is rough and rocky. Marjoram grows about a foot high. It can be distinguished by its egg-shaped leaves and closely packed heads of tiny purplish flowers, as well as by its aromatic scent.

CENTAURY AND ST. JOHN'S WORT. *Seen here on the edge of the wood among the bracken and bramble are centaury with its pink flowers, and perforate St. John's wort. The latter has bright yellow five-petalled blossoms, and oblong stalkless leaves which are thickly dotted with pellucid glands.*

A TYPICAL SANDY HEATH. *On sandy or gravelly soil grow such plants as may be seen in this picture. Gorse and broom flourish side by side with bracken and ling, and both silver birch and pine trees are a common sight.*

FLOWERS OF
MOUNTAIN AND MOOR

by

CHARLES A. HALL, F.R.M.S.

IN our mountain regions we find many lowland plants sufficiently hardy to withstand the climate of such altitudes. In such situations they are frequently dwarfed. The range of these plants is rather astonishing. Thus, it is found that coltsfoot, so well known in the lowlands, occurs in mountain regions 3,500 ft. high, and the little, seemingly tender woodland plant, wood sorrel, can exist at about the same altitude. The wood anemone has been noted at 2,750 feet above sea-level and the marsh violet at 4,000 feet. One comes across specimens of yarrow and dandelion at 3,900 feet, and wonders what they are doing at such a height, and daffodils grow in profusion on the mountainous heights of the Pennine range. Many other lowland plants exist on alpine heights, but these few are mentioned just to indicate that all plants found among the mountains are not specifically alpine. The relatively few truly alpine species found in·British mountain areas are survivors of an arctic climate which, in the Glacial Period, affected our islands. These are found at their best on sheltered rock ledges, where the soil is scanty, and it is necessary for the plants to produce long roots in order to secure water and food. When we realize the vicissitudes these plants endure and yet survive, we figuratively take off our hats to them. They are subjected to intense cold by night and in winter, and bright light by day. On their sheltered ledges they are not greatly affected by wind. A number of alpines are found on rocks by mountain streams and the way to discover them is to go up stream. The rainfall in mountain regions is heavy, yet the alpine is actually a "dry place" plant and has to provide against excessive evaporation of moisture from its tissues.

Searching for alpines is an arduous business. One has, perhaps, to negotiate bogs in the earlier part of the climb and at greater heights the going is hard. Sometimes a coveted specimen is on a rocky ledge beyond reach. On the mountain eminence one seems to be on top of the world. There is the bird's-eye view of the country below, and maybe, the inspiring sight of the distant sea as well as of other heights. And for the botanist there is the alpine plant, often a rarity, and always singularly interesting. Indeed, the alpine has a character all its own and what might be called an "atmosphere" which is indefinable. When one meets such a distinctive denizen of the mountain heights one feels as if in the presence of a native of an unfamiliar world. The reader is warned that he is by no means certain to find all the species about to be described on one mountain: maybe he will find only two or three, or even none at all.

Cultivators of rock gardens often specialize in saxifrages, as far as possible providing for them the alpine conditions in which they natively flourish. The species are imported from continental mountain regions, such as the Swiss Alps, the Pyrenees, or the Carpathians. But there are some species native to Britain: among them is the yellow mountain saxifrage, a charming little plant found on wet rocks by mountain

FOXGLOVE

streams in Scotland, northern England and Ireland, up to 3,000 feet. The leafy flowering stem may be five or six inches high: it is terminated by from one to three yellow flowers, about half an inch across, spotted with orange or red. Sometimes the flowers are more numerous, occurring in a loose cluster. The five sepals are joined at the base and almost as yellow as the five petals, and nearly as long. There are ten orange-yellow stamens. At the base of the plant there are flowerless stems with crowded, narrow, rather thick, spreading leaves, each about one inch long. The leaves scattered on the flowering stems are fringed with a few hairs. Plants of this species are often crowded together, forming bright-green cushions. The flowering period is June-July.

SAXIFRAGE

Cut-leaved or mossy saxifrage has flowerless prostrate stems which, where there is enough moisture, may be two or three inches long, but in drier places are reduced to dense tufts. Many of the leaves are unlobed, narrow, pointed, but others of larger size may have three or occasionally five lobes about half an inch long. The stems bearing flowers are three to six inches high, with few leaves. The flowers are creamy white, half to one inch across, and occur in a loose cluster terminating the stem. There are five narrow sepals, five petals and ten stamens. This species also forms cushions: the flowering season is May-July. The plant cannot be described as common, but it is frequently seen in moist rocky places in mountain areas in England, Wales, Scotland and Ireland. Starry saxifrage is also seen on wet rocks by streams in the mountains, having been noted up to over 4,000 feet. It bears white flowers, about three-eighths of an inch across, in loose clusters of two to eight, terminating a leafless stem rising direct from the root. The five sepals are

nearly free of each other, only being slightly joined at the base. The five white petals, twice as long as the sepals, each have two yellow spots at the base, and the anthers of the stamens are red. This species flowers July-August. It has been noted at the summit of Ben Nevis.

ALPINE LADY'S MANTLE

Perhaps one of the first alpines to catch the attention of a person making acquaintance with our mountain flora is alpine lady's mantle, a member of the Rose family and nearly related to common lady's mantle, described on page 304. Its attractiveness rests not so much in its branched clusters of small greenish-yellow flowers as in its leaves, which are green above, but on their undersides are white with silvery hairs, giving the effect of a lustrous material. The stem is covered with similar hairs. The leaves are deeply divided into five or seven segments. This alpine is quite common in the mountains of Scotland, northern England and parts of Ireland. Sibbaldia, named after Sibbald, a seventeenth century Scottish naturalist, is also of the Rose clan. Its perennial rootstock forms a short spreading tuft. The leaf-stalks are about half an inch long, and the leaf-blades are divided to the midrib into three inversely egg-shaped or wedge-shaped leaflets, each of which at its end has three teeth. The ascending flowering stems are leafy, three to five inches high, often much less, and they bear at their ends close clusters of a few small yellow flowers about a quarter of an inch across. The green calyces are more obvious than the very small pale-yellow petals, which, indeed, are occasionally conspicuous by their absence. Although Sibbaldia occurs abundantly in stony places in Scottish mountains, it does not appear elsewhere in Britain, so must be described as a rarity. Cloudberry, of the Rose family, is a bramble of sorts found in peaty places in the Scottish Highlands and in some subalpine areas in the north of England and Wales. From its creeping, branched rootstock, unbranched stems without prickles arise to about six inches, with leaves on their upper parts. The leaves are comparatively large, roundish or kidney-shaped, toothed. The white flowers, often over an inch across, occur singly on terminal flower-stalks. The fruit is a fairly large luscious berry on the bramble principle, but consists only of a few rather large juicy drupes (or stone-fruit) which at first are red and later become orange-red. This species flowers June-July.

CAMPION AND CHICKWEED

Moss or dwarf campion is of the Pink family, nearly related to the several campions of the lowlands. It is plentiful in the Scottish Highlands and may be found sparingly in the hills of the English Lakes and in North Wales. It forms bright-green moss-like cushions on alpine rocks. The short branches of the perennial rootstock are seen covered with withered leaves and terminate in dense clusters of very short green leaves which are linear. From these clusters many reddish purple, seldom white, flowers emerge, about half an inch across, with slightly notched inversely egg-shaped petals, often almost stalkless, otherwise on stalks hardly an inch long. This is a charming plant, altogether delightful to the eye, flowering June-August. In the same family we have alpine mouse-ear chickweed, which is fairly common in the Scottish Highlands, but less frequent in the heights of northern England, is a rarity in Wales and not found in Ireland. The plants like moist rocky sites. The stems are three to six inches high, branched at the base, swollen at the joints. The leaves are placed opposite to each other, broadly egg-shaped. The whole plant may be nearly smooth, but generally it is covered with long woolly hairs which are some-

times glandular, making the plant viscid. The flowers are up to one inch across, white, one or two on long stalks. The five sepals have membraneous margins and the five petals are notched and twice as long as the sepals.

Mountain everlasting is a Composite showing the distinctive features of the Daisy family, but quite unlike the familiar daisy. It is found in Scottish mountains up to 2,000 feet, and also on heaths in Scotland, Cornwall, Devon and Suffolk. Although not more than three to six inches high, it catches and pleases the eye on account of the white or pink bracts, which form the involucre of the flowerhead and have that nature which is commonly described as "everlasting." They outlive the flowers and leaves. The strap-shaped leaves are green above and cottony beneath. The few flowerheads form flat clusters. The small florets are all tubular and on one plant they are male and on another female. Dwarf cudweed is a rare Composite found only in the Scottish Highlands, growing on rocks and flowering July-August. It has tufts of slender leaves, almost pointed, from half to one inch long, covered beneath with silky wool. This wool often appears on the upper surface. The flowering spike, seldom more than three inches high, is cottony and almost leafless. There may be only one flowerhead, but usually there is a cluster of five or so. Each head is about one-third of an inch across and consists of brownish tubular florets, those in the centre male and the outer ones female. The bracts of the flower-heads are blackish-brown.

SPIKED WOODRUSH

Found only in rocky places on mountain heights from 1,000 to over 4,000 feet, in North Wales, Westmorland and Scotland, we have a small member of the Rush family, the spiked woodrush, which might be mistaken for

GOLDEN SAXIFRAGE. *A plant which may be found in the Welsh and Scottish mountains at altitudes of 3,000 feet, golden saxifrage has yellow flowers growing in small flat clusters. The leaves, which are almost round, have wavy margins, and those near the flowers are often streaked with yellow.*

like the sundews and butterworts, nourished by digesting insects, are found on peaty soils, and other plants like the heaths flourish there because they get food through fungi associated vitally with their roots—a remarkable co-operative arrangement. Moorland plants, although they may grow in boggy soil, cannot thrive on its acids, so they need to conserve fresh water: in this respect they have the same problem as plants of salt-marshes and dry places. Many typical moorland plants resist excessive evaporation by reducing the area of leaf surface exposed to heat and drying winds.

HEATHER FAMILY

In peaty moorland heather is dominant, particularly that abundant species known as ling. This hardly needs description, for it is well-known to all nature lovers. Its woody, much branched stems, up to two feet high, are covered with pairs of small, stalkless leaves and small lilac bell-shaped flowers are borne in erect spikelike clusters. The nectar extracted by bees from the flowers adds a delightful flavour to honey, and mutton from sheep fed on the plant is considered particularly toothsome. Less abundant, but common enough, we have bell heather or fine-leaved heath, which produces purplish-red urn-shaped flowers about one-eight of an inch across, in clusters terminating the woody stem. The very fine leaves, up to a quarter of an inch long, the edges of which are *not* curved inwards, usually grow in whorls of three. The whole plant, which flowers July-September, may be up to two feet high and its stems are much-branched. Cross-leaved heath produces drooping rose-coloured egg-shaped flowers in short, terminal, one-sided clusters. The small leaves, fringed with hairs, occur cross-

a kind of grass. The grass-like leaves, with long white hairs, are much shorter than the slender stem, which is from six to twelve inches high and has one or two leaves and bears a drooping spike-like cluster of very small brown flowers. The seed-capsule is of one cell and contains three seeds.

Moors are treeless regions, practically wildernesses, and in our country they comprise heather-clad hill-slopes, upland peat-bogs or lowland heaths. The soil of such areas is poor and more or less acid. The character of the moorland flora depends upon the quantity of peat present. There is little peat in chalk or limestone regions. Peat is only formed where bacterial action is negligible, and such action is favoured where lime and plenty of oxygen are available. Mineral food, so necessary to the life of many plants, is scarce in peaty soils, and only plants which can secure food from other sources can flourish there. Hence plants wise in circles of four and their edges are curled inwards. The wiry stems produce slender branches. The plant reaches a height of twelve to eighteen inches and flowers July-September.

The bilberry, blaeberry or whortle-berry is well-known on account of its small black berries covered with a bluish bloom, which many people appreciate in the form of puddings or tarts. The plant which produces these berries is a small shrub with sharply-angled branches, from a few inches to over a foot high. The egg-shaped leaves —scarcely an inch long, almost unstalked, toothed on their edges—turn red in the autumn prior to falling off the plant. The shortly-stalked little flowers from which the berries develop are only about a quarter of an inch long, nearly spherical, pale greenish-white often with a reddish tinge. They appear in spring. This plant thrives on heaths, especially in mountain areas, and also in woods, and is common throughout Britain except in the south-east. In the same genus we have cowberry or red whortle-berry, producing red berries, rather like those of the cranberry, which are used as food in the form of jam or jelly and are much liked by grouse. The plant is a much-branched straggling shrub with inversely egg-shaped shining leaves which are evergreen. The flowers are pink, bell-shaped, about a quarter of an inch long, and occur in dense terminal drooping clusters of five to twelve. This species is found on moors, heaths and in open woods in Scotland, Ireland, Wales, and the north and west of England: it flowers in the summer. It should be noted that the margins of the leaves curl inwards.

We might travel far before finding a more dainty and elegant little plant than

the native hare-bell. Its bell-like flowers seem to have absorbed the azure of the fairest sky, and although it is of fragile growth it can stand up to the high winds which buffet it in its exposed situation on a moor or heath. Sometimes a white flower is seen. The root-leaves are heart-shaped or roundish, with long stalks; they soon wither. The slender, wiry stem is up to twelve inches or so high, and it bears a few narrow, pointed leaves. The drooping flowers, about one inch long, with slender stalks, occur singly or in a loose cluster of two or three. Five petals are fused to form the corolla, as is seen by its five short lobes. This species is perennial and flowers July-September. Occurring commonly in dry heathy places, sheep's-bit is of the Campanula family, but looks more like a scabious or a member of the Daisy family. The fact is that what might have been campanulate flowers have had their corollas cut into five narrow, spreading segments. The calyx, also, has been

HEATHER. *Common everywhere on heaths and moors, heather has wiry stems, minute leaves and bell-shaped flowers.*

WILD DAFFODILS ON THE HILLSIDE. *Wild daffodils appear in March and April, the golden trumpets being in rich contrast with the pale, clear yellow of the*

floral leaves. Before blooming, the flower is enveloped in a thin, skin-like sheath. The leaves are straight and narrow, and of a blue-green colour; the rootstock is a bulb.

HEATHER FAMILY. *Above may be seen three types of heather common to the British Isles. From left to right they are bell-heather, which has purplish flowers; ling, whose corolla tube is split into four parts; and cross-leaved heath, which has pale rose flowers and frequently grows to the size of a small bush.*

reduced to five narrow slender lobes. The lilac-blue flowers, which are small, are clustered in dense heads, up to one inch across, terminating long stalks. The leaves are linear, or lance-shaped, more or less hairy. This species produces two-celled seed capsules with many seeds and is thus distinguished from the scabiouses with which it may easily be confused. It flowers July-September.

Gorse, whin or furze is almost too well-known as a moorland plant to need description. Its bright yellow pea-like flowers opening in early spring add brightness and cheer to what otherwise might be a depressing landscape. The majority of its leaves are reduced to thorns and the plant thus happens to be protected from the ravages of browsing animals, but the real reason for this reduction is prevention of excessive evaporation of moisture, or conservation of it. On dry, warm days in summer, one may hear a crackling amidst the bush, due to the sudden expulsion of seeds from the dry pods. The seeds are thus thrown some distance away and it is in this way that gorse extends its territory. Petty whin or needle-furze, like gorse, belongs to the Pea family. It is frequently found on commons, heaths and moors in England and much of Scotland, but does not seem to occur in Ireland. In comparison with common gorse it is a small plant, hardly a foot high. It is a branched, spreading shrub with a woody spinous stem, the lower branches being reduced to thorns. The upper branches have small egg-shaped or lance-shaped leaves and bear loose leafy clusters of yellow pea-like flowers which turn green when drying. It flowers May-June; its seed pods are about half an inch long, broad and inflated.

Broom is another familiar showy shrub found on commons, heaths, and in other dry places, flowering May-June. The stem may be as high as six feet, although it is often shorter. The leaves are split into three leaflets. The bright yellow flowers, about one inch long, are on short stalks, occurring one or two together in the axils of the leaves. On careful examination it will be seen that the style of the pistil is spirally coiled.

The carline thistle, a member of the Compositae, is locally abundant on dry grass-heaths, especially on chalk soils. It is a spiny plant with deeply lobed leaves, growing from a few inches to over a foot high. This species is easily distinguished from all other thistles by the straw-coloured, radiating inner bracts of the compound flowerheads. These resemble petals and have an "everlasting" texture. They respond remarkably to the atmosphere. When it is humid they rise and curve over the florets they protect, but in dry weather they lie flat. This plant is a biennial, flowering June-October. The melancholy thistle is rather rare, but it is locally abundant in swampy places of the limestone mountain pastures of the Pennines. The stem is erect, from two to four feet high, furrowed and cottony. This thistle differs from all others in having no prickles. The handsome purplish flower-

CROSS-LEAVED HEATH. *Found in boggy soils on heaths, the leaves of this plant are arranged in whorls of four on the main stem. The drooping flowers are rose-pink and clustered in a dense head on the stalk. They are rich in nectar.*

AUTUMN CROCUS. *Of the same family as the iris, the autumn crocus, found in upland meadows and pastures, flowers in September and October. A silky tube, which grows up from the rootstock, divides at the head to form the bright purple blossom. Long, narrow leaves appear in the spring following its blooming.*

heads usually occur singly on long stalks. The musk thistle is found on grass-heaths, especially on chalk, and is frequent in southern England, less common in the north and rare in Scotland. The stem, up to two or more feet high, furrowed, cottony, is winged with a continuation of the leaves. The leaves are deeply-lobed, wavy, hairy and very prickly. The large flowerheads, about an inch to an inch and a half across, have a drooping habit and are made up of crimson florets with purple anthers; their strong fragrance of musk gives the plant its name.

The stately foxglove, seen in its most vigorous growth in copses and on banks on low ground, also occurs on hilly wastes and moors, being noted in the Highlands, up to 2,000 feet. A valuable heart medicine is extracted from its leaves. The superficial observer would hardly associate the little eyebright with

so grand a species as the foxglove, yet structurally it is of the same family. It varies much in size, shape of leaf and in other respects, but usually it is a much-branched plant not more than six inches high, often much less, with small stalkless, opposite, egg-shaped, deeply-lobed leaves. The flowers occur in loose leafy spikes: they vary in size, but are small, hardly more than a quarter of an inch long. The tubular calyx is four-cleft. The corolla gapes; it is composed of five petals fused into a tube which, at its mouth, is two-lipped, the upper lip composed of two petals and the lower one of three. Yet these small flowers, white or pinkish, with purple streaks and a spot of yellow in the throat, are very charming. The plant occurs in many situations from sea-level up to about 4,000 feet, and is very common on heaths among grasses from which it steals some of its food. It is used by

GORSE IN BLOOM. *Gorse, also known as whin or furze, generally grows on poor, dry soils such as may be found on sandy heathland. It is a sturdy shrub, with golden-yellow scented flowers, and both leaves and branchlets are armed with sharp spines.*

373

herbalists as a remedy for eye troubles.

Wild thyme is a common moorland plant whose fragrance delights us on a warm summer day. It is a Labiate—that is, one of the many plants with square stems, opposite leaves and two-lipped flowers, like the deadnettles. The stems of thyme are wiry, slender, much-branched, rooting at the nodes, forming a cushion. The small egg-shaped leaves may be fringed with hairs.

The small scabious has a preference for chalky soils and is a common downland species. It has slender, branched, slightly hairy stems, one to two feet high, and bears flattened heads of small five-lobed lilac-blue flowers, the corollas of the outer flowers being larger and very irregular. The flowerhead is about one

inch in diameter. The leaves are deeply lobed and the narrow segments are often lobed as well. This is a charming plant, but less distinguished than the field scabious (page 301).

Slender St. John's wort occurs on commons and heaths, flowering July-August, bearing bright yellow five-petalled flowers half an inch or so across. These flowers are often tinged with red on the outside; the stamens are massed in three bundles. The many stems are upright, round, slender, smooth, one to two feet high. The leaves of the main stem are heart-shaped, clasping the stem at their bases, whilst those of the side stems are narrower. On holding the leaves up to the light it will be seen that they are marked with translucent dots. The petals are fringed with red glands. Trailing St. John's wort is found on stony heaths and in boggy places. It is a much branched prostrate plant with the pale yellow flowers characteristic of its genus. These are up to half an inch across. The sepals and petals are generally edged with black glands. The oblong stalkless opposing leaves usually have pellucid dots. This species flowers July-August.

The tuberous pea is occasionally seen on heather moors in the Peak District, but is more abundant in woods and thickets. It bears pea-like flowers up to three-quarters of an inch long: these are purple, variegated, and when faded are blue or green. They are borne in loose clusters of two to six, terminating long slender stalks. The stems, six to eighteen inches high, have leaves cut to the midrib into two and sometimes three or four leaflets. There are no tendrils. This pretty flower blooms May-July. Its roots produce small tubers which are said to be very nourishing.

Milkwort is a common heath and

EYEBRIGHT. *A branching plant (left) with pinkish or white flowers streaked with purple and rounded toothed leaves.*

DOWNLAND PLANTS. *Musk thistle* (*right*) *has large crimson flowerheads and prickly divided leaves; lady's bedstraw* (*below*) *has small yellow flowers.*

pasture plant hardy enough to survive the rigours of mountain heights up to 3,000 feet. Lowly as it is, its blue, pink or white flowers attract the careful observer's eye. Its many wiry stems, two to ten inches high, are leafy, the lower leaves oblong, the upper lance-shaped, all varying from half to one and a half inches long and with uncut margins. The flowers occur in loose clusters of ten to twenty, each one on a short stalk with a bract at its base. Of the five sepals, three are greenish and narrow; the other two are long and broad, coloured like the petals. The three to five petals are smaller than the sepals. The plant is subject to much variation. Mountain or purging flax, closely related to common flax, is not nearly so conspicuous a plant. It has very slender stems two to ten inches high, with opposing oblong leaves and small white flowers about a quarter of an inch across, occurring in loose terminal clusters of which the central flower opens first. It is found in heaths and pastures up to over 2,000 feet in the Highlands and is valued by herbalists as a laxative.

PARSLEY PIERT

Parsley piert is of the Rose family and a lady's mantle of sorts (see page 304). It is common in fields and waste places but is also found on grassy heaths. This is an inconspicuous many-branched species of erect or prostrate habit. The wedge-shaped leaves are three-lobed and the lobes are deeply cut. The minute greenish flowers, minus petals, occur in stalkless tufts in the axils of the leaves by which they are almost hidden. Tormentil, also of the Rose family, is very common on heaths and moors and is found on mountain heights. The root-

stock is woody. The stems are about six inches high. Leaves from the root are stalked, those from the stem unstalked, both are deeply cut into three-toothed leaflets which in their turn are also cut. The attractive yellow flowers, about half an inch across, are solitary, on long stalks. In the same family we have dropwort, related to the Spiraeas of the garden and the meadowsweet of moist meadows. It has a preference for chalk or limestone soils and occurs commonly on downs. The root-fibres are swollen into tubers at intervals. The plant reaches one to two feet high and has a similarity to meadowsweet, but its leaves have more and smaller leaflets. The flowers are larger and fewer: they are white, sometimes tipped with red, and the petals are pink outside before they open. The plant is scentless. Still another member of the Rose family, occurring on limestone

grassy heaths, limestone heaths and chalk downs. The wiry, much-branched stems, prostrate or ascending and from a few inches to two feet long, have circles of six to eight threadlike, shortly pointed leaves at their nodes. A closely related plant, heath bedstraw, is found on rocks and heaths and occurs in the Highlands up to over 3,500 feet. Its dense clusters of small star-like white flowers are not nearly so attractive as those of ladies' bedstraw, and the plant is much smaller, the stems being only about six inches long. The leaves are very small, stalkless, shortly pointed and arranged usually six in a circle round joints of the stem; they are often fringed with small prickles. June-August is the flowering season.

The fragrant orchis is an upland species, occurring in hill-pastures and heaths. Its root tubers are lobed; its leaves are narrow, lance-shaped, and the reddish unspotted flowers grow in a long spike from one to two feet high. On a warm day their delightful fragrance may be detected from some distance. Beneath each flower is a leafy three-nerved bract.

Heath rush is abundant on heaths and moors. At the base of the stem there are many narrow, grooved, spreading leaves hardly half the length of the stiff stem, which may be about one foot high. The small glossy-brown flowers terminate the stem in a compound panicle, but they are not usually clustered. The field wood-rush has relationship and some resemblance to the spiked wood-rush (page 351). It abounds in dry pastures and heaths, flowering March-May. The plant is grass-like, with leaves mainly from the root, two or three inches long, with a fringe of long white hairs. The brownish-green flowers, each with six yellow anthers, occur in loose clusters.

heaths and chalk downs, is salad burnet, with a woody stem six to eighteen inches high, smelling and tasting like cucumber —hence "salad"—the leaves being divided into five to ten pairs of opposing toothed leaflets and a terminal one. The small green crimson-tinged flowers are borne in clustered roundish heads.

Ladies' bedstraw, with its large compact clusters of small yellow flowers, adds colour through the summer to

LING IN BLOOM

RAGWORT

INDEX

NUMBERS IN ITALICS REFER TO ILLUSTRATIONS

INDEX

The publishers wish to acknowledge permission from E. J. Hosking for the pictures appearing on pp.: 13, 19, 20, 40, 41, 44, 46, 49, 61, 70, 71, 83, 95, 100, 102, 106, 108, 109, 110, 136, 137, 166, 193, 198, 200, 209, 226-7 and 370 ; J. Markham for pictures on pp. 23, 26, 28, 35, 36, 38, 68-9, 80, 149, 217, 296 and 341 ; Capt. C. W. R. Knight for pictures on pp. 8-9 and 99 ; from W. W. Nicholas for pictures on pp. 29 (lower), 37, 101, 114 and 175 ; and from A. R. Thompson for pictures on pp. 39 and 225. The colour plates of birds are reproduced from Gould's *The Birds of Great Britain* by permission of the trustees of the British Museum.